Aquatic WILD™

K-12 Curriculum & Activity Guide

CEE

COUNCIL FOR
ENVIRONMENTAL
EDUCATION

Council for Environmental Education
5555 Morningside Drive, Suite 212
Houston, TX 77005
Phone: (713) 520-1936 Fax: (713) 520-8008
E-mail: info@councilforee.org
Web: www.councilforee.org

C E E
COUNCIL FOR
ENVIRONMENTAL
EDUCATION

Project WILD State Sponsors

Alabama Department of Conservation and Natural
    Resources
Alaska Department of Fish and Game
(Arizona) White Mountain Wildlife and Nature
    Center
Arkansas Game and Fish Commission
California Department of Fish and Wildlife
Colorado Parks and Wildlife
Connecticut Department of Energy and
    Environmental Protection
Florida Fish and Wildlife Conservation Commission
Georgia Department of Natural Resources
Idaho Department of Fish and Game
Indiana Department of Natural Resources
Iowa Department of Natural Resources
Kansas Association for Conservation and
    Environmental Education
Kansas Department of Wildlife and Parks
Kentucky Department of Fish and Wildlife
    Resources
Louisiana Department of Agriculture and Forestry
Maine Department of Inland Fisheries and Wildlife
Maryland Department of Natural Resources
Massachusetts Division of Fisheries and Wildlife
Michigan Alliance for Environmental and Outdoor
    Education
Michigan Department of Natural Resources
Minnesota Department of Natural Resources
Mississippi Department of Wildlife, Fisheries and
    Parks

Montana Fish, Wildlife and Parks
Nebraska Game and Parks Commission
Nevada Department of Wildlife
New Hampshire Fish and Game Department
New Jersey Division of Fish and Wildlife
New Mexico Department of Game and Fish
New York State Department of Environmental
    Conservation
North Carolina Wildlife Resources Commission
Ohio Division of Wildlife
Oklahoma Department of Wildlife Conservation
(Oklahoma) University of Central Oklahoma
Oregon Department of Fish and Wildlife
Oregon State University
Pennsylvania Fish and Boat Commission
Pennsylvania Game Commission
Puerto Rico Department of Natural and
    Environmental Resources
Rhode Island Division of Fish and Wildlife
South Dakota Game, Fish, and Parks
Tennessee Wildlife Resources Agency
Texas Parks and Wildlife Department
Utah Society for Environmental Education
Vermont Department of Fish and Wildlife
Virginia Department of Game and Inland Fisheries
Washington Department of Fish and Wildlife
West Virginia Division of Natural Resources
Wisconsin Department of Natural Resources
Wyoming Project WILD

International Partners

Canadian Wildlife Federation ▪ Centre for Environment Education, Ahmedabad, India
Czech Junak, Czech Republic ▪ National Centre for Educational Materials, Iceland
Parks and Recreation Foundation of Japan ▪ Umea University, Sweden

Council for Environmental Education Board of Directors

Harold Aiken, MWH ▪ Dr. Bill Futrell, Wyoming Department of Education (Ret.)
Steve Huffaker, Idaho Fish and Game (Ret.) ▪ Cindy Jordy, Phillips 66
Barbara J. Price, Phillips Petroleum Company (Ret.)
Josetta Hawthorne, Council for Environmental Education (ex-officio)

Council for Environmental Education Staff

Josetta Hawthorne, Executive Director ▪ Marc LeFebre, Senior Program Manager
Jennifer Paschke, Senior Manager, Publications ▪ Sarah Livesay, Education Program Consultant
Julie Tran, Business Administrator ▪ Casey Bruns, Intern ▪ Raven-Deneice Grant, Intern

Awards and Recognition

Project WILD, its sponsors, and many of its participants have received a variety of awards and recognition. In 1983, the National Wildlife Federation presented the Council for Environmental Education with its Conservation Achievement Award for "outstanding contributions to the wise use and management of the nation's natural resources."

Project WILD was honored at the White House in 1991 as one of the first recipients of the Gold Medal for Education and Communications in the President's Environment and Conservation Challenge Award program. This award was bestowed "for excellence in developing innovative solutions to the nation's environmental challenges."

Project WILD has also received the Conservation Education Award from The Wildlife Society. The National Environmental Education Foundation recognized the Council for Environmental Education with the 1997 National Environmental Education Achievement Award for leadership in conservation education.

Project WILD's early childhood program, Growing Up WILD, received the Family Choice Award in 2009 and the 2011 Renewable Natural Resources Foundation Award for Excellence in Journalism. Project WILD materials have been endorsed by the National Council for Social Studies and are consistent with recommendations of the National Science Teachers Association.

Table of Contents

Wildlife Management (WM)

Responsible Action and Service (RA)

Appendices

Welcome to Project WILD!

Project WILD is an interdisciplinary conservation and environmental education program emphasizing wildlife. The goal of Project WILD is to assist learners of any age in developing awareness, knowledge, skills, and commitment resulting in informed decisions, responsible behavior, and constructive actions concerning wildlife and the environment.

The waters of the earth, in some form, are within walking distance from anywhere on the planet. The *Aquatic WILD K–12 Curriculum and Activity Guide* serves as an invitation to explore and understand the fascinating world of water and the aquatic habitats it supports.

Water in all its forms is one of the most dramatic of today's arenas in which informed, responsible, and constructive actions are needed. Water is one of the basic components of habitat for people and for wildlife—it is essential to all life. Aquatic species and aquatic ecosystems give humans early and clear warning about the quality of the water environment upon which we all depend.

For instructional purposes in Project WILD, wildlife is defined as any nondomesticated animal. Wildlife may be as small as a microscopic organism or as large as a Blue Whale. Wildlife includes but is not limited to insects, spiders, amphibians, birds, fish, and mammals, if nondomesticated. For instructional purposes in Aquatic WILD, aquatic wildlife refers to any wild animals that depend upon aquatic environments for survival.

Project WILD was launched in 1983 as a joint project of the Council for Environmental Education (CEE) (formerly Western Regional Environmental Education Council, Inc. [WREEC]) and the Western Association of Fish and Wildlife Agencies (WAFWA) in 13 western states. WREEC was founded in 1970 in a unique and visionary effort to create a partnership between education and natural resource professionals and has since grown to become a national environmental education organization. WAFWA now represents 23 states and Canadian provinces and is comprised of directors of the public agencies responsible for management of wildlife.

CEE's mission is to provide environmental education programs and services that promote stewardship of the environment and further the capacity of learners to make informed decisions. To accomplish its mission, CEE supports programs and partnerships for environmental education.

Over One Million Educators Gone WILD!

Since Project WILD was introduced in 1983, more than 1.3 million educators in the United States have participated in Project WILD and Aquatic WILD workshops. Those educators, in turn, have reached over 100 million youth since the program was first introduced. (See *www.projectwild.org* for more information.) This success, which has made Project WILD one of the largest wildlife education programs in the world, is possible only through the enthusiastic support of Project WILD's extensive and talented network of Project WILD sponsors, coordinators, and facilitators. Project WILD is endorsed by both the National Council for Social Studies and the Association of Fish and Wildlife Agencies.

Project WILD's primary audience is educators of pre-kindergarten through high school students. This approach does not limit the usefulness of Project WILD to formal educational settings, however. Volunteers working with students in pre-school and after-school programs; representatives of private conservation, industry, and other community groups; and personnel involved in preparation of future educators are all among those who effectively use the instructional resources of this program. Project WILD is sponsored throughout the United States, the District of Columbia, Puerto Rico, and three countries in addition to the United States.

Project WILD's educational materials are provided to educators through practical, interactive workshops conducted by representatives of sponsoring state wildlife, natural resources, and educational agencies. The dedication and commitment of teachers, wildlife biologists, environmental educators, interested citizens, school administrators, and other enthusiasts who volunteer hours of time and effort make Project WILD possible at the state and local levels.

The Board and staff of the Council for Environmental Education; Project WILD Program Committee; WAFWA and AFWA members and all the organizational, state, and international sponsors; and others associated with the program are dedicated to achieving the highest possible standards of professional quality, factual accuracy, and objectivity in all programs, activities, and materials bearing the Project WILD name. Project WILD has adopted policies and guidelines that state the program's commitment to neutrality on controversial issues, treating such issues fairly and honestly without advocating any one particular point of view and recognizing that people need information from a variety of sources to make their own informed decisions. Project WILD programs, activities, and materials are not to be used to promote agency or organizational policies or political points of view.

We welcome you to Project WILD! We hope you and your students gain a deeper understanding of the environment around you, the issues we face in the 21st century, and how you can contribute to the stewardship of our natural resources.

For Additional Information

For additional information about participation in Project WILD as an associate, contributing, or international sponsor, please contact:

Project WILD National Office
Council for Environmental Education
5555 Morningside Drive, Suite 212
Houston, TX 77005
Phone: (713) 520-1936
E-mail: **info@projectwild.org**
Web: **www.projectwild.org**

Introduction

I n 2007, the Council for Environmental Education lost an inspirational leader, Rudy Schafer, our founder, passionate advocate, and long-time board member. The following is an introduction Rudy crafted to share Project WILD's early beginnings and core values.

A concern for the land, its resources, and its continuing viability is basic to our survival and well-being. . . as individuals, as a nation, and as members of the world community. Two groups within society play important roles in shaping future environments: resource management professionals and educators. Educators have the responsibility for equipping learners with the skills and knowledge necessary to access and evaluate information upon which sound judgments can be made. Resource management professionals provide us with the information and technology necessary to achieve our goals.

Project WILD was created by the Western Regional Environmental Education Council (WREEC), which was founded in 1970 to bring together state-level resource management professionals and education administrators from 13 western states to work on environmental education programs of regional and, ultimately, national importance. Funding and support were provided by the Western Association of Fish and Wildlife Agencies (WAFWA).

Based on WREEC's successful Project Learning Tree model, the Project WILD conceptual outline was developed with input from educators, preservationists, conservationists, wildlife managers, business and industry representatives, and others. Learning activities in a variety of subject matter and skill areas were written by classroom teachers in regional writing workshops, and their work was tested extensively by other educators before being edited and assembled in final form. WREEC did not seek to produce a course of study, but aimed to develop a collection of good learning activities that could be used in many settings and content areas.

As with all good educational materials, Project WILD is concerned with providing information, as well as helping students to evaluate choices and to make responsible decisions. In short, Project WILD's mission is to help students learn how to think, not what to think.

Project WILD adheres to those strict efforts for balance and objectivity, backed by sound educational practices and theory. It also represents the work of many within the fields of education and natural resource management from across the country. The materials are available to those who attend instructional workshops offered by certified leaders and supported by a network of sponsoring state, national, and international agencies.

We are pleased to bring you Project WILD in an easy-to-use format that organizes activities by thematic topic, subject matter, and grade level. If you are new to Project WILD, we hope that this curriculum guide will become a most valued educational resource.

Personally, I take great pride in being part of the Council for Environmental Education and the great Project WILD family that has done so much for literally millions of students over the years. For those who are just now joining us, a hearty and sincere welcome. Yes, working together we can make a difference!

Rudolph J. H. Schafer

Founder,
Western Regional Environmental Education Council

What's New for Aquatic WILD?

Ongoing updates to Project WILD and Aquatic WILD materials build upon developments in wildlife conservation needs as well as advances in instructional methodology in Pre-K through 12th grade education. A key milestone in the expansion of Project WILD is this 2013 edition of the *Aquatic WILD K–12 Curriculum and Activity Guide*. New content in this edition of Aquatic WILD includes seven new activities, many of which address the need for students to take a leading role in investigating aquatic habitats and resources and implementing water stewardship activities in their communities. Expanded content in this new edition also helps educators and their students to explore careers and occupations in the field of wildlife management and conservation. Additionally, new activity components help strengthen science, technology, engineering, and mathematics (STEM) instruction. Below is an overview of the expanded content:

Field Investigation Activities

New field investigation activities and resources guide K–12 educators and students in researching environmental topics or issues in local areas by implementing outdoor field investigations. Through new and expanded Aquatic WILD activities, students learn methods and protocol for conducting scientific investigations, including how to formulate a research question, choosing a viable study site, engaging in systematic data collection, and applying field ethics. Student-guided investigations will mirror the processes undertaken by professional wildlife biologists, while also providing opportunities for educators to strengthen service-learning efforts. Each field investigation activity is clearly identified with a special icon for easy reference.

"In Step with STEM" Activity Extensions

A new STEM component allows educators to delve even deeper into science, technology, engineering, and mathematics (STEM) content. STEM extensions make use of a variety of tools and instruments, from litmus tests to smartphone applications, and involve students in the application of technology, science concepts, and math skills as part of their problem-solving efforts. The STEM extensions for each activity in this edition of Aquatic WILD also provide links for additional online resources at *www.projectwild.org/aquatic*.

"Working for Wildlife"

This new activity explores occupations in wildlife conservation and involves middle and high school students in a simulated job fair and interview process. Students research and interview for wildlife-related jobs in state fish and wildlife agencies, private industry, and nonprofit organizations.

"WILD Work"

A career component has been added to all activities to tie in real occupations in the fields of wildlife management and conservation with every lesson. Supplementary online resources to use in conjunction with WILD Work extensions are now linked through an expanded Project WILD website, *www.projectwild.org/aquatic*. For every job or career listed in a WILD Work text box, students and educators can follow a link to corresponding videos or other online resources to learn more about the qualifications, daily duties, or other facets of the job within a wildlife management or conservation organization.

Outdoor Components

In an effort to maximize student time outdoors, outdoor components are now included in all activities, whether through expanding activity procedures, extensions, or "In Step with STEM" activity extensions.

Activities on Fish Conservation and Angling

Fishing is both fun and educational! New activities help teachers team up with state agencies and nonformal educators to get kids outdoors. The new activity "Gone Fishing!" combines angling and student investigations of local fish species and aquatic habitats. In the activity "Conservation Messaging," students research fish conservation issues in order to produce video and/or online media for the delivery of conservation messages.

New Reference Information

An expanded Appendices provides resources for planning subject matter (teaching) units, methods for conducting site inventories with students, resource pages, and expanded grade level correlations for each activity.

New and Expanded Activities

"Water Works" and "Urban Waterway Checkup" explore issues in urban water quality and water as a shared resource. "Got Water?" and "Water Safari" are new field investigation activities that involve elementary students in exploring the accessibility and arrangement of water as a habitat component. Additionally, the middle level and high school activities "Puddle Wonders" and "Where Does Water Run?" have been re-developed as expanded field investigation activities (see "Aquatic WILD Field Investigations" for additional information).

New Background Information

Many Aquatic WILD activities include new background information that addresses developing trends, issues, and new research in the field of wildlife conservation and management.

What's New for Aquatic WILD?
© Council for Environmental Education (CEE)

Project WILD: Supporting Student Achievement

Project WILD helps educators meet accountability measures for student achievement by providing standards-based, scientifically sound materials and high-quality professional development for in-service and pre-service educators. Project WILD materials and professional development use educational practices that are proven effective.

Project WILD is Standards-Based

Academic learning and assessment standards anchor our country's effort to improve every student's opportunity for success. Standards set clear expectations for teaching and student performance.

Explicit links between educational standards and the Project WILD curriculum guides make it easy for instructors to use Project WILD activities as part of a standards-based curriculum. In most states, Project WILD instructional materials have been correlated with state educational standards in discipline areas such as science and social studies.

Additionally, ongoing updates of Project WILD correlations to national standards in science, environmental education, mathematics, and language arts also help in efforts to integrate Project WILD into school curriculum and youth programs. Go to *www.projectwild.org/educators* for additional information on correlations to national standards, including: *Next Generation Science Standards*, *Common Core Standards*, North American Association for Environmental Education (NAAEE)'s *Guidelines for Excellence*, and Association of Fish and Wildlife Agencies (AFWA)'s *Scope and Sequence for Conservation Education*.

Project WILD Provides Scientifically Sound Materials

Project WILD materials are grounded in proven instructional approaches. Activities emphasize hands-on, inquiry-based, and cooperative learning strategies with demonstrated classroom effectiveness.[1] These strategies are included among research-based instructional practices approved by schools and districts across the nation.

Project WILD also relies on well-proven techniques such as simulations, nonlinguistic representations, and learning activities that encourage higher-order reasoning skills such as comparison and classification.[2]

Project WILD materials follow a conceptual framework that was developed through a rigorous process to ensure its accuracy, balance, and educational validity. Over 500 professionals critiqued and reviewed the *Project WILD K–12 Curriculum and Activity Guide* and the *Aquatic WILD K–12 Curriculum and Activity Guide*. Project WILD curriculum and activity guides are updated regularly to incorporate new information and respond to educator feedback.

Project WILD Helps Prepare Highly Qualified Teachers

Well-prepared teachers who know what to teach, how to teach, and have a command of subject matter being taught are an important link to student success in school. Research suggests that teachers who emphasize higher-order thinking skills and hands-on learning activities help boost their student's performance significantly.

Project WILD's education materials rely strongly on these hands-on, minds-on instructional techniques. Our training programs help educators apply knowledge and techniques in the classroom to teach subject matter and skills pertinent to a range of disciplines. Surveys completed by teachers tell us they learn new skills and practices through Project WILD that translate into more effective instruction.

Project WILD increases teachers' knowledge of academic subjects, particularly in the sciences and social studies. Project WILD training, advanced courses, and extended pre-service training programs in addition to the classroom materials enhance educators' content base, especially as it relates to wildlife and conservation.

Project WILD Offers Effective Professional Development

Like our activities, Project WILD workshops are committed to addressing pre-K–12 classroom priorities. Results from workshop surveys indicate that educators consistently give Project WILD high marks for content, quality, and usefulness. Project WILD workshops and educator institutes are offered throughout the year in most states. Many Project WILD training workshops are offered in conjunction with university teacher training programs or university-affiliated museums and nature centers. In most states, a teacher's first Project WILD workshop introduces them to the state fish and wildlife agency, a unique partner that provides resources, support, and advanced training in special topics and classroom techniques. Ongoing contact with the state Project WILD coordinator is the primary link to an active network that provides quality resources and professional development.

Project WILD workshops and training programs meet key characteristics of high-quality professional development—sustained, intensive, classroom-focused, and rich in academic subject content.

Project WILD is Proven Effective

Project WILD training programs and educational materials are proven effective, fair and balanced, and engaging for instructors and students alike. Over 40 studies at the national and state level have evaluated Project WILD activities, materials, and professional development offerings. Visit *www.projectwild.org* to access research studies about Project WILD, including summaries of research that have been published over the past thirty years.

Project WILD's success is due in large part to emphasis on classroom testing and experience, input from subject matter and education experts, teacher feedback, extensive evaluation, and quality training programs. Educators can feel confident that Project WILD materials are classroom tested for effectiveness, attainment of instructional objectives, quality of the activity, and student involvement.

Over the years, Project WILD has responded to changes in education practices with correlations to state and national curriculum standards; development of pre-service training to complement our in-service training programs; instructional focus on hands-on, learner-centered, and cooperative learning strategies to involve students; incorporating student use of technologies and scientific inquiry; and collaborating with state education departments to develop more intensive, sustained trainings to meet educators' needs for professional development.

---

[1] These strategies have been the subject of hundreds of scientifically rigorous studies, as reviewed and reported in Marzano, R.J. (2003). *What Works in Schools: Translating Research into Action.* Alexandria, VA: Association for Supervision and Curriculum Development, 78–87. See also Hattie, J. (1992). *Measuring the Effects of Schooling.* Australian Journal of Education, 362, 99–136 and Wenglinksy, H. 2000.

[2] See Marzano 2003, and Hattie 1992.

Evaluation of Project WILD Materials

Ongoing review, testing, and evaluation of Project WILD materials help in the development of well-conceived, tested, current, and effective instructional resources.

Expert Review

Project WILD's activities and conceptual framework have been reviewed for educational soundness, balance, and content accuracy. Classroom teachers, often in cooperation with nonformal educators and wildlife specialists, wrote the initial instructional activities. Reviewers throughout each stage of Project WILD's development have included classroom teachers, university faculty, wildlife biologists, wildlife and natural resource agency personnel, representatives of animal welfare organizations, sportsmen, school administrators, curriculum developers, environmental education specialists, nonformal educators, representatives of private industry, and others. Results of this review process have been used in editing and improving the Project WILD instructional materials throughout the history of the program.

Pilot Test

A pilot test and revision process was developed and implemented by a respected team of independent researchers for the initial versions of the Project WILD Elementary and Secondary Activity Guides as well as Aquatic WILD. Each instructional activity appearing in Project WILD materials was tested by educators to ensure quality and appropriateness of content. Through testing, both major and minor activity revisions were made and a few activities were eliminated entirely. Each activity has been determined to be effective in accomplishing its stated objectives. A similar pilot was conducted by CEE staff for the 2013 expansion of Aquatic WILD, primarily involving the addition of field investigations.

Field Test

Following pilot testing, a field test implemented by a team of independent researchers helped assess the effectiveness of the materials when used by teachers with their students. The field test was conducted in three states, in three demographic areas (urban, suburban, and rural), and across all elementary and secondary grade levels during a full school year. Two hundred fifty-nine teachers and more than 6,000 students were involved. Field testing demonstrated significant gains in learning and students' development of attitudes toward wildlife that are consistent with the goals of Project WILD. Educators generally found the activities stimulating and worthwhile in their classes and were able to integrate the activities into their curricula. A direct relationship was evidenced between the number of Project WILD instructional activities used by teachers and the students' gains in knowledge and attitudes. Statistical significance was found where teachers used seven or more Project WILD instructional activities. Project WILD was shown to be effective in urban, suburban, and rural areas. In addition to initial testing, field testing continues to be a key phase of activity development as materials are updated and expanded.

Additional Studies

Several studies conducted by conservation organizations as well as research for master's theses and doctoral dissertations have focused on Project WILD throughout the United States and abroad.[1] Research results indicate Project WILD has a positive impact on student knowledge and attitudes about wildlife and constructs about wildlife. For more information, visit *www.projectwild.org*.

---

[1] Pitman, Barbara J. (2004). *Project WILD: A Summary of Research Findings, 1983–1995 and 1996–2003*, Houston, TX: Council for Environmental Education.

Teach Outside!

An emerging collection of research confirms the importance of outdoor time for children. With many activities that work well in outdoor settings, and several more designed specifically for the outdoors, Aquatic WILD is a perfect fit with efforts to get young people outside.

Connecting Children to Nature

Interaction with nature plays an important role in children's well-being and development. Research illustrates the positive effects outdoor education has on test scores, increased grade point averages, measures of knowledge transfer,[1] and childhood creativity.[2] Aquatic WILD provides educators and caregivers with outdoor opportunities that aim to establish the nature connection, nurture children's curiosity about nature, and assist in the development of informed adult citizens that make environmentally sustainable choices.

Outdoor Learning and Exploration

In many communities children's access to time in nature and outdoors is diminishing. Aquatic WILD addresses this dilemma by prioritizing outdoor learning and exploration, whether the available space is a forest, a city park, or an asphalt playground. Resources in this guide to help educators teach outside include:

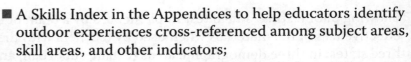

- A Skills Index in the Appendices to help educators identify outdoor experiences cross-referenced among subject areas, skill areas, and other indicators;

- Extensions at the end of Aquatic WILD activities that suggest how to transition an activity into service-learning opportunities. In this way, student learners gain not only the benefits of the outdoor experience, but also the fulfillment of community service and outreach;

- Several outdoor field investigation activities that involve learners in the systematic collection of data to answer questions, solve problems, and develop a scientific understanding of their local environment. A quick reference to Aquatic WILD activities that include field investigations can be found in the Skills Index in the Appendices, along with a sample field investigation Data Collection Form.

Tips for Getting Ready

A few key guidelines will help ensure outdoor activities are educational, safe, and engaging. (1) *Know the area*: spend a little time to familiarize yourself with the local outdoor area or study site before taking students outside; invite an expert to help identify plants, animals, and other natural features students might encounter. (2) *Prepare the parents*: at the beginning of each school year, hold a meeting or send informational materials to parents about the importance of including outdoor education in the syllabus; let parents know in advance when students will be going outside. (3) *Prepare the students*: review directions, expectations, and any safety concerns before leaving the classroom; plan accommodations for students with special needs to ensure participation in the outdoor activities. (4) *Maintain structure*: allow time for self-guided exploration and play, but also provide students with a focused and well-defined goal; set specific boundaries for students, particularly if they will have unstructured time. (5) *Follow-up*: have students write entries into their science notebooks or journals; these student-generated records can serve as planning or assessment tools when used throughout the school year.

[1] Faber, Taylor. A. & Kuo. F.E. (2006). Is contact with nature important for healthy child development? State of the evidence. In Spencer & Blades, (Eds.), Children and Their Environments. (pp. 124–140).

[2] Kirkby, M. (1989). Nature as refuge in children's environments. Children's Environments Quarterly 6, 1–12

Aquatic WILD Field Investigations

Why Conduct Field Investigations with Students?

Field investigations are evidence-based studies that bring the scientific process out of the laboratory and into the natural world. By asking questions and observing wildlife, habitat, and ecological systems around them, students are able to learn how the scientific process works while gaining firsthand experience of the natural world.

Field Investigations teach students...

... how to conduct scientific inquiry.

The field investigation activities in the *Aquatic WILD K–12 Curriculum and Activity Guide* are designed to mirror the scientific process used by professional scientists every day. During the investigation, students observe and ask questions about their environment, collect and analyze data, and draw conclusions based on the evidence they have collected. These practices teach students reasoning and problem-solving skills they will use for the rest of their lives.

... the importance of experimenting in uncontrolled environments.

Using structured observations of the natural world, students learn how science works away from a carefully structured laboratory setting. Professionals like wildlife biologists, ecologists, oceanographers, and engineers often do research in settings where they have little control over the numerous interacting variables that affect their work. Field investigations help students learn how to identify, isolate, and measure the factors that will allow them to answer questions about their environment.

... how to think about systems.

Students discover interconnected relationships in the environment and develop an understanding of how the interrelated parts of an ecosystem work together. Students gain insights and solve problems by examining not just isolated aspects of a system, but also how the parts of a whole relate and interact.

... with firsthand experience.

A firsthand, multi-sensory connection with the natural world provides a powerful learning experience for students. The memorable nature of outdoor learning helps students retain material, and outdoor fieldwork can increase students' motivation to learn.[1]

... important STEM skills.

The last decade has seen advances in education and policy to strengthen the teaching of STEM disciplines (science, technology, engineering, and mathematics). The U.S. Department of Commerce's Economics and Statistics Administration predicts STEM job growth to be 17 percent from 2008–2018 compared to 9.8 percent for non-STEM occupations, and employment in fields such as environmental and civil engineering, environmental science, and mathematics is expected to grow even faster. Reaching students early is the first step in fostering their interest in these important areas.

... in accordance with national standards.

Field investigations support *A Framework for K–12 Science Education*[2] and *The Next Generation Science Standards* by emphasizing scientific practices and providing opportunities to explore crosscutting concepts such as patterns, cause and effect, scale, systems, and change. Outdoor studies also support national social studies standards by helping students understand the relationships between people, technology, and the environment.

---

1 See Rickinson, M., et. al. (2004). *A Review of Research on Outdoor Learning.* National Foundation for Educational Research & Kings College London.

2 National Research Council. (2012). *A Framework for K–12 Science Education: Practices, Crosscutting Concepts, and Core Ideas.* National Academies Press.

Field Investigation Activities

In short, field investigation activities in Aquatic WILD involve students in outdoor settings making firsthand observations and collecting and analyzing data in order to answer questions about natural processes in the local environment. To help educators locate field investigations in this guide, each of the eight field investigation activities is designated with this icon:

Expanded Field Investigation Activities

Following the style and approach to inquiry of many Project WILD and Aquatic WILD activities, questions on the subject matter for each activity are provided in the procedures in field investigation activities. The educator or activity leader then decides the best way to use the questions: whether to assign the group to investigate, as suggestions for guiding group discussion, to encourage critical thinking, to further stimulate inquiry among learners, or simply as hints the educator may use to better prepare for questions students may raise.

Aquatic WILD Field Investigation Activities involve...

- **K–12 Students**
- **Outdoor Settings**
- **Local Environments**
- **Firsthand Observations**
- **Data Collection**
- **Data Analysis**
- **Evidence-based Conclusions**

The practice of developing and articulating investigative questions and procedures is key to carrying out scientific investigations. For this reason, a subset of the field investigations in this guide has been expanded with greater focus on student-generated questions and research procedures.

Aquatic WILD Field Investigations

Activity Title	Grade Levels	Activity Description
Edge of Home	Upper Elementary & Middle School	Students explore the concept of ecotones by investigating places where habitats overlap.
Gone Fishing! *	Middle School & High School	As a method of data collection, students go fishing to investigate local fish species and fish habitat.
Got Water? *	Upper Elementary	Students evaluate habitat in the schoolyard or local study site to determine if sources of food, water, and shelter are in an appropriate arrangement for a specific animal species to survive.
Puddle Wonders! *	Middle School	Students observe water that accumulates in puddles; measure and record the depth, area, and volume of the puddles; and look for evidence of wildlife using the puddles.
Water Canaries	Middle School & High School	Students investigate a stream or pond using sampling techniques.
Water Safari *	Lower Elementary	Students investigate wildlife and signs of wildlife in the schoolyard or other outdoor study site, as well as the locations of water that wildlife might use.
Watershed	Middle School & High School	Students measure the area of a local watershed, calculate the amount of water it receives each year, and discuss the varied roles the watershed plays in human and wildlife habitats.
Where Does Water Run? *	Middle School & High School	Students design and implement a field investigation involving relationships between levels of precipitation, runoff, and percentage of impervious ground cover.

* Five expanded field investigations in this edition of *Aquatic WILD K-12 Curriculum and Activity Guide* include more in-depth guidelines for involving students in developing investigative questions, procedures, data collection, and analysis.

These expanded field investigations also provide a model for further implementation of student-directed investigations. See the "Aquatic WILD Field Investigations" table for more information about the field investigation activities. For ideas about other topics students could investigate through field investigations, see the "Examples of Additional Student Field Investigations" text box in this section.

Expanded Field Investigation Activity Format

Expanded field investigation activities balance educators' need for curriculum resources on specific environmental topics and students' need to choose research topics on local environmental conditions they find interesting and relevant. Within the context of teacher-directed discussion and procedures, students are provided opportunities to articulate investigative questions, to further develop investigation procedures, to draw conclusions, and to communicate their findings.

Each Project WILD and Aquatic WILD activity contains reference information and subheadings that mirror traditional lesson plan formats, such as grade level recommendations, content areas, learning objectives, key vocabulary, background information, procedures, assessment guidelines, etc. The expanded field investigations, however, help students and educators go deeper into the investigative process through six additional activity

sections. These sections are further described in items I-VI below.

I. Study Site

Each expanded field investigation activity will include advice on how to select a study site that fits the needs of the group and the specific activity. Many of the activities can be done in easy-to-reach places like schoolyards and local parks. Some investigations can also be implemented on a larger scale, for example at a lakeshore, river, or forest. Whatever location is chosen, clear boundaries for the study site should be identified in order to ensure feasibility, accurate data collection, and safety. As a general rule of thumb, when planning a field investigation it is important to choose a study site that is not too large. Consider, for example, if students are planning to measure distances across a study site. Will they have the time and tools to do so? Will the study site allow for all students to remain in the educator's field of vision and voice range?

II. Introducing the Field Investigation

Introduce the field investigation to students by providing the background information necessary for the activity. This may include a class discussion, individual or team research done by students, or a site visit before the investigation so that students can begin building knowledge about the habitat and natural features they will be studying, as well as what methods they will use to collect and analyze data.

III. Forming the Field Investigation Question

The number of questions students can raise when preparing for a field investigation may seem endless. Guiding discussion to help students articulate a single, testable question is key for students' success if they are involved in planning and implementing a field investigation. Students will often start by asking far-reaching questions such as "How can we preserve the environment?" or "What is the best habitat for wildlife?" These big-picture or essential questions cannot be addressed with a single field investigation; however, students can often explore questions that address a smaller part of these complex issues. Questions that can be answered through direct observation in a field investigation are researchable questions.

A good researchable question will rely on variables that can be measured by students. For example, the question "Is it warmer close to the school building or farther away?" can be answered with a thermometer and tape measure. The investigative question should also have a narrow focus, meaning it addresses only a few variables in a specific area at a specific time. For example, a student who asks "How healthy is the river in our town?" can be guided toward a more specific question such as "How does the pH level in the river change when the season changes?" or "How many species of fish can be found in the river in the morning?"

To help determine what type of observations are needed in an investigation, researchable questions can be grouped into three categories:

- **Descriptive questions** describe a particular part of a natural system and can be answered using written descriptions, lists, or maps. Examples include "How many squirrels are there in the schoolyard?", "What is the temperature of a lake?", and "When do dandelions bloom?"

- **Comparative questions** require data collection on a single measurable variable in two or more locations, populations, groups, or times. Examples include "Is there a difference between the number of squirrels in the schoolyard and a local park?" and "Are there more dandelions in the spring or in the summer?"

Examples of Additional Student Field Investigations

Researchable question: What kinds of macroinvertebrates live in waterways?

Study site: Puddle, river, lake, or stream.

Type of question: Descriptive.

Variable(s): Number of species.

Procedure: Students collect, observe, and categorize macroinvertebrates from a puddle, river, lake, or stream.

Data organization: List of species; student illustrations; pie or bar chart depicting number of individuals of each species found.

Researchable question: How is the temperature of a body of water different at morning and at night?

Study site: River, lake, or stream.

Type of question: Comparative.

Variable(s): Manipulated—time of day; responding—temperature.

Procedure: Students take the temperature of a body of water at morning and night.

Data organization: Averages of multiple temperature samples; bar chart; number line.

Researchable question: How does the pH of a body of water change with rainfall?

Study site: River, lake, or stream.

Type of question: Correlative.

Variable(s): Manipulated—amount of rainfall; responding—pH level.

Procedure: Students take measurements of pH levels of a body of water before and after rain events.

Data organization: Averages of multiple pH samples; bar chart; t-test.

■ **Correlative questions** require measurement of two variables in search of a pattern. Examples include "How does the number of squirrels in the schoolyard change with the temperature?" and "What is the relationship between dandelion blooms and rainfall?"

(Adapted from *Field Investigations: Using Outdoor Environments to Foster Student Learning of the Scientific Process.* 2007. Pacific Education Institute and Association of Fish & Wildlife Agencies.)

The *What's My Question?* sheet on page 388 will help students formulate and categorize researchable questions.

Each expanded field investigation in Aquatic WILD will provide examples of researchable questions. For young students, educators may want to spend less time exploring possible avenues of research and simply assign students a question. Older students can be guided by educators toward one of the questions provided in the activity or allowed to develop their own researchable questions. No matter the age of the students, however, a goal of all field investigation activities is to eventually get students asking their own questions about their environment and determining how they would go about answering those questions.

IV. Conducting the Field Investigation

To ensure accuracy, procedures for data collection that are consistent across groups and time periods are necessary; in other words, every student should be collecting and recording data in the same way,

Tip: Try starting with descriptive investigations. Once students become knowledgeable about their study site and are able to describe the site's characteristics—the how much, how many, what, and where—they will then be better equipped to raise questions that compare attributes or help explain relationships between phenomena. Conducting an inventory of the study site or mapping the site are basic ways for students to answer descriptive questions about the site. See the "Guidelines for Mapping" (page xxi) and "Inventory Methods" (page 335).

thereby implementing the same controlled variables. A detailed and specific procedure is especially important if students are comparing data between groups or with data from another site or time period.

Younger students can be given step-by-step instruction, while educators may want to lead older students in developing and writing their own procedures. When doing so, students should identify the variables to be observed in order to answer their investigative question and decide how these variables will be measured. Descriptive questions may only require a single variable, such as air temperature, number of animals seen, or the amount of rainfall. Older students working on comparative or correlative questions may also identify types of variables. These include:

■ **Control:** the variables being held constant.

■ **Manipulated:** the part of the system that is being deliberately changed or altered. Although we typically cannot manipulate natural phenomena, it is possible to make observations of a variable at different times or locations or under different conditions. The manipulated variable is also an independent variable. That is, manipulated variables are not changed by other variables being measured. They do not depend on or are not caused by changes in responding (or dependent) variables. Thus, any change in the manipulated variable is independent of changes in the responding (dependent) variable.

- ■ **Responding:** the part of the system that responds to changes in the manipulated variable. These "dependent variables" change depending on changes in the manipulated (independent) variables.

For example, if students are investigating the relationship between air temperature and distance from the school building, one of the controlled variables would likely be the time of day air temperature is measured. The manipulated variable would be the location at which temperature is measured, and the responding variable would be the temperature.

Once variables have been identified and the procedure has been developed, students should write a hypothesis or prediction about the outcome of their investigation.

Mapping is an important activity that can be used by all grade levels to collect, organize, and analyze data. For more information on using maps in field investigations, see "Guidelines for Mapping."

V. Organizing and Analyzing Data

During the investigation, students can collect data on a data collection sheet or in their science notebooks (see the section on "Science Notebooks" for more information). If educators or students customize a data collection sheet, each form should include a place to record the date, time, weather conditions, and variables being measured. A sample data collection form can be found on page 390. See also "Criteria for Developing Student Data Sheets" in this section.

Expanded field investigations will provide students with guidelines for compiling and analyzing data once data collection is complete. Possible methods of organization include lists, graphic organizers, spreadsheets, and maps. Analysis can include determining patterns over time, identifying spatial relationships, or conducting statistical calculations.

VI. Drawing Conclusions

Once the data has been organized and analyzed, students can make inferences based on their observations to answer the investigative question. At this stage in the investigation, encourage students to articulate clear, concise statements that answer their question. Conclusions should be limited to the time and place being studied. For example, a student's answer to the question "Is it warmer near the school building or farther away?" could state "In the mornings on the south side of the school building, it was 63°F one meter from the building and 58°F 100 meters away. Therefore, it was warmer closer to the building."

If an hypothesis was made, students should address whether their predictions were correct and explain the reasoning for their conclusion. If students are unable to answer the investigative question, their conclusion statements should state why and suggest alternative steps or measurements that might be needed to answer the question.

Students should be encouraged to think about possible explanations for their data. Inconsistencies in the data should also be addressed by students. Were there problems in the procedure that led to incorrect data collection? What other factors might have affected the field investigation?

Finally, students should be asked to examine their study in the context of larger systems. What does this field investigation suggest about the habitat or ecosystem being studied? How might this information help make real world decisions? What new questions does the field investigation raise? For example, if it is warmer near the building, students may wonder how this influences local plants and animals or how this temperature difference changes throughout the day.

The *Conclusions and Next Steps* sheet on page 389 will help students develop answers and explanations that address their research questions as well as consider the implications of their investigations and potential new directions for research.

> **Tip:** for comparative and correlative investigations, good questions describe what variable is changed (the manipulated variable). For example, in the question "will more species of wildlife be observed on the study site in the autumn or in the spring?" the season (autumn or spring) is the changed variable. The changed variable is also known as the independent or manipulated variable.

Criteria for Developing Student Data Sheets

You will find examples of data sheets in several of the field investigation activities in this guide, as well as on page 390 in the Appendix. However, as students develop additional questions to investigate, they will make new observations and record new categories of data. Working with students to customize a data collection form as they plan their investigation will help them organize and analyze data.

A data collection form should include the following items:

1. Name(s) of individual(s) collecting the data.

2. The research question.

3. A prediction or hypothesis that answers the question.

4. Study site conditions—including date, time, location, and weather conditions.

5. A description of the study site, in writing, and if the question involves spatial variables, a map as well (see "Guidelines for Mapping" on page xxi).

6. A data table that includes the following components:

   a. A clear title describing what is changed (manipulated variable) and what is observed/measured (responding variable).

   b. A clearly labeled column on the left-hand side of the table to record observations of the manipulated variable.

   c. Responding variable labeled across the top row.

   d. Spaces to record multiple observations or trials.

   e. Observations, counts, and measurements made with proper units.

(Adapted from *Field Investigations: Using Outdoor Environments to Foster Student Learning of Scientific Processes*, 2007. Pacific Education Institute and Association of Fish & Wildlife Agencies.)

Guidelines for Mapping Field Study Sites

Maps are an important tool in field investigations. They are the most efficient and effective means for the collection, analysis, and communication of spatial data. Constructing maps helps us think systemically about the environment and convey complex information about relationships, processes, and scale. Using maps also allows data from different groups, locations, and time periods to be accurately compiled or compared. Even young children will benefit from constructing simple maps, and they can be used to introduce basic concepts such as boundaries, direction, area, overhead view, symbolic representation, and scale. Older and more advanced students will benefit from opportunities to use Geographic Information System (GIS) programs that combine maps and information databases to produce graphic displays. Use of GIS programs are becoming ever more accessible and user friendly as we enter the era of cloud computing. They allow students and educators to see and manipulate data in new ways.

Components of a Map

Every map should have five basic components: (1) a title, (2) a legend, (3) a scale, (4) a compass, and (5) a date. These features will allow students to easily share and compare maps and will also make it possible to refer back to the maps at a future date. Other details can be added to fit the demands of

a particular field investigation. For example, grid lines can be added to help students easily pinpoint locations, and timelines can be added to maps related to long-term investigations. Map content should also be structured to fit the study questions. Possible features to identify include permanent structures (e.g., buildings, driveways, sidewalks), vegetation, topography (i.e., slope of the land), bodies of water, weather, signs of animal life, and areas of sun or shade.

How to Map

The type of map required will depend on the particular field investigation. Often all that's needed is for students to make simple sketches in their field notebooks. Images from Google Earth or other online databases can also be used to create simple maps, and floor plans can be used to create maps of schoolyards and other natural areas located near buildings (students can identify features by their location relative to parts of the building).

> **Tip:** Particularly for younger students, maps do not always need to be drawn exactly to scale to be useful for data collection and analysis.

More advanced students can construct precisely-scaled maps using graph paper. Students should measure the field study site and find an appropriate scale to use (for example, a 20 x 20 yard site can be scaled at one yard per square). They can then measure and map the relevant features at the site. Having all students use the same scale will allow them to easily compile data and also compare observations across dates and locations.

Students may also construct field site maps by using transects (straight lines along which observations are made). With a compass or GPS unit, students should create transect lines sufficiently spaced to cover the field study site (for small sites transects can be laid out using rope or string). Students then walk the transect and record relevant features along with their distance from the starting point and the transect line, then transfer those observations to a map. See "Inventory Methods" in the Appendix for more information about this technique.

Observations and Inferences

Learning how to be observant and learning how to make inferences are two important skills. Students can develop these skills when participating in several Aquatic WILD instructional activities, and they are particularly relevant when implementing field investigation activities. Because many students seem to confuse observations and inferences, this section is intended to help distinguish between the two.

Observations are descriptions of characteristics or attributes—for example, of objects, processes, or events. Inferences are judgments or interpretations about things such as objects, processes, or events.

If a student sees a fish in the water and describes the fish's coloration, length, width, thickness, mobility, fin pattern, scale configuration, and eye characteristics, that student is making an observation. A student who sees a fish darting about near some fish eggs in the water and says it is a female fish protecting a nest has made an inference.

Observations are objective in the sense that what is said about objects, processes, or events can usually be agreed upon by any observer. Descriptions of characteristics such as measurements, weights, color, fin patterns, etc. may usually be the same for any observer, while inferences—derived from judgments or interpretations—go beyond descriptions.

For many students, the act of labeling something becomes an end in itself. For example, a student may observe a fish and identify it as a trout.

Observationally, the student may be seeing an animal of about ten inches in length with a body two inches thick and three inches deep that lives in an aquatic environment. Inferentially, the student may decide that the fish is protecting a nest. Inferences go beyond objective information of the kind obtained by observation and involve efforts to determine correlative relationships with other elements. Inference requires students to use observations in combination with information they may be missing in order to establish what are intended to be informed cognitive leaps, or inferences.

In scientific study, observations typically are gathered. Later, when patterns begin to emerge, the process of inference begins. The distinction between these two modes of inquiry becomes especially important when we consider how willingly some tend to come to conclusions on the basis of inferences with no grounding in observational experience. At best, such inferences reflect guessing and, at worst, superstition and prejudice. Learning the skills of observation adds richness to the database from which inferences are made. As students learn these skills of observation, mature inferences tend to emerge, which in turn lead to new investigative questions, hypotheses, and theories in science.

Use of Notebooks and Journals in Field Investigations

What are science notebooks?

Science notebooks are a tool used by teachers that offers many opportunities to benefit both student and teacher. Just as professional scientists keep notebooks with their observations, thoughts, and ideas, students too can keep notebooks to develop various skills to better engage in science. While science notebooks can take many forms, there are several proven formats that are appropriate for different grade levels. You will find online resources for setting up and using science notebooks at *www. projectwild.org/aquatic.*

Science notebooks can be bound and self-contained, or they can be composed of loose-leaf pages in a binder that can be added to and removed. The notebooks can be filled with whichever types of class material a teacher sees fit. They generally include a dedicated section in the front and back for a table of contents and a glossary of definitions. They might include separate blank pages for a student's illustrations, charts, and diagrams.

How do they benefit students?

The scientific process involves much more than recording observations or data. The ability to make sense of information and communicate scientific concepts is essential to forming a true understanding of those concepts. Science notebooks allow students to create an organized record of their observations, formulate ideas in writing, and ultimately communicate their thinking. Scientific writing requires students to think critically and reprocess information.

Over time, science notebooks become a valuable accumulation of class material as well as an evolving record of a student's own thoughts. The personal nature of a notebook can prompt students to place value on the information inside and make it more likely for them to use their notebooks as references throughout the year.

Additionally, science notebooks can be integrated with classroom discussions for students to compare their thoughts to those of other students. Knowledge that is personally meaningful is created socially through shared understandings. Further, science notebooks offer various opportunities for collaborative learning, which can further develop communication skills. Opportunities for young learners to acquire skills that science notebooks help develop will allow students to better integrate data observation and collection skills into science activities in later years.

How do they benefit teachers?

Science notebooks provide teachers with an evolving record of a student's true level of conceptual understanding and thus can be used as an excellent evaluation tool. There are many opportunities for both informal and formal assessment. Teachers are also able to use the notebooks to gain a sense of how a student's learning has progressed. The student responses in science notebooks can also guide teachers in adapting instruction to address student interests or misconceptions. Finally, science notebooks provide an excellent way for teachers to leave feedback for students and communicate with students on an individual level.

How are field journals different?

While science notebooks are an excellent tool for students to use inside the classroom, field journals are a separate tool for students to use while engaging in outside field investigations. While much of the basic setup may be similar, field journals are intended to provide a convenient and organized way for students to record their observations in the field. This is important, as time in the field is often limited.

Scientists of all types have been using journals for centuries, and these journals have become significant, historical scientific resources. For scientists and students, field journals act as historical records for a certain place and time. As students make long-term observations in their field journals, they can also gain a valuable understanding of ecological changes. Sketches and drawings of observations, such as the one in the image below, are an important part of any field journal. Students should be reminded, however, that getting exact detail is not as important as capturing the important scientific components of what they are observing.

Teachers who involve their classes in the same study site year after year may want to keep one or several students' field journals to serve as a data source in future years, as well as a model for journaling from which other students can learn. Keeping a "class journal" with combined information from several students can be another effective way to collect data over time.

Organization of This Guide

P roject WILD and Aquatic WILD were designed to be instructional resources for educators who want to introduce students to hands-on activities that encourage problem-solving and decision-making skills about the environment they share with wildlife.

Supporting Academic Concepts Required in the Classroom

The activities found in Aquatic WILD are intended for use in both classroom and nonformal settings. The instructional materials are designed to support state and national academic standards appropriate for grades K–12. The activities can easily be adapted to meet the learning requirements for academic disciplines ranging from science and environmental education to social studies, math, and language arts. Educators may choose one or numerous Aquatic WILD activities to teach a concept or skill. The activities may be integrated into existing courses of study, or an entire set of activities may serve as the basis for a specific course.

Organization of Materials

The Aquatic WILD supplementary curriculum is organized into three sections: (1) Ecological Knowledge, (2) Social and Political Knowledge, and (3) Sustaining Fish and Wildlife Resources. Each of these sections is divided into topic areas that correspond directly to the conceptual framework found in the back of the guide. The activities within each topic are ordered by complexity, moving the student from basic conceptual understanding to application. Therefore, educators may find activities in the beginning of a topic area more applicable to elementary classrooms, while those at the end may be more suited for higher grade levels. Within these sections are designated "Field Investigation" activities, which involve pursuing a research question using scientific techniques for gathering data in the field (see "Aquatic WILD Field Investigations" on page xiv.

Section One: Ecological Knowledge

Activities found in this section are designed to develop a basis of understanding for the characteristics of environments and to comprehend how they function. This section establishes a foundation for most of the activities that follow. There are five areas of study: (1) *wildlife populations*, addressing characteristics and population dynamics; (2) *habitats, ecosystems, and niches*, addressing distribution and importance of these concepts; (3) *interdependence*, addressing commonalties and interactions among living things; (4) *changes and adaptations*, addressing environmental changes and organism adaptations; and (5) *biodiversity*, addressing types of biodiversity, human influence, and the importance of habitat.

Section One:
Ecological Knowledge

Section Two: Social and Political Knowledge

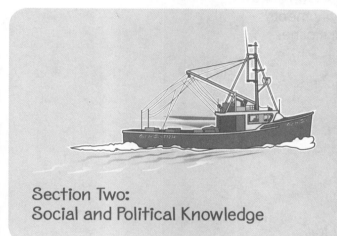

Section Two:
Social and Political Knowledge

In this section, students examine the way human cultures, economics, and politics have affected people's attitudes toward natural resources. There are four areas of study: (1) *cultural perspectives*, addressing cultural development, expressions, and appreciation of wildlife and natural resources; (2) *economic, commercial, and recreational considerations*; (3) *historical and geographic development*, addressing the development of society and commerce as related to natural resources; and (4) *political and legislative frameworks*, both domestic and international.

Section Three: Sustaining Fish and Wildlife Resources

Activities found in this final section of the guide are designed to encourage students to recognize, evaluate, and make responsible choices in their own lives regarding natural resources while reflecting on the knowledge and skills they have acquired in earlier activities. There are five areas of study: (1) *attitudes and awareness*, including human perspectives and values; (2) *human impacts*, both positive and negative; (3) *issues and trends in global perspectives*, including land use, consumptive and nonconsumptive uses of wildlife, and wildlife populations; (4) *wildlife management*, addressing basic concepts related to management considerations and practices; and (5) *responsible action and service*, focusing on how students and others can take action on behalf of wildlife and the environment.

Section Three:
Sustaining Fish and Wildlife Resources

Activity Format

Activity Sidebar

Grade Level: Indicates the appropriate level for the activity based on national subject standards. Aquatic WILD grade level designations include Lower Elementary (K–2); Upper Elementary (3–5); Middle School (6–8); and High School (9–12).

Content Areas: Includes specific subjects as well as general disciplines to which each activity applies. Subject areas listed in this section indicate that the activity meets specific national learning standards for that discipline.

Method:
Summarizes the instructional methods, concepts, and procedures within the activity.

Materials:
Provides a listing of all materials required to conduct the activity including student worksheets, supplies, and equipment.

Activity Time:
Enables the educator to plan accordingly for preparation, activity, and discussion time.

People Power: Serves as a guide for an educator to ensure the activity is appropriate for his or her group's size.

Setting: Indicates whether indoor or outdoor spaces—or both—are needed for the activity.

Conceptual Framework
Topic Reference:
References each activity's place within the conceptual framework of the guide. The two code letters indicate the topic section within the conceptual framework on page 371.

Terms to Know: Introduces words that are central to understanding the concepts taught in the activity. Most Terms to Know are included in the glossary.

Appendices:
Lists supplemental sections within the guide that support or enhance the activity.

Opening Statement

A one-line introduction offers a first glimpse of what the activity entails and can be used as an ice-breaker to capture student interest.

Objectives

This section identifies the concepts and skills students gain through participation in the activity.

Background

Educators can read this section as preparation for class discussion. It provides relevant information regarding the science content, activity concepts, and teaching strategies for conducting the activity.

Procedure

This section provides step-by-step directions to conduct the activity from student introduction through completion. Select field investigations also have the following activity components:

- Study Site
- Introducing the Field Investigation
- Forming the Question
- Conducting the Field Investigation
- Organizing and Analyzing Data
- Drawing Conclusions

(see page xvi for more information.)

Variation

Allowing for flexibility in conducting the activity, this section provides alternate suggestions or options for some activities.

Extensions

Extensions suggest additional activities for continued investigation into concepts addressed in the activity, as well as additional opportunities for assessment and service learning.

Evaluation

The activity ends with diverse assessment strategies that relate to the objectives stated for the lesson.

Additional Resources

This section contains free online resources that provide further information or real-time data to strengthen the concepts presented in the activity.

Student Pages

Activity cards and worksheets meant to be used directly by the student are designated with this icon. FOR STUDENTS These pages may also be downloaded from *www.projectwild.org/aquatic* under Resources.

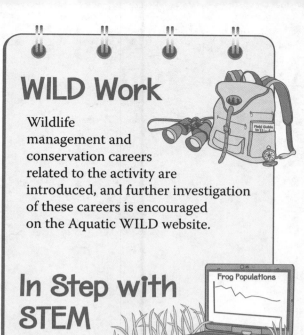

WILD Work

Wildlife management and conservation careers related to the activity are introduced, and further investigation of these careers is encouraged on the Aquatic WILD website.

In Step with STEM

Frog Populations

These extensions offer science, technology, engineering, and math (STEM) lessons to further involve students in the problem-solving applications of the activity's concepts.

Sidebar quotations draw attention to important ideas and information.

Questions to Investigate

Found in a subset of field investigation activities, these sample questions can help educators guide student discussion in articulating a single, testable field investigation question.

- Sample descriptive question
- Sample comparative question
- Sample correlative question

Ecological Knowledge

Activities found in this section are designed
to develop a basis of understanding for
the characteristics of environments and to
comprehend how they function. This section establishes
a foundation for most of the activities that follow. There
are five areas of study: (1) *wildlife populations*, addressing
characteristics and population dynamics; (2) *habitats,
ecosystems, and niches*, addressing distribution and
importance of these concepts; (3) *interdependence*,
addressing commonalities and interactions among
living things; (4) *changes and adaptations*, addressing
environmental changes and organism adaptations;
and (5) *biodiversity*, addressing types of biodiversity,
human influence, and the importance of habitat.

Are You Me?

Grade Level: Lower Elementary

Content Areas:
Science, Environmental Education

Method:
Using picture cards, students match pairs of juvenile and adult aquatic animals.

Materials:
Cardboard for making cards, art supplies

Activity Time:
one or two 20-minute sessions, preparation time for students to bring family pictures to class

People Power:
small groups of three or four students each

Setting:
indoors

Conceptual Framework Topic Reference:
WPIB

Terms to Know:
aquatic animals, grow, change, adult, young, metamorphosis, pupae, larva, nymph

Students investigate magnificent metamorphosis!

Objectives

Students will recognize various young stages of aquatic animals and match them with corresponding adult stages.

Background

Many animals look significantly different in their earliest stages of development when compared to adulthood.

This difference is especially apparent for some aquatic insects. Many aquatic insects undergo metamorphosis, which means change during growth. Some insects experience simple metamorphosis while others undergo complete metamorphosis. In simple metamorphosis, the insect egg develops into a nymph. Nymphs resemble adults but can vary considerably from their adult form in coloration or appendages like wings. Insects that experience complete metamorphosis begin as eggs that develop into larvae. The larvae grow through several stages and then change into pupae. Pupae are usually encased in a protective cover for their next stage of growth. From the pupae emerge the soft-bodied, often pale-colored adults. They differ remarkably in appearance from their earlier forms but are not yet completely formed. Gradually, the soft pale bodies develop firmness and color. In complete metamorphosis, there is little resemblance between adult and earlier forms.

There are also remarkable similarities and differences between other aquatic animals in different life stages. The eggs of many animals hide their eventual form (e.g., alligators, turtles, birds). Pelican hatchlings, for example, closely resemble miniature dinosaurs. Aquatic mammals often are easier to recognize. In general, they do not change as dramatically as other animals in overall appearance as they grow from young to adult stages.

The major purpose of this activity is for students to recognize differences in the life stages of aquatic animals. Students will increase their appreciation of the diversity of wildlife as well as their understanding of growth and change in animals.

Procedure

1. Make pairs of aquatic animal cards such as a pair of beavers, a pair of pelicans, etc. One animal in the pair should be an adult; the other should be at a younger stage of development. The pairs might include adult, larva, nymph, hatchling, juvenile, infant, or egg forms of aquatic animals. Educators can refer to the masters provided on pages 5–8.

2. Ask students to bring two pictures of the same person from home: one as an adult, the other as a child.

3. Divide the class into small groups of three or four students, and have each group stand around a table. Have students at each table place the adult-child pictures on the table and mix them randomly. Once the adult-child pictures are mixed at each table, have the entire group shift to another table so there will not be anyone at the table where his or her own pictures are placed.

4. At the new table, have group members attempt to match pairs of adult-child or student-infant photos.

5. When students at each table have completed their efforts to match pairs, ask all groups to return to the tables where they started this activity. Are the matches correct? Ask students to change any pairs that are not correctly matched. Discuss how difficult or easy it was to correctly match pairs. Introduce the idea that many animals look remarkably different as adults from how they appeared in younger forms. Ask students to think of any young animals that look different as adults. Tell students they are about to learn how to match young and adult forms of many different kinds of aquatic animals.

6. Introduce the aquatic animal cards, and divide the class into groups. Designate one group as "adults" and the other half as "young animals." Give each student in the adult group an adult animal image. Give each student in the young animal group a young animal image. Make sure there is a corresponding match, adult or juvenile, for each card given. Instruct students to look for their match by pairing appropriate adult and juvenile forms.

7. When all students have made their choices, let the group check that the matches are correct. Educators may show the students the matched images on the master.

8. Have all students examine the correctly matched pairs. Look for the similarities and differences in how aquatic animals grow and change, such as in number of legs, presence of wings, or body shape.

NOTE: This activity can be repeated several times by shuffling the adult and young images so that each student becomes familiar with a wider array of animals.

WILD Work

Ask students to discuss the types of things a **Wildlife Biologist** might do each day. Encourage them to share stories of people they may have seen on television who work with animals. What do they think these jobs might be called?

Research the answers to these questions with students by going to *www.projectwild.org/aquatic*.

In Step with STEM

■ Students can photograph stages of a butterfly, from caterpillar to adult.

■ Students can use rulers to measure changes in their height over an extended time period. Graph and compare results.

■ Create a scatter-plot diagram to post as a wall chart that allows students to analyze the relationship between a person's height (on the vertical axis) and age (on the horizontal axis). Each individual in the classroom plots his or her height using an adhesive dot. Expand the data over time and keep the diagram updated by plotting the height/age of classroom visitors.

Many aquatic insects undergo metamorphosis, which means change during growth.

Many animals look significantly different in their earliest stages of development when compared to adulthood. This difference is especially apparent for some aquatic insects.

Extensions

1. Research some of the habitats in which these animals live.

2. Visit some of the habitats where the animals are actually found.

3. Select a pair of images, and research the animal shown to learn more about its life cycle.

4. Discuss and/or pantomime the concept of metamorphosis. Implement a project that demonstrates ecological balance between humans and wildlife in association with an aquatic environment.

Evaluation

1. Choose two aquatic animals. Draw a picture of each animal as an adult and another picture of each animal as it looks when it is young, circling any physical changes that are different between the two stages. Discuss how these changes may make it easier for the adult to live in its habitat.

An adult dragonfly dries its wings.

4

Are You Me?

Are You Me? Cards

Whirligig Beetle		**Whirligig Larva**
Caddisfly		**Caddisfly Larva**
Dragonfly		**Dragonfly Nymph**
Stonefly		**Stonefly Nymph**
Osprey		**Osprey Chicks**

Are You Me? Cards

Mayfly		**Mayfly Nymph**
Pelican		**Pelican Eggs**
Butterfly		**Butterfly Larva**
Duck		**Ducklings**
Frog		**Tadpole**

Are You Me?

Are You Me? Cards

Sea Turtle		**Sea Turtle Eggs**
Sea Otter		**Young Sea Otters**
Cranefly		**Cranefly Larva**
Manatee		**Young Manatee**
Skate		**Skate Egg Case**

Are You Me? Cards

Alligator		**Alligator Hatchling**
Black Fly		**Black Fly Larva**
Dolphin		**Young Dolphin**
Mosquito		**Mosquito Larva**
Beaver		**Young Beavers**

Fishy Who's Who

Students create fish "biographies" to learn more about fish in their local area.

Objectives

Students will (1) recognize and identify the major species of freshwater or saltwater fish that live in their area, (2) describe the value of fish species in some aquatic communities, and (3) locate places where the fish species live.

Background

Fish play a variety of roles in aquatic ecosystems. Some are predators on other aquatic life, while others feed on plant material. Still others scavenge or feed on detritus. Fish also exhibit a wide range of behaviors and have many different characteristics and adaptations. For example, some species deposit eggs in special nests; some have live young. While some fish species are better known or seen more often by people, all fish species play important roles in freshwater and saltwater ecosystems.

Procedure

1. Ask students what fish species they think inhabit waterbodies in their community, state, or region. What different fish species have they seen, caught, heard of, or read about? Make a list of these different kinds of fish and post it in the classroom.

2. Obtain a large map of the area or region. Make sure the map identifies landforms as well as major bodies of water like lakes, rivers, large streams, bays, and oceans. Identify each kind of aquatic habitat located on the map as freshwater or saltwater. Choose a certain area to be studied more closely by the class. A simple way of making a large wall map is to create a slide featuring an appropriate map image using digital presentation software and, using a digital projector, projecting the image onto a piece of paper taped to the wall. Then, trace around the part of the map to be studied.

Grade Level: Upper Elementary

Content Areas:
Science, Language Arts, Expressive Arts, Social Studies, Environmental Education

Method:
Students complete an inventory of fish habitats that exist in their area, obtain information about the various fish species that live in these habitats, and locate the fish species on a map.

Materials:
Paper, pencils, large piece of paper for wall map, state map, digital projector, art materials for illustrations, colored string or yarn, tape, thumbtacks or pushpins

Activity Time:
three 45-minute sessions

People Power: small groups

Setting: indoors,

Conceptual Framework Topic Reference:
WPID

Terms to Know:
biography, habitat, hatchery, freshwater, saltwater

Appendices:
Let's Go Fishing!, Inventory Methods, Using Local Resources, Agencies and Organizations

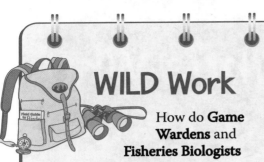

WILD Work

How do **Game Wardens** and **Fisheries Biologists** both contribute to ensuring healthy fish populations?

What types of information would a **Fishing Guide** need to know in order to help provide anglers with the best fishing opportunities?

Research the answers to these questions with students by going to *www.projectwild.org/aquatic*.

In Step with STEM

Use a vinyl tablecloth or recyclable butcher paper to create a "habitat mat." Draw a stream and add natural materials such as rocks and sticks to make a more realistic habitat. Ask students to locate potential habitat spots and place their fish drawing or plastic fish toys in appropriate spots along the stream.

While some fish species

are better known or

seen more often by

people, all fish species

play important roles in

freshwater and saltwater

ecosystems.

3. Divide the class into teams. Have each team identify possible sources of information about fish and fish habitats in the community, state, or region and then develop plans for obtaining the information. State wildlife agency personnel, water-quality specialists, and marine and aquatic biologists may be of assistance. State and federal agencies can also be contacted for materials. Local wildlife clubs, state wildlife agencies, and private groups and organizations often have useful publications. Other sources might include the school or public library and the Internet (visit *www.takemefishing.org* for information on fish that can be found in your area). Have each team use its sources and develop "biographies" for as many of the fish as possible that occur in the study area.

NOTE: Each "biography" could include the fish's name (common and scientific), where it lives, and its habits. It could also include specific information about the kind of habitat (freshwater, estuarine, or marine) the fish needs to survive. In addition to biological information about the fish and its habitat, the "biographies" could include information about ecological, scientific, recreational, economic, political, cultural, aesthetic, and intrinsic reasons for which fish are valuable.

4. Ask each team to create a set of paintings, sketches, or other illustrations of the fish they have written about in their biographies, as well as an illustration of the fish's habitat. These drawings should be large enough to be seen easily in a wall display.

5. Have teams meet and compare the research information from different sources. In some cases, the information they have found may not be consistent. If so, students might try to determine why. Through this process of comparing research notes, students might be able to improve the accuracy and comprehensiveness of their descriptions of various fish and habitat.

6. Returning to the large wall map, ask teams to post the biographies (on cards or other suitable format) and artwork depictions of the fish and their habitat on the map near the locations where the fish live. If the fish biographies begin to overlap, post the cards on the outer edges of the map and extend colored string or yarn from the cards and artwork to the areas where the various fish species live. Use tape, thumbtacks, or pushpins to attach the yarn to the artwork and map.

7. Finally, have students compare their original list of fish from Step 1 with the current information on the map.

Extensions

1. Research why some fish species occur widely throughout various habitats while others are more restricted or specialized.

Provide examples of fish that have special habitat or food needs. What special adaptations do they possess?

2. Invite a local fish biologist to speak to the class about fish and fish habitat in the state.

3. Locate any local hatcheries, fish research stations, or other places doing research with fish and fish habitat. If possible, arrange a tour of one of these facilities for the class or group.

4. Are there any special fish habitat "hot spots" in your state—places where fish are in danger because of human or natural actions? Note these on your wall map and describe the nature of the problem.

5. Investigate fish populations in your area by conducting a "creel survey." Interview people you find fishing (e.g., along streams and rivers, in lakes, at the ocean shore, on piers, at marinas, even at urban parks) and collect data about the fish they catch. For links to more information about creel surveys, visit *www.projectwild.org/ aquatic*.

Evaluation

1. Identify five species of fish that live in your state.

2. Describe where in the state each of these fish is most apt to live and in what types of habitat.

3. Write a story or chain of events that could occur as a result of the loss of one of the local species identified in the activity.

Fish play a variety of roles in aquatic ecosystems. Some are predators on other aquatic life, while others feed on plant material. Still others scavenge or feed on detritus.

BROOK TROUT

Whale of a Tail

Grade Level: Middle School

Content Areas:
Mathematics, Expressive Arts, Language Arts, Environmental Education

Method:
Students use computational, graphing, and measuring techniques to draw or sculpt life-size replicas of whales.

Materials: Large sheets of paper (flip chart or butcher paper); 1-inch grid paper; 200–300 feet (60–90 meters) of twine; writing materials; measuring devices (meter sticks, yardsticks, tape measures); chalk (preferably sidewalk chalk)
OPTIONAL: carpenter's chalk line (extremely useful)

Activity Time: three or four 20- to 60-minute sessions

People Power: teams of five students each

Setting:
indoors and outdoors

Conceptual Framework Topic Reference:
WPIA2

Terms to Know: Cetacea, scale, grid, baleen, buoyancy

Appendix:
Metric Conversion Chart

How many of you could fit inside of a whale?

Objective

Students will describe the sizes of different whales compared to their own body sizes.

Background

Whales, or any of the marine mammals constituting the order Cetacea, are unique among mammals in that they live their entire lives in the water. The term "Cetacean" encompasses over 80 known species of whales, dolphins, and porpoises.

Most smaller whales and all dolphins and porpoises belong to the toothed whale suborder, possessing teeth that are uniform in size and shape. They feed on fish and invertebrates such as squid and crustaceans. Most larger whales belong to the baleen whale suborder. Instead of teeth, whales in this group have large baleen plates that hang from the upper jaw and filter the plankton or krill on which the animals subsist. Probably the largest animal ever to have lived is a baleen whale, the Blue Whale, which has been measured up to 100 feet (30 m) in length, with a weight of more than 220 tons (200 metric tons).

The whale's body is enveloped in a layer of blubber that aids in buoyancy, preserves body heat, and serves as a source of stored energy. Whales breathe air through one or two nostrils on the top of the head, and they can dive deeply.

Whale reproduction is essentially the same as in other mammals. The pregnant female carries her unborn young for 9 to 16 months; usually a single calf is born underwater. A healthy calf can swim from the instant it is born. It begins to nurse soon after. A whale reaches sexual maturity at 6 to 13 years of age. The life span ranges from about 30 years for smaller toothed whales to as long as 80 years for baleen whales.

Typical lengths and weights for mature whales are listed in the table at the bottom of this page.

The most difficult part of this activity for students may be transferring the smaller grid to the larger grid. Although it may appear to be somewhat formidable, the process is rich and rewarding. Students use mathematics, art, and measurement skills. The process is also invaluable in providing students with a lasting awareness of these huge marine creatures.

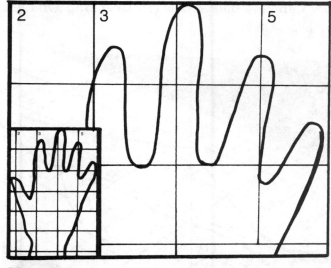
Diagram A

Procedure

1. This activity requires students to draw life-size whales. Divide the class into groups of five, and assign a different whale species to each group.

2. Have students research the average size, including length, of their whale species. Students can also gather information about the life history of the whale to report to the class. Research topics include what characteristics the whale has, what it eats, how it reproduces and cares for its young, what its migration routes are, what its history is in terms of whaling, and what its current status is (endangered, threatened, etc.).

3. Once the size and natural history information have been compiled, students can learn how to use grids to draw the whale to scale. Provide students with grid paper and have them to make a drawing of the outline of their hand as shown in Diagram A.

4. After they have finished drawing the outlines of their hands, have each student make a grid on a much larger paper (i.e., flip chart or butcher paper). The grid squares on the large paper should be three to five times bigger than the squares on the smaller grid paper. Once students have a larger grid made, have them transfer the small drawing of their hand to the larger paper, keeping the same proportions as much as possible. See Diagram A.

NOTE: It helps to number the squares on both pieces of paper. Matching the numbers of the squares on the two pieces of paper helps to transfer the drawing.

Type of Whale	Length		Weight	
	Feet	Meters	Tons	Metric Tons
Humpback Whale	50	15.0	50	45.0
Sperm Whale	55	16.5	47	42.3
Finback Whale	70	21.0	50	45.0
Gray Whale	40	12.0	35	31.5
Right Whale	55	16.5	47	42.3
Blue Whale	90	27.0	75	67.5

5. Students will use the same method to draw life-size whales. First, have students make a drawing of a whale on a clean sheet of 1-inch grid paper. For this drawing, 1-inch squares represent 10 feet on each side.

For example, a Blue Whale is 90 feet long. On the 1-inch grid paper, the drawing will be nine squares long. See Diagram B.

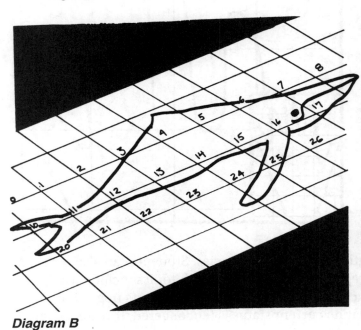

Diagram B

6. Using chalk, students next create a large grid on a parking lot or other open site. The site should be large enough to accommodate the full size of a whale. Make each of the grid squares at the site 10 feet on each side. Transferring the whale image from the 1-inch grid to the 10-foot grid may be made easier by the following:

■ Use two or three long strings with markers every 10 feet. (Knots, short strings tied to the main string, or magic marker spots at 12-inch intervals all work well.)

■ If available, use a carpenter's chalk line.

■ Make sure to number the squares on the drawing and have them numbered the same on the site.

■ The site grid does not have to be exactly square, so don't let this part of the process become too burdensome.

NOTE: Whales can also be created using the metric scale. On 1-centimeter grid paper a Blue Whale, for example, would be 27 squares long (see table on page 13). Make the large squares at the site 1 meter on each side.

7. After the grid is transferred to the study site, students can begin drawing the whale.

Depending on how large the study site is, the class may be able to do only one whale at a time. If this is the case, make enough copies of the 1-inch grid drawing of the selected whale so that each group can have its own copy. Each group can then select a portion of the whale and transfer a section. Collectively, the groups will accomplish the transfer.

8. Have the class gather around the image of the whale. Invite students to join hands to see if the class can make a continuous chain that surrounds the whale. Ask them to stand inside the outline of the whale. How many students could fit inside the whale drawing? How many cars could park on the drawing of the whale?

HUMPBACK WHALE

Whale of a Tail

9. Next, have the groups report on the whale species they have researched. If more than one whale was drawn, repeat the process with each whale group.

10. Summarize by asking students how this activity has broadened their awareness and appreciation of the variety and size of the different species of whales.

Extensions

1. Have students draw the actual size of an African elephant or a brachiosaurus among the whales.

2. Have students research the current status of several species of whales. Find out about the work of the International Whaling Commission.

3. Have students investigate several nonprofit organizations with a mission to conserve whales. How are their activities similar? How are they different? (For example, some groups take direct action to disrupt whaling operations while others focus on policy issues.)

Evaluation

Draw the outline of a person and the outline of several whales researched in this activity. Draw the sketches according to scale. Place the sketches in order from smallest to largest.

WILD Work

Marine Biologists monitor marine plant and animal life and habitat conditions. They collect data on whales that could lead to new hypotheses and theories about the future of whales in the oceans.

Illustrators, Writers, Dancers, Poets, and other artists use their work to inform the public about the natural world. The artwork produced in this activity could be an example of environmental art that raises awareness about an endangered species of whale.

For links to more information on these occupations, see the WILD Work link at *www. projectwild.org/aquatic*.

In Step with STEM

- Have each student compare his or her own height to the length of various whale species. Express findings as ratios.

- Make a life-size inflatable whale out of heavy-weight plastic according to the pattern provided at the end of this activity.

The term "Cetacean" encompasses over 80 known species of whales, dolphins, and porpoises.

Pattern for Life-Size Whale

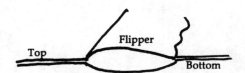

List of Materials

1. Black plastic, 4 mil, 24 feet (7.2 m) by 100 feet (30 m)
2. Clear/White plastic, 4 mil, 16 feet by 100 feet (4.8 m by 30 m)
3. Clear 2 inch (5 cm) wide plastic tape—20 rolls

Tools Needed

1. Tape measures, 100 feet (30 m) and 26 feet (8 m)
2. Scissors to cut the plastic and tape
3. High-speed fan

Steps

1. Lay plastic on 10-foot (1 m) grid.
2. Cut out all parts; cut out some of the flippers or tail flukes from the cutout sections of the whale body.
3. Tape together the flippers and tail flukes (remember the right and left sides for both), and tape together the top dorsal fin. Do not tape the body (straight side) connection.
4. After taping the "fins," turn inside out, placing the tape seam inside.
5. Tape together the cutout sections of the whale's top section as indicated on the plan.
6. Tape together the cutout sections of the whale's bottom section as indicated on the plan.
7. Place the tail flukes and flippers on the bottom section of the whale at their locations.

8. Start taping the top section to the bottom section, using the tail flukes as side walls where they connect to the body; start at the tail section on each side and work toward the mouth area.
9. Do not tape the end of the tail section together.
10. Mouth area—the clear/white plastic will have to be pleated to meet the side area taping; start in the center of the mouth and work out the sides—about 2 inches (5 m) for each pleat.
11. Once the whale is fully taped, place the fan in the tail opening and inflate the whale. One person will go into the whale to the nose section and pull the nose section out through the tail opening, inverting the seams and letting the flippers and tail flukes to the outside.
12. Mount the top dorsal fin on the black top section in the center of the tail section about 58 feet (17.4 m) from the front of the whale.
13. Place the-9 inch (22 cm) eye drawings on the top section, just in front of the flippers. 9" (22 cm)
14. Inflate the model with the high-speed fan; step back and give it room.

Tail Flukes

2 black and 2 clear/white pieces
(Will create right and left tail sections)

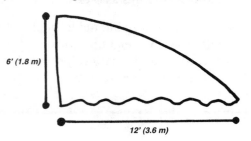

6' (1.8 m)

12' (3.6 m)

Top Dorsal Fin

2 black pieces

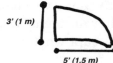

3' (1 m)

5' (1.5 m)
(This side attaches to body of whale)

Flippers

2 black and clear/white pieces
(Will create right and left flipper sections)

6' (1.8 m)

16' (3.8 m)

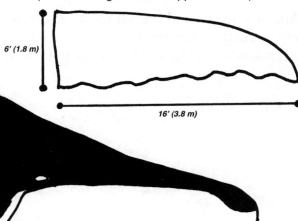

Activity courtesy of Needham Science Center, Needham, Mass.

Pattern for Life-Size Whale

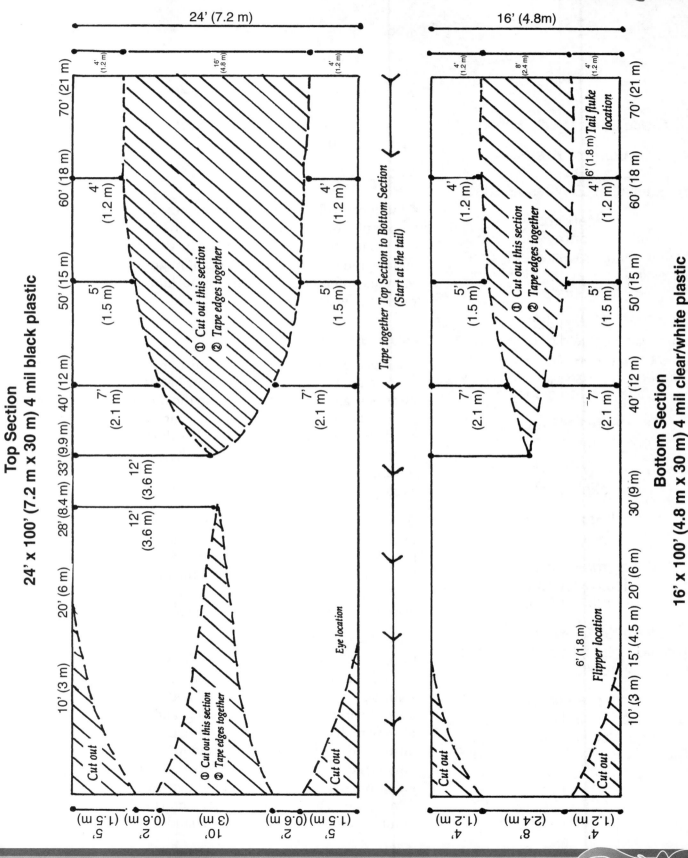

Top Section
24' x 100' (7.2 m x 30 m) 4 mil black plastic

24' (7.2 m)

4' (1.2 m)   16' (4.8 m)   4' (1.2 m)

70' (21 m)

60' (18 m)   4' (1.2 m)

① Cut out this section
② Tape edges together

50' (15 m)   5' (1.5 m)

40' (12 m)   7' (2.1 m)

33' (9.9 m)

12' (3.6 m)   12' (3.6 m)

28' (8.4 m)

30' (9 m)

20' (6 m)

Eye location

① Cut out this section
② Tape edges together

10' (3 m)

Cut out   Cut out

5' (1.5 m)   2' (0.6 m)   10' (3 m)   2' (0.6 m)   5' (1.5 m)

4' (1.2 m)   16' (4.8 m)   4' (1.2 m)

Tape together Top Section to Bottom Section
(Start at the tail)

Bottom Section
16' x 100' (4.8 m x 30 m) 4 mil clear/white plastic

16' (4.8m)

4' (1.2 m)   8' (2.4 m)   4' (1.2 m)

70' (21 m)

Tail fluke location

6' (1.8 m)

60' (18 m)   4' (1.2 m)   4' (1.2 m)

① Cut out this section
② Tape edges together

50' (15 m)   5' (1.5 m)   5' (1.5 m)

40' (12 m)   7' (2.1 m)   7' (2.1 m)

20' (6 m)   15' (4.5 m)   10' (3 m)

6' (1.8 m)
Flipper location

Cut out   Cut out

4' (1.2 m)   8' (2.4 m)   4' (1.2 m)

Migration Headache

Grade Level: Middle School

Content Areas:
Science, Environmental Education, Expressive Arts

Method:
Students portray migrating waterbirds traveling between nesting habitats and wintering grounds.

Materials:
Large playing field or gymnasium; one base (paper plates or carpet squares, for example) for every two or three students

Activity Time:
one 45-minute session

People Power: 20 to 40 students or more

Setting: outdoors or large indoor area

Conceptual Framework Topic Reference:
WPIIA2b2, WPIIA2a2a

Terms to Know: migration, limiting factors, habitat, wetlands, waterbirds, shorebirds

Appendices:
Using Local Resources, Agencies and Organizations, The Ecosystem and Project WILD, Climate Change

If you were a bird, would you survive your winter trek down south?

Objectives

Students will (1) list limiting factors affecting habitats and populations of migrating waterbirds; (2) predict the effects of such limiting factors; (3) describe the effects of habitat loss and degradation on populations of migrating waterbirds; and (4) make inferences about the importance of suitable habitat for migrating waterbirds.

Background

Birds that migrate depend not just on having one suitable habitat, but two and often three habitats. For example, some birds nest and raise their young in the northern limits of their ranges. The same birds may also require suitable habitat in the southern limits of their ranges to live during winter. Because migrating birds travel hundreds or thousands of miles between nesting and wintering grounds, resting and feeding sites (known as stopovers) are crucial.

A variety of remarkable migrating shorebirds and waterfowl inhabit the skies and waters of the United States. Many migrating birds—ducks, geese, cranes, herons, rails, terns, and plovers, for example—require wetlands in their breeding, stopover, and wintering grounds. Without wetlands, dozens of species of waterbirds face loss of necessary habitat.

Over the past 150 years, waterbird populations have been threatened by the alteration of habitats and direct mortality of birds. Numerous populations of waterbirds have declined, some significantly. Destruction of wetland habitat reduces the quantity of suitable nesting, feeding, and resting areas. Alteration of wetland habitats often reduces their quality, making them unsuitable for waterbirds. Wetland habitat, usually found in low, fertile plains along watercourses, was historically prized for conversion to farmland and settlements. Agriculture and development, both residential and industrial, have reduced the number and quality of natural wetlands.

Direct mortality of waterbirds occurs in various ways. The migration routes of North American waterbirds are well known. Before the passage of regulations regarding the hunting of waterbirds, market hunters of the 19th century and very early 20th century decimated flocks by taking advantage of the vast numbers of waterbirds that concentrated at strategic points along these routes. Pollution, through insecticides and herbicides, for example, has also taken a toll. Birds may ingest poisons that have been concentrated as they move through the food web, sometimes with lethal effects. In some cases, pesticides also kill the birds' food, reducing their food supply.

Many international, federal, state, and private groups recognize the importance of wetland habitat to wildlife conservation. In the early 1900s, several laws and treaties were enacted that regulated the hunting of waterbirds and protected the habitat on which they depended. Laws that conserve and enhance wetland habitats have slowed the alteration of these habitats. The Clean Water Act of 1977 and the Farm Bill of 1985 are two major pieces of such legislation. In addition, techniques have been developed to build new wetlands as well as enhance the quality of existing wetlands. The U.S. Fish and Wildlife Service (USFWS) has principal legal responsibility in the United States for managing migratory wildlife at the federal level. State wildlife agencies share some responsibilities with the USFWS for conserving migratory waterbirds.

The effects of natural occurrences and human management efforts during the 1990s have produced mixed results. The North American Waterfowl Management Plan, coordinated by the USFWS, has worked through private-public partnerships to conserve and enhance waterfowl habitat in Canada, Mexico, and the United States. This effort, aided by several years of plentiful rain and snow, has allowed populations of many species of waterfowl (ducks, geese, and swans) to rebound from near record lows in the 1980s and early 1990s to near historic high numbers. In fact the populations of many waterfowl species were larger in 2012 than they were in 1986. Conversely, shorebirds like plovers, terns, and the Red Knot continue to suffer losses because of habitat loss and alteration along coastal regions. In 2001, the U.S. Supreme Court removed isolated wetland ecosystems such as Texas pocket prairies from protection under the Clean Water Act and determined that waterfowl cannot be the sole justification for preserving natural space. In 2006, the Supreme Court once again suggested narrowing the scope of the Act by only including waters with a relatively permanent flow. Many organizations are working to reverse these decisions.

In addition, many waterfowl conservationists are now studying predicted effects of climate change on waterbirds. Rising sea levels could contribute to coastal habitat loss and unusual weather

WILD Work

A **Wetlands Scientist** is responsible for field data collection (plant and animal surveys, soil sampling, etc.), data analysis, and report writing. Education requirements to become a Wetlands Scientist typically include a bachelor's degree in biology or environmental science and expertise in wetland ecology and waterfowl and shorebird biology. This type of scientist often works outdoors in various weather conditions. To find more information on this occupation, visit *www.projectwild.org/aquatic*.

In Step with STEM

Conduct a web search to identify and map sites designated as Important Bird Areas in your state or region.

Many migrating birds— ducks, geese, cranes, herons, rails, terns, and plovers, for example— require wetlands in their breeding, stopover, and wintering grounds.

conditions may disrupt migration patterns for many waterbird species. Increasingly warmer seasons across the upper Midwest have altered some insect life cycles, affecting the timing of food availability for arriving birds. Resources and research are needed to understand shifting conservation concerns for waterbirds in decades to come.

In this activity, each student (assuming a class of 30) represents thousands, if not tens of thousands, of waterbirds. Thus, occasional losses to predation and other events of relatively minor magnitude during the course of migration are not emphasized in the simulation. The major purpose of this activity is for students to dynamically experience some important factors that affect habitat quality and the associated survival of migratory waterbird populations.

Procedure

1. Select a large playing area about 70 feet in length. Place an equal number of bases in three areas on the playing field as shown below:

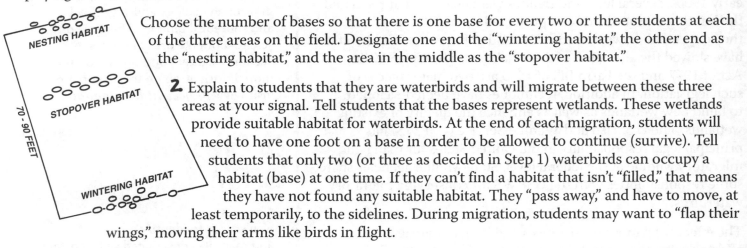

Choose the number of bases so that there is one base for every two or three students at each of the three areas on the field. Designate one end the "wintering habitat," the other end as the "nesting habitat," and the area in the middle as the "stopover habitat."

2. Explain to students that they are waterbirds and will migrate between these three areas at your signal. Tell students that the bases represent wetlands. These wetlands provide suitable habitat for waterbirds. At the end of each migration, students will need to have one foot on a base in order to be allowed to continue (survive). Tell students that only two (or three as decided in Step 1) waterbirds can occupy a habitat (base) at one time. If they can't find a habitat that isn't "filled," that means they have not found any suitable habitat. They "pass away," and have to move, at least temporarily, to the sidelines. During migration, students may want to "flap their wings," moving their arms like birds in flight.

3. Explain to students that many factors will limit the survival of populations of migrating waterbirds. Some involve changes in the wintering, stopover, and nesting habitats. There will be periods of time when food, water, shelter, and space are suitably arranged to meet the habitat requirements of the birds. There will be other times when the habitat is stressed, with many factors limiting the potential for the birds' survival.

4. Begin the activity with all students at the wintering habitat. Announce the start of the first migration. Have students migrate slowly until they become familiar with the process. Then they can speed up. On the first try, all the birds will successfully migrate to the stopover habitat.

5. Explain that most waterbirds need these areas to rest and eat before continuing the migratory journey. Then have them migrate from the stopover habitat to the nesting habitat. Explain that there has been no loss of available high-quality habitat in the area. Thus, a successful nesting season is at hand.

6. Before students migrate back "south," remove one base from the stopover habitat. Explain that a developer has received a permit to drain a wetland to build a mall. Repeat the instruction to migrate, and send the birds to the stopover habitat. Have students who could not find available habitat stand on the sideline. Tell students that these birds died as a result of habitat loss. Remind any "deceased" birds that they will have a chance to get back into the activity. They can come back as surviving hatchlings when favorable conditions prevail and there is habitat available in the nesting ground.

NOTE: the migrations can be graphed as shown in the sidebar on the following page.

7. Continue the migrations by reading *Habitat Scenarios* at the end of this activity. Educators may want to appoint two students as monitors to remove and add bases (habitats) as required for each scenario.

8. After the activity, ask students to identify factors that caused waterbird populations to decline or increase. What are the short- and long-term effects of the decline or increase? Which factors are human-caused? Which are natural? Which factors reduced or enhanced the quality of the habitat? What are the benefits and liabilities related to these factors for the community?

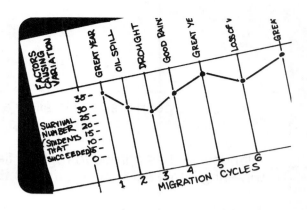

Extensions

1. Research a species of waterbird. Conduct this activity again with each student representing a specific kind of waterbird.

2. Explore the major factors affecting habitat loss and alteration, or gain and restoration, in your area. Research the causes for long-term habitat loss, as well as any major efforts underway to prevent these increasing losses.

3. Using a map, plot the major migratory routes of North American birds.

4. Visit a national wildlife refuge, state wildlife area, bird observatory, private sanctuary, seashore, or other habitat for migratory waterbirds.

5. What other animals migrate? Are the problems they face similar to those of migratory birds? Research these questions online.

6. There are national laws and international treaties protecting migratory species. Identify some of these. What are their histories? Are they effective? Are there problems enforcing them? What migrating species, if any, are unprotected by such laws?

7. Find out how wetlands have changed or remained the same in your community throughout the past 100 years. Are there wetland regulations or zoning laws in your community?

Evaluation

1. Name two human activities and two environmental factors that might interfere with waterbird migration. For each activity and factor, describe the possible effects on waterbirds.

2. Distinguish between effects on individual birds and effects on populations of birds. Indicate if an effect is short term or long term.

3. Why is suitable habitat important for migrating waterbirds? Include in your response a description of the different kinds of habitat that are needed by migrating waterbirds.

4. Is habitat loss a greater threat to the survival of migrating populations than for stationary populations of wildlife? Explain your answer.

Birds that migrate depend not just on having one suitable habitat, but two and often three habitats.

A flock of Willets migrating in their winter plumage.

Habitat Scenarios

A marsh has been dredged to allow a marina to be built.
Remove one habitat from the *stopover* habitat.

A landowner has agreed to re-flood fields after harvesting, increasing acreage for wintering birds. **Add one habitat to the *wintering* habitat.**

A joint federal and state wetland restoration project involved removing "drain tiles" (perforated pipes), allowing a former wetland to flood and return to its natural state. **Add one habitat to the *stopover* habitat.**

A large increase in the number of mink and raccoons has reduced the value of a marsh nesting area. **Remove one habitat from the *nesting* habitat.**

Wintering habitat is reduced by the conversion of bottomland hardwood forests to cropland. **Remove one habitat from the *wintering* habitat.**

New legislation restricts motorboat traffic on a number of lakes and large marshes, reducing the human disturbance to wildlife. **Add one habitat to *stopover* habitat.**

Several years of sufficient rain and snow has replenished the water supply, thus increasing the food supply. **Add one habitat to the *nesting* habitat.**

A timber company has agreed to preserve a forested wetland in exchange for tax credits. **Add one habitat to the *stopover* habitat.**

Filling and diking reduces the amount of tidal wetlands available to waterfowl. **Remove one habitat from the *wintering* habitat.**

A large condominium development has been built on a drained marsh that was prime duck wintering habitat. **Remove one "habitat haven" from the *wintering* habitat.**

A large oil spill from a supertanker has severely damaged a number of salt marshes that were prime wintering areas. **Remove three "habitat havens" from the *wintering* habitat.**

A canal was constructed to remove boat traffic from a river that was used by a large number of waterfowl years ago. It is returning to its natural state. **Add one "habitat haven" to the *stopover* habitat.**

A number of consecutive dry years have occurred, resulting in numerous small wetlands drying up. **Remove one "habitat haven" from the *nesting* habitat.**

A prime wetland area has just been included in a new National Park. Because human disturbance is reduced in the area, **add one "habitat haven" to the *wintering* habitat.**

A coastal resort town has annexed a nearby area containing a wetland, which it has drained to allow tourist hotel development. **Remove one "habitat haven" from the *wintering* habitat.**

Habitat Scenarios

A "cookie cutter" (machinery that removes some vegetation and exposes a small area of water) has been brought to a marsh to improve waterfowl habitat.
Add one "habitat haven" to the *nesting* habitat.

Acid rain has reduced the number of invertebrates needed by hens during nesting.
Remove two "habitat havens" from the *nesting* habitat.

A marsh has been dredged to allow a marina to be built.
Remove one "habitat haven" from the *wintering* habitat.

Prime waterfowl habitat has been severely damaged by the use of a marsh as an irrigation pond. **Remove one "habitat haven" from the *stopover* habitat.**

Water in a human-made marsh has been drawn down to speed decomposition and consolidate the bottom. **Remove one "habitat haven" for a season and then add two "habitat havens" the next season because of the improvement in *nesting* habitat.**

A large increase in the number of mink and racoons has reduced the value of a marsh as a nesting habitat for waterfowl. **Remove one "habitat haven" from the *nesting* habitat.**

The muskrat population explodes, "eating out" cattails in a dense marsh. This makes the marsh more suitable for waterfowl. **Add one "habitat haven" to the *nesting* habitat.**

The owners of fragile wetland areas agree to place their lands in a wetland conservation program. **Add one "habitat haven" to the *wintering* habitat.**

A new dam is built on a river, creating a lake that covers the wetlands above it. **Remove two "habitat havens" from the *wintering* area.** However, the following year the area below the dam is declared a wildlife sanctuary. **Add one "habitat haven" to the *wintering* habitat.**

Pesticides infiltrate marsh water, altering the food web and affecting resistance to disease.
Remove one "habitat haven" from the *nesting* habitat.

Rough fish, such as carp, that stir up bottom sediments are prevented from entering a wetland by a fish trap. This improves the water quality and habitat for waterfowl.
Add one "habitat haven" to the *stopover* habitat.

Filling and diking reduces the amount of tidal wetlands available to waterfowl.
Remove one "habitat haven" from the *wintering* habitat.

New federal laws ban the use of lead shot nationwide. This reduces waterfowl deaths due to lead poisoning. **Add one "habitat haven" to the *stopover* habitat.**

Heavy spring rains in the nesting habitat stimulate aquatic plant and invertebrate growth, creating more food sources for waterfowl. **Add one "habitat haven" to the *nesting* habitat.**

A new water treatment plant reduces the amount of pollutants released into a wetland.
Add one "habitat haven" to the *nesting* habitat.

Got Water?

Field Investigation

Grade Level: Upper Elementary

Content Areas: Science, Math, Environmental Education

Method: Students read about the natural history of several wild animals that might live in their state and discuss how these animals meet their basic needs. Students explore their schoolyard or neighborhood to determine if an assigned animal can obtain the needed food, water, and shelter within an accessible distance or area.

Materials: This field investigation requires special materials. See page 25 for a full list.

Activity Time: one 45-minute preparation period; two 45-minute sessions to conduct activity

People Power: small groups of 2–4 students

Setting: indoors and outdoors

Conceptual Framework Topic Reference: WPIC, HNIB, HNIIA, IDIA

Terms to Know: habitat, arrangement, meter, home range, population, field investigation, limiting factor, predator, prey, wildlife manager

Appendices: Inventory Methods, Using Local Resources, Field Ethics, The Ecosystem and Project WILD

Have you ever considered what an ant has to go through just to get a drink of water?

Objectives

Students will (1) be able to explain the importance of accessible water to the survival of an animal; (2) describe the types and locations of three habitat components (food, water, and shelter) for two different species; (3) measure the distance between the source of food, water, and shelter for each species; (4) compare and contrast the home range for two species and discuss differences; and (5) evaluate a habitat to determine if the sources of food, water, and shelter are in an appropriate arrangement for an animal to survive.

Study Site

Determine where on your schoolyard or alternate local outdoor area you will conduct this field investigation. Select a location where students can see common animals—songbirds, squirrels, rabbits, spiders, insects, etc. If the school site is not appropriate, locate a nearby park or area (even a vacant lot); be sure to get permission if the site is on private property. An alternative is to instruct students to choose an animal they see at home and conduct their investigation in their backyard or at a local park as homework.

Background

All animals need food, water, shelter, and space for survival. The area where animals find the arrangement of food, water, shelter, and space suitable to their needs is called their habitat. Wild animals must find their own food, water, and shelter. The more time they spend meeting their needs (i.e., the further they travel to gather food, water, and shelter), the more energy they use, leaving less energy available for health maintenance and reproduction. They are also more exposed to predators and the elements when searching for food and water. Therefore, the arrangement of food, water, and shelter in an

© Council for Environmental Education (CEE)

animal's home range is critical to the survival of the individual animal, as well as the population of that animal. Biologists have determined an average home range for many wildlife species based on the entire area (space) the animal typically travels to find the food, water, and shelter needed for living and reproduction. The typical home range of a small animal, such as a spider or deer mouse, is much smaller than that of a larger animal, like a bear.

Food supplies the energy an animal needs to survive. Shelter is important for safety and reproduction. Water is critical to an animal's survival for a variety of reasons, from maintaining overall health to cleaning fur or feathers. Water helps animals digest food and regulate body temperature. Snakes need water to keep their skin moist when shedding. Amphibians need water for taking in oxygen through their skin, so they can lay their eggs, and for larval development. And for fish, staying in water is the only way to breathe oxygen!

How much water does an animal need to survive? Does the animal have to drink from a creek or will a small puddle do? Does the water have to be pure and of high quality? Where does an animal find its water? Does the animal even drink its water? Answers to these questions vary greatly for different species.

When evaluating an area to determine if it provides suitable habitat for a species, wildlife managers look at type, quality, and quantity of water, food, and shelter, as well as how they are arranged. The lack of any of these components within a given area will limit the number and types of animals that can live there. The component (food, water, shelter, space, disease, predation, climactic conditions, pollution, hunting, etc.) that limits the number or type of animals in an area is called a limiting factor. Therefore, an important consideration in a habitat evaluation is the distance between sources of water and other habitat components.

As discussed earlier, home ranges of different species vary in size, so measuring the distance between habitat components for different species may require different tools. For the squirrel, a long string marked in meter increments, a tape measure (like those used for track and field events), or a surveyor's wheel would work well. On the other hand, a ruler or shorter tape measure would work better for measuring a caterpillar's home range. In the case of a large animal—coyote, raccoon, or opossum—a hand-held Global Positioning System (GPS) unit might be the best tool to determine distances between its food, water, and shelter. **NOTE:** Use measuring devices with which students are familiar, or have a separate lesson before the investigation to learn how to use chosen devices.

Materials

- ☑ *Habitat Evaluation Data Form* (page 31; one copy per student team)
- ☑ *Field Investigation Analysis* (page 32)
- ☑ *Home Range and Habitat* (page 33)
- ☑ clipboards
- ☑ pencils
- ☑ field guides to local wildlife (bird guides, insect field guides, mammals, etc.)
- ☑ books or websites on natural history of wild animals found locally
- ☑ access to a computer for students to conduct research
- ☑ measuring instruments (surveyor's wheel, GPS used as an odometer trundle wheel, long distance measuring tape, or long string and a meter stick)

NOTE: A long distance measuring tape may be borrowed from a track team; a surveyor's wheel could be borrowed from a local engineering or surveying firm; or if the distance between two sites is significant, a hand-held GPS can be used. Google Earth and topographic maps can also be used for long distance measurements.

OPTIONAL: *What's My Question?* and *Conclusions and Next Steps* (in Appendices); students' science notebooks

All animals need food, water, shelter, and space for survival.

Introducing the Field Investigation

1. Begin with a discussion of wildlife that students have seen near school and in their neighborhoods. What animals (big and small) do students commonly see? Make a class list of wild animals students have seen in the area. Why are the animals there? (If needed, review the definition of habitat and its basic components: food, water, shelter, space. Discuss the importance of each component for the animal's survival.) Where in the area do students think animals find food? Shelter? Water? Point out that when we examine animals' habitats, water sources often are overlooked. Have students brainstorm where different species of animals might get their water and record the answers.

Ask students how far they think each of the animals listed might travel to meet its needs for food, water, and shelter. Animals need energy to maintain body temperature, to move, and to reproduce. How does the distance between basic needs in an area affect their use of energy? (**NOTE:** the more energy used to travel and meet its basic needs, the less energy an animal has to grow and reproduce.)

How might changes in an animal's habitat (flood, drought, development, etc.) affect the amount of energy it needs? Why?

Discuss how animals find what they need to survive in their habitats and distances they may need to travel to meet their needs. Explain to students that all animals (and plants) have a habitat. Even the students have a habitat! Where do they get their water? Where do they get their food? Where do they get their shelter (be open-minded about this—house, apartment, schools, tent, car, trailer, etc.)? Explain that different animals have different habitats, but they also have differently-sized home ranges. The area (distance) the animal travels to survive and reproduce is its home range. For a chipmunk that lives in a forest, the forest is the chipmunk's habitat. But, how far does the chipmunk travel to find its needs? Will a chipmunk travel ten miles or less than one mile? How far would you travel to find your needs? Ask students to list all of the places found in their home range. Using a road map of your surrounding study site area, have each student use a different color marker to draw lines between where students travel for food, water, and shelter. Compare and contrast their home ranges.

ACORN WOODPECKER

Got Water?
© *Council for Environmental Education (CEE)*

2 Provide each student the opportunity (or assign for homework) to research one species from the classroom list that lives in their area. From the information gathered, have each student create a short paragraph, list, drawing, or presentation detailing the natural history of his or her animal including habitat, food requirements, typical water sources, and the size of the home range. Because finding information on home range may be difficult, examples of home range sizes for different types of animals are provided in this activity (see *Home Range and Habitat*).

3 Next, ask students to share their information with a partner. Pair those students who researched really small animals, like a caterpillar or ant, with those who researched a larger animal, like a chipmunk or frog. Ask each student pair to develop a chart or Venn diagram to compare and contrast habitat, food, water, shelter, and space (home range) of the two animals. Students should notice that different animals live in different habitats and have different needs. Different species also have different home range sizes and therefore require different amounts of space to survive. Re-emphasize that food, water, shelter, and space need to be in the proper arrangement for an animal to survive.

Discuss how animals obtain what they need to survive, with a special focus on the importance of water to animals. Ask students to make a list of different water sources animals might use.

4 Explain to students that partner pairs will go outside to investigate and evaluate wildlife habitat for the two animal species they researched. Show students an aerial map to identify boundaries and give a visual reference of the study site (Google Maps, Google Earth, or a local environmental agency are good source of aerial maps). Ask students what they know from previous visits to the site or what they can observe from the aerial photograph or map. Discuss where the species they researched might be found.

5 Before going to the study site, provide each student pair with a clipboard, pencils, graph or drawing paper, and one *Habitat Evaluation Data Form*. Have student pairs complete the Part 1 sections of the *Habitat Evaluation Data Form* using the natural history information they previously researched about their species. You can also provide field guides if students want to look up more information about their species, or do additional research in the library or online.

Ask students what types of devices they might use to measure distances between food, water, and shelter for the species they researched. Collect enough suggested devices (measuring tapes, rulers, Global Positioning System, etc.) to enable students to have multiple measuring device options.

WILD Work

Wildlife habitat in urban areas often results in wild animals coming into close proximity to people. Attracting wildlife is sometimes intentional, such as bird-feeding or when creating a butterfly garden. Other times, people's actions may attract wildlife in unintentional ways, possibly causing problems for people and animals. Invite an **Urban Biologist** or **Urban Wildlife Specialist** to present on actions people can take to minimize problems between people and wildlife in urban areas. For additional information about Urban Wildlife Biologists or Urban Wildlife Specialists, go to ***www.projectwild. org/aquatic.***

Students can search for lizards in a variety of habitats.

Water is critical to an animal's survival for a variety of reasons, from maintaining overall health to cleaning fur or feathers.

Forming the Question

1. Take students to the study site. Make sure students understand to alternate measuring and recording duties between partners. Ask them where they might look for wildlife or evidence that wildlife have been in the area (e.g., under rocks, in mulch, under leaf litter for smaller animals, nests in trees, burrows in the ground, scat, a feather or tuft of hair on the ground, a pile of eaten acorns or nuts, animal tracks, etc.).

2. Have students prepare a simple map of the study site. This can be done either inside using an aerial photograph or map or once you get outside, when students can view the study site. Maps can be drawn in the students' notebooks or on a piece of graph or writing paper. The map will be used to mark the locations of food, water, and shelter for each of their two animals.

3. Ask students to think about what their assigned animals eat and how much water and what type of water their animals would need (water types include stream, pond, dew, food consumed, etc.). Have students consider what type of shelter their animals prefer (under a rock, in a nest in the trees, in a burrow, under a large pine tree, in the grass). Ask students if they think their animals could find the food, water, and shelter they need in a suitable arrangement on this study site. Task student pairs to make predictions on whether this site is suitable or unsuitable for each of their two animal species.

As a class or in groups, develop a field investigation question around the central theme of habitat suitability. See the "Questions to Investigate" text box in the sidebar for examples of researchable questions. As an option, students can also use *What's My Question?* (page 388) to help them develop a question they are able to investigate.

Conducting the Investigation

1. Ask students what they need to know in order to determine if the study site is suitable habitat or if water is available, etc. Based on research and discussions of home range, students should understand they will need to first find sources of food, water, and shelter. Second, they will need to measure the distance between the food, water, and shelter sources to see if they are within a reasonable distance and space for the animal to travel (this is where home range is important).

2. Give student pairs time to investigate the study site and find what they believe to be their species' sources of food, water, and shelter. (It is fine if they choose the wrong source of food, water, or shelter for their species; they will have an opportunity to learn more about it.) Have them record the location and describe or illustrate the source of their species' food, water, and shelter on the study site maps they created during the previous "Forming the Question" section.

3. Once student pairs have found and recorded potential sources of food, water, and shelter, have them select measuring devices from the array they identified earlier and measure the distance between each species' food, water, and shelter. Have students draw lines and record the distances on their maps. They should also record this information on Part 2 of their *Habitat Evaluation Data Forms*. Remind students to include units with measurements on maps and data sheets. **NOTE:** Students could also capture digital photos of different habitat components to include with their data sheets.

Organizing and Analyzing the Data

1. After completing remaining portions of the *Habitat Evaluation Data Form*, students should analyze the distances between each species' food, water, and shelter sources. Are the distances reasonable for the animal to travel for its basic needs? (Hint: How do these distances compare with the animal's home range)?

2. Have each student complete the *Field Investigation Analysis* included with this activity. For more advanced students, consider having students complete the *Conclusions and Next Steps* field investigation page (see Appendix).

Drawing Conclusions

As a class, discuss each pair's findings. Discuss the answers on the *Field Investigation Analysis* page. How do students relate distance between an animal's food, water, and shelter and whether or not a habitat is suitable? They should begin to demonstrate an understanding that if one component is too far away from the others, it limits the ability of the animal to live in the area and is considered a limiting factor.

The animal needs to live in habitat where the components are arranged so it does not use too much of its energy meeting its basic needs; otherwise, it must move to a new area or has difficulty surviving. The time an animal spends traveling between its sources of food, water, and shelter limits time to mate and care for young. Time spent away from shelter, looking for food or water, can make the animal more vulnerable to predators.

In Step with STEM

Frog Populations

- Design the ideal habitat for one of the animals researched, including food, water, and shelter requirements. Select a site to inventory for existing habitat components. Then create a restoration plan to help provide the missing habitat components the species needs to survive.

- Research common native plants that provide habitat for native wildlife species in your area. Sources of information can include websites, interviews with natural resource professionals, or field guides. Work with a local nursery or habitat stewardship group to organize and host a native plant sale.

- While this activity frequently involves small animals that have relatively small home ranges, also consider larger animals to research. Calculate the difference in home ranges for local wildlife species of various sizes. What natural circumstances will cause home ranges to fluctuate?

- Using an aerial map or photograph of the study site, assess if the species researched in this activity must travel over human-dominated landscapes that involve dangers of vehicles, domesticated pets, habitat intrusion, etc. Design "safety corridors" for the travel of these species. Ideas may be under-roadway passages, increased edge vegetation plantings, or proposals to city officials to request legal protection of existing wild areas in the neighborhood.

A dragonfly finds an urban water source.

The component (food, water, shelter, space, disease, predation, climactic conditions, pollution, hunting, etc.) that limits the number or type of animals in an area is called the limiting factor.

If the study site includes bird baths and bird feeders, these can be recorded as water and food sources.

Evaluation

1. Was there suitable habitat at the study site for each species? Provide evidence from observations to support your answer.

2. How might the arrangement of food, water, and shelter at the study site be changed to improve its suitability for the species researched (i.e., reduce time and energy used to meet its basic needs)?

3. For each species, describe what people could do to improve the habitat for that species. **NOTE:** Discuss appropriate habitat restoration with students in contrast to detrimental wildlife interactions such as providing human food, relocation, or direct contact with wild animals, which are unwise and unlawful.

4. Overall, is this site a good habitat for a diversity of species that might live in this area? Present evidence from class findings to support your claim. (Hint: Does it have several sources of water, a wide variety of food sources, and many different kinds of shelter?)

5. Select one species from the list that was found to have a good habitat at the study site and compare with a species that was not found to have a suitable habitat at the site. What are the differences in what the two species need to live? Why did the study site provide good habitat for one species and not the other?

Extensions

1. Ask students if people have impacted habitat on the study site in any way. How? Did these impacts improve or degrade the habitat? Have each student write a short paragraph explaining his or her point of view that includes evidence from observations at the site.

2. Have groups of students make a scale drawing of the study site. Be sure they label each of their species' sources of food, water, and shelter on their scale map. Then, have students draw lines between the habitat components and label the distance.

3. Visit a new area. Take a few minutes to compare your initial study site with this new site. What animals might be found at this site but not at your initial study site? Why? Students should include evidence from their observations that support their claims.

4. Have students choose another native animal found in your area. Have students draw a map of the "perfect" habitat for this species. Or, draw a picture labeling the animal's food, water, and shelter.

Habitat Evaluation Data Form

Date: _____ **Study Site Location:** _____	**Species #1:** _____ **Distance of Home Range** *(if traveling in a straight line):* _____	**Species #2:** _____ **Distance of Home Range** *(if traveling in a straight line):* _____
Part 1: Food Source (examples: acorns, nectar)		
Part 2: Location of Food (examples: oak tree by slide, flowers by front door)		
Part 1: Water Source (examples: dew, pond)		
Part 2: Location of Water (examples: dew on grass, small pond near the trees)		
Part 1: Shelter (examples: nest, burrow, rock)		
Part 2: Location of Shelter (examples: nest in pine tree, hole in the hill along fence)		
Distance between Food and Water		
Distance between Water and Shelter		
Distance between Food and Shelter		

Field Investigation Analysis

1. How far must the animal travel if it goes from its shelter to a food source, then to a water source, and then back to its shelter?

2. Based on your earlier research, how does the distance the animal must travel compare with the animal's home range?

3. If the animal's food, water, and shelter are too far for the animal to travel, what do you think the animal would need to do in order to survive?

4. Do you think this site is a good habitat for your animal? Why or why not?

5. Can you answer your original field investigation question based on the information you gathered? If yes, answer the question in one or more complete sentences. If no, explain what additional information you might need to answer the question.

6. What things have people done to change habitat in this area?

7. What things could people do to make this site a more suitable habitat for your species? Would these actions affect other species?

Home Range and Habitat

Home range can be defined as the area within which an animal normally lives and finds what it needs for survival. Basically, the home range is the area that an animal travels for its normal daily activities. Many factors influence the size of a home range, including: species, number of animals (density) in an area, the time of year, the sex of the animal, and the type and quality of the habitat. Typically home range sizes fall within a range, for example, the home range of a gray squirrel varies from 1.2 acres to 8 acres. This is very dependent on the number of squirrels in the area and the quality of the habitat. The table below provides a comparison of home ranges and habitat components for four common animals.

Animal	Gray Squirrel	Eastern Bluebird	Night Crawler	Ant
Possible sizes of home range (as area or volume)	0.5–3.2 hectares	0.8–2.2 hectares during spring, summer. Often larger in fall, winter up to 240 acres.	1500 cubic centimeters– 1 cubic meter	5,000 square meters
Typical size of home range (as area or volume)	0.5 hectares	0.8 hectares during spring, summer, early fall	1 cubic meter	1,000 square meters
Size of home range if traveling in a straight line (as distance)	137 meters	122 meters in spring, summer, early fall	100 centimeters	Up to 100 meters
Water	Stream, pond, creek, dew, and some from succulent plant material	Ponds, creeks, bird baths. Prefer running water.	Rain, dew. Skin must stay moist.	Dew, moisture, or liquids from foods they eat, anywhere they can find water.
Food	Variety of nuts (acorns, walnuts), buds, flowers fungi	Mostly insects. Some berries, such as dogwood	Dead leaves, soil, microorganisms, and animal remains	Fruits, plant materials, insects. A variety of foods depending on the species.
Shelter	Trees, tree cavities, leaf nests	Prefer running water.	Underground tunnels in soil	Most in soil underground. Some build ant hills. Others live in logs or other rotting plant material.
Habitat Type	Forest, woodlots, parks, backyards. Must have trees.	Fields, shrubby fields, parks, backyards with scattered trees	Most not native to U.S. Live in soil in forests, fields, gardens.	Found in a variety of habitats from deserts to forests. Not found in Antarctica or the Arctic.

Designing a Habitat

Grade Level: Upper Elementary, Middle School

Content Areas:
Science, Language Arts, Expressive Arts, Environmental Education

Method:
Students design a habitat suitable for aquatic wildlife to survive in a zoo or an aquarium.

Materials:
3" x 5" cards, art supplies, writing materials, papier mâché, modeling clay, gallon jars, string, cardboard, cardboard boxes (to use as frames for models)

Activity Time:
two or more 45-minute sessions

People Power:
groups of two to four students each (can be modified to accommodate different numbers)

Setting:
indoors

Conceptual Framework Topic Reference:
HNIB1, HNIIA, HNIIA1

Terms to Know:
habitat, zoo, aquarium

Appendices: Using Local Resources, Field Ethics, Animals in the Classroom, Benefits of a Classroom Aquarium, Agencies and Organizations

Ever wonder if that gorilla at the zoo is comfortable?

Objectives

Students will identify the components of habitat that are essential for most aquatic animals to survive.

Background

Zoos and aquaria are, for the most part, artificial habitats. The basic life-giving conditions of food, shelter, air, water, and space in a suitable arrangement for animals to survive seem obvious. However, in aquaria, water is a uniquely sensitive part of the habitat. The surrounding envelope of water must meet specific requirements for different aquatic life forms. Slight changes in salinity, pH, and dissolved oxygen plus the presence of a wide range of pollutants can spell disaster for certain aquatic organisms.

To successfully house aquatic wildlife in zoos and aquaria, those facilities must pay careful attention to the range of conditions that each life form can tolerate. There are also certain physical requirements in terms of the shape and dynamics of the exhibit that must be compatible with each creature. For example, some fish require moving water or currents. Others prefer almost static conditions. Some prefer deep water and others shallow rocky bottoms. Penguins prefer refrigerated settings. The variations are remarkable when one considers designing habitats for microorganisms in pond water and mammoth habitats for Killer Whales and walruses.

Concern for the physical requirements of animals must go beyond meeting minimum survival needs. Attention is also given to the animals' comfort, creating conditions as similar to those in their natural habitats as possible.

In the growing practices of aquaculture (human cultivation of freshwater organisms) and mariculture (human cultivation of oceanic organisms), research is conducted regarding habitat requirements. Often natural streams, rivers, lakes, and even the ocean are used in these enterprises. Attention to water quality and disease control is just as important in these settings as it is in the confined habitats of zoos and aquaria.

The major purpose of this activity is for students to recognize and appreciate the complex life requirements of aquatic wildlife by focusing on the artificial habitat conditions of zoos and aquaria.

Procedure

1. Prepare 3" x 5" cards with the name of one of the following animals written on each card: trout, shark, goldfish, sturgeon, Sea Otter, Largemouth Bass, water strider, beaver, Diving Beetle, Killer Whale, penguin, sea turtle, alligator, Siamese Fighting Fish, frog, and oyster (expand the choices as appropriate).

2. Divide the group into teams of two to four. Have each team draw one card from a container.

3. Each team will be responsible for designing an artificial habitat in which its animal could successfully live. Inform students that each team will be expected to conduct research and consult reference materials or experts to determine the life requirements of each creature. In addition, students will investigate and establish the characteristics of the natural habitat of the animals.

4. When the research is complete, each team of students is to design and build a model or small replica of a zoo exhibit or aquarium habitat that would be suitable for the animal's survival and comfort in captivity. Establish a scale for the exhibits (for example, 1 inch = 5 feet for the large animals; actual size for the insects).

5. Once the models are complete, ask each team to report to the rest of the class. Each report should include a description of the basic biological needs of each animal as well as a description of the characteristics of its natural habitat. Students should point out how their models are designed to meet the needs of the animal.

OPTIONAL: Once all the reports are finished, have students arrange their models in a larger plan for a zoo or an aquarium.

6. Ask students to summarize the components of habitat that seemed to be necessary for the survival of the aquatic animals they studied. (Food, water, shelter, air, and space in a suitable arrangement would be the minimum necessary components.)

WILD Work

How could an **Animal Nutritionist**, an **Animal Physiologist**, and an **Animal Well-being Specialist** work together to create suitable habitats for aquatic wildlife at a zoo or an aquarium?

To find more information on these careers, head to: *www.projectwild.org/aquatic*.

In Step with STEM

Prior to designing a habitat, research habitat requirements of select species using the American Zoological Association's Animal Care Manuals available online. See *www.projectwild.org/aquatic* for the link.

To successfully house aquatic wildlife in zoos and aquaria, those facilities must pay careful attention to the range of conditions that each life form can tolerate.

Concern for the physical requirements of animals must go beyond meeting minimum survival needs. Attention is also given to the animals' comfort, creating conditions as similar to those in their natural habitats as possible.

Extensions

1. Visit an aquarium and arrange for a staff person to explain how the aquarium addresses the same basic requirements for animals that the students did—that is, the components of habitat.

2. Design habitat outdoors using natural materials such as sticks, leaves, soil, clay, and sand.

3. Create a balanced aquarium for the classroom.

4. Discuss the reasons for and against keeping aquatic wildlife in captivity in zoos and aquaria.

Evaluation

1. List the components of suitable habitat that are necessary for most aquatic animals to survive.

2. Choose an aquatic mammal, fish, amphibian, or other aquatic animal. Describe the biological characteristics of the animal and the kind of habitat requirements it has in order to survive. Compare similarities and differences between this aquatic animal and another aquatic animal. What things, if any, do they both need to survive? What things, if any, must be different in their habitats for each kind of animal to survive?

Designing a Habitat
© *Council for Environmental Education (CEE)*

Water Safari

Where might wild animals get water?

Objectives

Students will observe, identify, describe, and illustrate wildlife and potential sources of water for wildlife on a study site.

Study Site

This field investigation activity can be done in a variety of outdoor areas. It is especially well-suited for urban environments or for those without access to large natural areas. Possible locations include school grounds, a nearby park, wild areas such as a field or forest, or even a vacant lot. Ensure that the appropriate permission has been granted for any areas outside the school property.

Background

Animals that are not domesticated are considered wildlife. Generally, wild animals must find their own food, shelter, and water. These resources can be found throughout natural environments, but even in urban settings many species of wild animals are able to find necessities of life. Urban wildlife can include mammals, birds, fish, reptiles, amphibians, insects, spiders, and other invertebrates.

Every animal needs food, shelter, air, water, and space to survive, and all of these resources need to be found in the proper arrangement. For example, smaller animals like insects and squirrels require a water source that is near their shelter and source of food. Animals that can travel longer distances, like birds and deer, may be able to use water sources located farther away. Depending on the animal, habitats can be as small as a crack in the sidewalk or a single tree, or as large as a city park or mountain range.

All wildlife, no matter where it lives, must have water to survive. For small invertebrates like insects and spiders, tiny drops of water on or under leaves or in pavement cracks may be enough to sustain them. Larger animals such as birds, mammals, and

Grade Level: Lower Elementary

Content Areas:
Science, Language Arts, Environmental Education

Method: Students will conduct a field investigation at an outdoor study site to discover wildlife, signs of wildlife, and the locations of water sources which wildlife may use on the site.

Materials:
Clipboards or other hard writing surfaces, pencils, copy of *Wildlife and Water Source Note Cards* (page 43) for each student, binoculars, magnifiers.
OPTIONAL: flashlight, camera, field guide

Activity Time: one or two 45-minute sessions

People Power:
any

Setting:
indoors and outdoors

Conceptual Framework Topic Reference:
HNIIA, HNIIB, WPIA, WPIC

Terms to Know: wildlife, habitat, water source, conservation, nocturnal, diurnal, shelter, safari, domesticated

Appendix: Inventory Methods, Field Ethics, The Ecosystem and Project WILD

reptiles may use permanent water sources (such as ponds, streams, or fountains) or temporary ones (such as puddles in a field or rainwater that collects in parking lots and on trash can lids). Many animals get a majority of their water from moisture in the food they eat.

Students will identify water sources on a safari hike to an outdoor study site. Because a water source is any place where a living organism gets the water it needs to survive, sources identified on the safari will depend on the study site surveyed. Observations from urban sites are likely to include human-made water sources such as fountains, sprinklers, and drainage channels. Natural sources of water may include streams, puddles, or dew. Study sites may have a mix of both natural and human-made water sources. Natural water sources can be subject to seasonal conditions or weather-related events such as flooding or drought. These conditions may also create municipally-imposed water restrictions on human-made water sources such as sprinkler systems and fountains, reducing these sources on the study site.

The types of wildlife students find will also depend on the habitat they search. In the soil surrounding the school building, students might discover small specimens of wildlife such as wolf spiders, carpenter ants, or earthworms. Farther from buildings, they may see a wider variety of insects and larger animals such as birds, mammals (squirrels or rodents), reptiles, or amphibians. The time of day (nocturnal vs. diurnal animals), season, and weather conditions will also play a role in wildlife viewing on the study site. Emphasis should be placed on students searching for wildlife signs or clues in addition to the actual animal to ensure a more successful safari. Animal signs, including animal droppings; wasp, squirrel, or bird nests; feathers; tracks near the water source; chewed nuts; etc., are more frequently encountered and offer the student an "up-close" experience.

Introducing the Field Investigation

1. Ask students to think about the things they need to survive (food, water, shelter, and space). Ask students where they get water for drinking, bathing, washing, swimming, cooking, etc. Discuss the origin of your local water source with students, including if this source is a groundwater source like an aquifer or a surface-level source such as a lake or river. This information can be obtained from your local water utility company or other area environmental agency. Also, discuss with students that the beverages and food that they eat and drink are also a source of water for their bodies.

2 Ask students if people are the only living organisms that need water to survive. Have students provide examples of other organisms that depend on water along with how each uses water (drinking, bathing, washing, swimming, etc.). Students will note that animals and people use water in similar ways.

3 Ask students to define wildlife. Help students understand the difference between wild and domesticated animals. Domesticated animals depend on people for food, shelter, and water, while wild animals must find these resources for themselves. Have students create a comparative class list that provides examples of wild and domesticated animals that live in their neighborhoods.

4 Inform students that they will be conducting an investigation to explore what wild animals can be found at the study site, as well as where those animals might find water.

Forming the Question

1 Ask students where they think wild animals find water. Explain that a water source is any place where a living organism gets the water it needs to survive. Ask students for examples of water sources that animals may use in their neighborhoods. Students may suggest large bodies of water such as lakes and rivers. Also discuss smaller water sources like puddles, dew on grass or leaves, and water in the food animals eat.

2 Together as a class, create a list of researchable questions about the wildlife and water sources they might find at the study site. From the list, determine which questions the class can try to find answers to by exploring the outdoor site. See "Questions to Investigate" in the sidebar for a list of questions students may generate.

Conducting the Field Investigation

1 Prepare students for their "safari." Have them assist in packing for the trip: you might want to include magnifiers, binoculars, a flashlight to illuminate corners and cracks, a camera, and field guides of plants or animals. Students might want to make paper safari hats or take binoculars made from cardboard tubes.

2 Give each student a copy of the *Wildlife and Water Source Note Cards*, a clipboard or other hard writing surface, and a pencil. Explain that they will be acting as scientists trying to find answers to the questions they created back in the classroom. To answer the questions, they should be looking for wildlife or clues that wildlife have been in the area (e.g., animal droppings, wasp

Questions to Investigate

Questions could include...

Where in the school yard or study site can water be found?

What are the different kinds of water sources?

What wildlife can we find at the site?

What animal is most commonly observed on the study site?

What clues can we find that wildlife have been in the area?

Where on the site will we find wildlife or clues of wildlife?

Generally, wild animals must find their own food, shelter, and water. These resources can be found throughout natural environments, but even in urban settings many species of wild animals are able to find necessities of life.

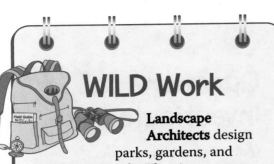

WILD Work

Landscape Architects design parks, gardens, and building grounds. They incorporate plants, water sources, and other natural features into their designs to help support local wildlife. For more information on the role of Landscape Architects in wildlife conservation and management, see the WILD Work resources at *www.projectwild.org/aquatic*.

In Step with STEM

■ Make simple graphs or pie charts that describe quantities of wildlife species identified in the investigation.

■ Draw a map of the field site (in a science notebook or drawing paper) that includes the locations of water sources and where students observed animals or signs of wildlife.

■ Discuss if human activities on the study site have affected water availability for wildlife. Consider how building design, structures, landscaping, and land use on the site affect water availability.

All wildlife, no matter where it lives, must have water to survive.

---

nests, bird feathers, tracks, and borings in wood structures), as well as sources of water near each wildlife sighting (e.g., dew on or under leaves, puddles, rain in sidewalk cracks, etc.).

3. At the study site, have students explore and look for wildlife. Students should write or illustrate each animal they observe on their *Wildlife Note Cards*. Next to the 👁 symbol, students will write or draw the location where they saw that animal or sign of wildlife.

4. If students find an animal that no one can identify, direct their attention to describing the animal's appearance. How many legs does it have? What type of body covering does it have? What other characteristics are distinctive? Students should sketch the animal in their science notebooks or take a photograph. If possible, have students use a field guide to try to identify the animal. Keep in mind that the point of the safari is to help students understand where wildlife gets water, not to identify all the animals they find.

5. Next, have students explore and look for water sources. Students should write or illustrate each water source they observe on their *Water Source Note Cards*. Then, write or draw the location where they saw the water source next to the 👁 symbol.

Organizing and Analyzing the Data

1. Using a blackboard, whiteboard, or flip chart, compile a class list of all animal sightings, clues of animals, and water sources observed by students. This can be done at the field site or back in the classroom as one large display.

2. Create a large map of the study site on which students can help mark the location of each animal sighting, clues of animals, and water sources. The maps do not have to be to exact scale (see "Guidelines for Mapping" on page xxi). Likewise many online programs, including Google Earth, will allow you to print an aerial photo that can be enlarged for this mapping exercise.

Drawing Conclusions

1. Have students review the classroom list of animals, signs, and water sources identified, as well as the map plotting these locations. Ask students if they see any patterns or conclusions based on their investigations (continue to Step 4 if students did not identify any water sources or signs of wildlife). What type of animal was seen most often? What types of water sources were most abundant? Was there something they expected to see but did not? Have students reference the data to support their answers.

Water Safari

2. Ask students to discuss what other questions they have now that they have completed the investigation. Topics that students might discuss include how seasonal changes, time of day, and weather affect sources of water at the study site and whether adding new, human-made water sources would change the type of wildlife seen at the study site.

3. Reinforce the idea that water is essential to the survival of wildlife. How do students think the presence or absence of water affected the wildlife they observed? Do they think water sources observed on the study site provided water for wildlife that was observed? Why or why not? How could we find out?

4. If students did not find any water sources on their safari, ask them to think of possible reasons to explain why they were unsuccessful. These may include:

- water sources may be very small, such as a dew drop, and have escaped students' notice;

- water sources may be hidden in an area inaccessible to students on safari, such as underground or inside a leaf;

- water sources may be temporary, such as dew or puddles; or

- there has been no rain for a long time, or verified drought conditions exist for your area.

Similarly, if no signs of wildlife were found, discuss possible reasons, such as:

- the animal's home range (where it travels to find what it needs to live) may be much larger than the area covered on the safari;

- animals such as tiny insects or spiders may be too small to see, or they may be hidden;

- not enough water, food, or shelter is available;

- the water, food, or shelter available at the study site is not the right type needed for animals that live in this area;

- animals were hiding due to student noise; or

- animals may be nocturnal (active during the night) and not active during the daytime safari visit.

Ask students what the relationship is between the presence of water and the presence of wildlife. Are there any actions we could take to help wildlife or improve water availability on our study site? If we carry out these actions, how can we find out if our actions were successful?

Ask students what the relationship is between the presence of water and the presence of wildlife. Are there any actions we could take to help wildlife or improve water availability on our study site?

Extensions

1. Students can turn their observations of wildlife into a field guide by stapling their *Wildlife Note Cards* together. Students can then color their pictures and decorate the cover.

2. Help students classify the organisms recorded on their safari into categories such as mammals, reptiles, birds, fish, and invertebrates. Ask students which category has the most organisms and why.

3. As you walk around the schoolyard or neighborhood, have students use small plastic bottles to collect water samples from various sources. Back in the classroom, students can describe the water in each vial. If available, use a microscope to view droplets of water to look for the small, almost invisible creatures that live in water.

4. Using an online mapping tool or watershed map from a local utility company or environmental agency, have students trace the path of drinking water from the source to their school.

5. Have students investigate if their city or township has water restriction guidelines in place for times of drought conditions. Would restrictions affect any of the water sources on the study site?

Evaluation

1. Identify three places wild animals can find water on the study site.

2. Describe three ways students could improve water sources for animals in the area around their school.

3. Categorize water sources based on use by the wildlife or signs of wildlife found on the study site. Examples include bathing, drinking, or habitat.

Wildlife and Water Source Note Cards

 Wildlife Signs

 Wildlife Signs

 _____

 _____

Water Sources

Water Sources

 _____

 _____

Where Does Water Run?

Grade Level: Middle, High School

Content Areas: Mathematics, Science, Environmental Education, Language Arts

Method: Students will design and implement a field investigation involving relationships between levels of precipitation, runoff, and percentage of impervious ground cover.

Materials: See the following page.

Activity Time: three 45- to 60-minute sessions; two periods if dimensions of the grounds are provided and rainfall data for the study site are known

People Power: two or more students

Setting: outdoors and indoors

Conceptual Framework Topic Reference: HNIB1, HNIIA, HIIA, HIIIB3, HIIIB4, HIC2

Terms to Know: area, erosion, impervious, pervious, infiltration, nonpoint source pollution, precipitation, runoff, volume, velocity, water cycle, sediment. For advanced students: descriptive, comparative, and correlative questions; manipulated (independent) variable; responding (dependent) variable; controlled variable; permeability

Appendices: Climate Change, Metric Conversion Chart

Take a closer look at what happens when it rains.

Objectives

Students will (1) calculate or research rainfall; (2) measure a study site and calculate impervious cover; (3) develop and write questions and detailed procedures for investigating runoff; and (4) collect, organize, and analyze data to draw conclusions.

Study Site

In this activity, students calculate the percentages of pervious and impervious surface, as well as the approximate amount of precipitation that falls on both surface types. The study site can be a small plot, the entire school ground, or other community site. Select an area that contains some human-made structures (buildings, sidewalks, etc.) and some natural or lawn areas. Arrange permission to use the site for the field component, if necessary.

Background

Developing an understanding of precipitation and runoff is an important part of understanding the water cycle (see Diagram A). Rainfall is one form of precipitation and represents one way water re-enters aquatic habitats. Once rain falls upon a surface, water begins to move both laterally outward and vertically downward. The vertical movement of water, called infiltration, allows water to seep into the soil and porous rock and to recharge groundwater supplies.

The lateral movement of water is runoff, which eventually flows into streams, rivers, lakes, and the ocean. Runoff is the predominant way water flows from one location to another. Runoff waters are necessary to renew many aquatic habitats that depend on inflow of water; for instance, runoff prevent lakes from shrinking because of evaporation or streams from flowing below minimum levels.

Water pollution is often blamed on discharge from pipes; however, runoff can also be a major carrier of pollutants into streams, lakes, rivers, and other aquatic systems that eventually empty into coastal waters. As water moves across streets, fields, parking lots, and pavement, it picks up litter, paint, oil, garden insecticides, bacteria and nutrients from livestock, and other contaminants. These widely dispersed pollutants are known as nonpoint source pollution and can affect the wildlife and plants living in aquatic ecosystems.

Impervious surfaces such as paved areas, buildings, and compacted soil do not absorb water. Reduced infiltration can greatly affect the surrounding vegetation and the underlying groundwater. With less water seeping into the soil, more water runs off. The more impervious an area becomes, the greater the amount of runoff.

Although water runoff helps maintain aquatic ecosystems, too much can have detrimental effects. An increase in the quantity and velocity of runoff increases soil erosion, flash flooding, and the potential for water to pick up and carry pollutants. More pervious surfaces, such as natural areas with well-rooted vegetation, allow water to infiltrate the ground.

Water erosion is the wearing away of soil and rock as water moves across it. Improper agriculture, development, and landscaping practices result in soil being washed away. Runoff transports soil sediments to local streams and other surface

Materials

- ☑ pencils
- ☑ science notebooks
- ☑ computer(s) with Internet access
- ☑ copies of *Pervious vs. Impervious Investigation* (page 53), *What's My Question?* (page 388), and *Conclusions and Next Steps* (page 389)
- ☑ graph paper for mapping study site
- ☑ meter or yard sticks
- ☑ long piece of twine with marks every yard or meter
- ☑ watershed map or aerial photos of the region (available online)
- ☑ local rainfall data

OPTIONAL: calculator, rain gauge, and devices for measuring distances such as a pedometer or trundle wheel (a device with a wheel that is pushed along a surface—available for purchase at building supply stores, or ask to borrow from local surveying, engineering, or architecture firms).

The Water Cycle

Diagram A

Water is diverted to prevent flooding on impervious surfaces.

Although water runoff helps maintain aquatic ecosystems, too much can have detrimental effects. An increase in the quantity and velocity of runoff increases soil erosion, flash flooding, and the potential for water to pick up and carry pollutants.

A human-made drainage ditch controls agricultural runoff.

waters. Sediment can settle in lakes, streams, and rivers or ultimately be carried to the ocean. Too much sediment makes the water murky and prevents sunlight from penetrating the water, which affects plant growth. Sediments can fill in important habitat at the bottom of lakes and reduce lake volumes. They can also clog the gills of fish and affect other aquatic wildlife.

Excess runoff can cause flooding. In areas with buildings, high proportions of paved surfaces, and piped drainage systems, over 80 percent of rainfall can become runoff. Steps can be taken to reduce runoff, which in turn can reduce flood risks. A few examples of measures towns can adopt include: permeable or porous pavements for roads and parking lots; retention basins (an artificial lake surrounded by vegetation that helps to hold runoff and prevent flooding); infiltration basins (vegetated depressions that catch runoff from impermeable surfaces and slowly filter it back into groundwater); and wide buffer strips of deeply rooted natural vegetation along paved areas.

Schools and homeowners can reduce runoff by installing rain gardens and rain barrels (for ideas and resources, visit *www. projectwild.org/aquatic*). Trees, shrubs, and other plants around homes and schools increase infiltration and reduce direct runoff into streams and rivers.

This activity helps students better understand the connections between runoff and the health of aquatic ecosystems. It also encourages them to think about ways excess runoff can be controlled to benefit the environment.

Introducing the Field Investigation

1. Discuss the following questions with students:

- How much rain falls here?
- How much rain falls at any one time?
- Where does water go after a heavy rainfall?
- Why does it matter where the water goes?
- Does the type of surface that rainwater falls upon affect what happens to the water once it lands?
- Does falling water affect various types of ground surfaces in different ways? How so?

2. Introduce the "Terms to Know," such as pervious and impervious surfaces, infiltration, sediment, and nonpoint source pollution. Have students define each term using appropriate resources (online or hard copy dictionaries, science texts, or other reference materials). Discuss the relationship of these concepts and their importance in understanding the health of the local ecosystem.

Where Does Water Run?

3. In class or as homework, have students research the annual rainfall for your region, including amounts of rain (in centimeters, meters, or inches), as well as any patterns, such as more rain during specific times of year. Students may use various reference materials including:

- Annual rainfall data (such as the 30-year average)

- Last year's rainfall

- Local report of individual precipitation events (Does most of the annual rainfall occur during a few heavy rains or a greater number of light rains?)

NOTE: For longer term projects, students can also measure precipitation over a time period using a rain gauge.

4. Students should also research the path water flows as it travels from the vicinity of your study site to the ocean. Students may use maps, books, or online sources such as aerial or satellite images, watershed maps, or topographic maps. In their science notebooks, students can list and/or sketch the names of streams, rivers, or other bodies of water, in the order by which the water flows.

5. Revisit the questions from Step 1. Can students expand their answers to these questions? What information/evidence do they have to support their answers?

6. Discuss plans to further investigate the flow of water on the school grounds or at a local site. Ask students what questions they would like to explore about runoff on the study site. Record questions on a board or flipchart. "Big picture" questions that may arise during class discussion include:

- How does the flow of water affect plants, wildlife, and people in our region?

- How does the type of surface or surfaces on our study site affect the environment?

- How do human activities in our region affect water quality?

- How do human activities affect wildlife?

7. Prepare to conduct the "Initial Mapping Activity" (as described on the following pages). Explain to students that in order to explore questions they may have about water on their study site, the first phase of the investigation will involve mapping the site to determine the amount of pervious and impervious surfaces and the amount of potential runoff. This knowledge can then help students in further articulating other research questions.

WILD Work

Hydrologists examine the physical characteristics, distribution, and circulation of water above and below the earth's surface. They study rainfall and other precipitation and determine the path precipitation takes.

Similarly, **Hydraulic Engineers** study the flow of fluids like water and sewage and design a system of structures and machines to handle their movement, such as storm drains, retention basins, and pumping stations. For more information on these occupations, see *www.projectwild.org/aquatic*.

In Step with STEM

Knowledge of the rate at which rainwater enters soil (infiltration rate) can be applied to irrigation projects, land use decisions, and flood control measures. Infiltration rate can be measured using a coffee can (or other cylinder) with the top and bottom removed. Place one end of the can one inch into soil, taking care to disturb the soil as little as possible. Pour a half gallon (or other predetermined amount) of water into the cylinder and record the time it takes to be absorbed into the soil. The rate of infiltration is determined as the amount of water per surface area and time unit in which that amount penetrates the soil.

For instructional videos and other resources on measuring infiltration rate, see *www.projectwild.org/aquatic*. You will also find links to other resources and data regarding runoff and water flow.

Initial Mapping Activity:
An Investigation of Impervious vs. Pervious Surfaces

1. Review impervious cover. What makes a surface impervious? How do we know if a surface is impervious? The opposite is pervious. What does that mean? After you believe your students understand the terms, tell them that before they formulate their research questions about runoff on their school grounds, they are first going to map their school campus and do comparative and descriptive investigations to answer two questions:

- Is the school campus (or study site) covered more with pervious or impervious surfaces?

- What is the potential runoff of water from the school campus (study site)?

most accurate

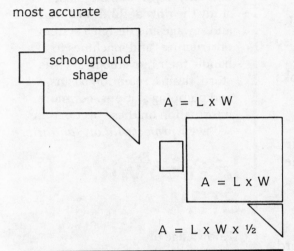

schoolground shape

A = L x W

A = L x W

A = L x W x ½

A = L x W

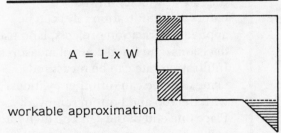

workable approximation

Cement tiles with porous limestone underneath can absorb water and help slow runoff.

2. Take students outside and have them predict if there are more pervious or impervious surfaces on their school campus (study site). Students' predictions can be recorded on the *Pervious vs. Impervious Investigation* page.

3. In groups of two or three have students measure and map the study area, differentiating between types of surfaces rainfall would land on (such as concrete, grass, roof top, parking lot, exposed soil, gravel). Graph paper will help students produce maps that are to scale and that display various surfaces of the study site (see Guidelines for Mapping in the "Aquatic WILD Field Investigations" section of this guide). Make sure students show the entire study site on their maps.

4. While outside, students should also record observations, measurements, and notes on any other factors that might affect runoff or help inform what the class investigative question should be. These could include the path water flows during rain; the location of potential sources of pollution on the study site (oil in the parking lot, animal waste, pesticide); sediment that may wash away in rain (such as exposed soil from a construction project); the slope of the land at different locations on the site; chemical tests (such as pH or dissolved oxygen); or the amount of precipitation as measured by a rain gauge.

5. Either in the field or back in the classroom, have students determine 1) the total area of the study site, and 2) the areas of each surface type they have described on their maps (from Step 3 above). For rectangular-shaped areas, apply the formula, area = length x width (A=L x W). There are many ways to determine the area of irregular-shaped areas of the study site—each group should use a method that makes sense to them. Coach students as needed and expect a few trials before students settle on one method on which to base their data. Students can enter their data on the *Pervious vs. Impervious Investigation* page.

6. Back in the classroom, have students compare and discuss their maps and come to agreement on the calculated areas for each surface type. Each group should be able to describe their methods and rationale. Mirroring methods used by teams of professional scientists, the goal is for students to compare their maps in order to generate a single map of the site. The class should also generate a single chart that indicates the total area of the study site as well as the area of each surface type.

7. Review again the meaning of pervious and impervious. Have students categorize the surfaces in the chart as either pervious or impervious. Finally, calculate the total percentage of impervious cover in the study site by adding all the impervious surface areas and dividing by the total area. Record answers on the *Pervious vs. Impervious Investigation* page.

8. Using the *Pervious vs. Impervious Investigation* page, have students write a statement that answers the investigative question, "Is the study site covered more with pervious or impervious surfaces?" Statements should give the percentage of which type of surface is greater on the site.

9. Using data on rainfall in your region or data collected on site from a water gauge, have students 1) calculate the volume of rainfall on the study site, and 2) calculate the potential runoff on the site. Make sure all measurements are first converted to either metric or standard units before making calculations. Students should record answers on the *Pervious vs. Impervious Investigation* page.

The vertical movement of water, called infiltration, allows water to seep into the soil and porous rock and to recharge groundwater supplies.

Agricultural runoff carries pesticides and excess nutrients from fertilizers into nearby waterways.

Impervious surfaces such as paved areas, buildings, and compacted soil do not absorb water. ...With less water seeping into the soil, more water runs off. The more impervious an area becomes, the greater the amount of runoff.

Forming the Question

1. Now that students have mapped and investigated the pervious and impervious surfaces on their campus (study site), have them generate more possible questions to investigate.

2. Discuss students' questions. Identify and record which questions can be answered through observations and measurements at the study site. Help students decide what researchable question will be investigated. Using guiding questions, coach students to refine their researchable question so that it is answerable with one (or a few) simple investigations given the tools you have on hand.

3. Students can record their questions, including big picture questions and the single investigation question, on the ***What's My Question?*** page. Examples of investigation questions involving runoff are listed in the "Questions to Investigate" box in the sidebar on the following page.

4. For more advanced students, ask if they think their field investigation question is a descriptive, comparative, or correlative question (see "Aquatic WILD Field Investigations" for more information).

Conducting the Investigation

1. Once students have decided on an investigative question either in groups or as a class, discuss and plan what type of data should be collected and how data will be collected. What type of information and observations will be needed to answer the research question? How will you go about collecting data? Why is it important for all students to take measurements the same way? Similarly, why is it important to take measurements the same way when collecting data at different times or locations?

2. Coach students to help them identify variables in their investigation. For comparative and correlative questions, help students identify a) which conditions will be changed (manipulated variable), and b) which conditions will be measured (responding variable). Help students identify a third type of variable—the controlled variable. Explain that when we determine a way to control how we take measurements, collect samples, or make observations in order to ensure we are doing it the same way each time, this is known as a controlled variable.

3. Have students write a plan for conducting the investigation, including:

a) A prediction or hypothesis about what they will find or how their question will be answered;

b) Materials they will need to conduct the investigation;

Students can contact local agencies for opportunities to be involved in water quality sampling.

c) For comparative and correlative investigations, the manipulated variable, the responding variable, and at least one controlled variable; and

d) Each step they will take, with enough detail so others could read the steps to conduct the same investigation.

4. Prepare a data collection sheet for the class investigation question or have students create their own data collection sheets for their group investigations. See Criteria for Student Data Forms in the "Aquatic WILD Field Investigations" section.

5. In groups of three or four, have students go outside and collect data for their investigation question.

Organizing and Analyzing the Data

1. Use a whiteboard, flipchart, or projector to record and display a summary of the cumulative results.

2. What calculations will help answer the research question? How can the data be best displayed graphically? Are any patterns found in the data?

3. For comparative and correlative investigations, describe how sampling, measurements, and observations were kept consistent for the two or more conditions, locations, times, or organisms (your controlled variables) and how they were random and representative of the site.

NOTE: For investigations that involve the volume of runoff, see Extension #1 on the next page for calculating the volume of rain.

Drawing Conclusions

1. Have students write a clear statement explaining the answer to the research question and support their statement with data from their data table. As an option, students can complete the *Conclusions and Next Steps* page.

2. Ask students to describe any problems they may have experienced when collecting data. Were there any factors that might have impacted the research (time of day, weather, etc.)?

3. Were the procedures developed by students logical and sufficiently detailed to provide data needed to answer the research question? If not, how could the procedures be modified?

4. What other data would help answer the research question?

5. What additional research questions do students have?

Questions to Investigate

Questions that help **describe** . . .

- What path does the runoff follow on the study site?

- Can any pollutants be observed that are carried by the runoff?

- Are there any features that slow the flow of runoff (such as ponds or infiltration basins)?

- Are there any places where water tends to pool?

Questions that help **compare** . . .

- Which sections (quadrants) on the site have the largest amount of impermeable surfaces?

- Which location on the site has the fastest runoff rate?

- Which type of land surface (concrete, grass, soil, mulch) infiltrates water the fastest?

- Which type of land surface (concrete, grass, soil, mulch) has the greatest amount of sediment in the runoff?

Questions that help **correlate** . . .

- Is there a relationship between surface area of human-made structures (buildings, concrete) and the speed of runoff?

- Is there a relationship between permeability rate and the amount of sediment observed in runoff?

- Is there a relationship between speed of runoff and the amount of sediment in the runoff?

Excess runoff can cause flooding. In areas with buildings, high proportions of paved surfaces, and piped drainage systems, over 80 percent of rainfall can become runoff. Steps can be taken to reduce runoff, which in turn can reduce flood risks.

Excessive runoff causes a flash flood in a surburban neighborhood.

Extensions

1. Calculate the volume of rain (in cubic meters) by multiplying the area of the study site by depth of rain. Rain depth may be found in pre-existing weather data or measured by a rain gauge. To help visualize the quantity of rainwater, determine the number of 1-liter soda bottles necessary to contain water from annual rainfall. 1 cubic meter = 1,000 liters.

Example: For a 20,000 square meter study site, the annual rainfall is 15 centimeters, or 0.15 meters. The volume of rain is calculated as follows:

20,000 sq. meters x 0.15 meters of rain = 3,000 cubic meters of rain

Therefore 3,000 cubic meters of rain would fit in 3,000,000 1-liter soda bottles.

2. Have students perform water quality tests on the rainwater and then repeat the tests on runoff water from the same rainfall. Compare water quality tests on runoff from a slow, steady rain to a hard, fast rain.

3. Research and write plans for developing and sustaining a rain garden, small pond, wetland, or aquatic ecosystem on your site (see *www.projectwild.org/aquatic* for resources). How can existing features of the landscape help determine the best location for a pond?

4. The contamination of groundwater is an important environmental issue in many communities. How might water in the groundwater table or aquifer become contaminated and potentially pose a threat to human health? To the health of other animals, including wildlife? Identify as many possible sources of contamination to groundwater and runoff in your community as possible. What can be, or is being done, to reduce or eliminate these sources and their effects?

Evaluation

1. Have students list other questions they generated during the field investigation that they did not explore. Which of these questions are researchable? How would they find the answers to these questions?

2. Ask students to explain how their conclusions relate to environmental stewardship. Why might it be important to know what was learned? How can knowledge of runoff and types of ground cover be applied to environmental management?

3. What can students do to help reduce problems that are sometimes associated with runoff, such as nonpoint source pollution, erosion, lower recharge rates of groundwater supplies, and flooding?

Pervious vs. Impervious Investigation

Date: _____ Time: _____ Study Site: _____

Names of field investigators: _____

Questions:

A. Is the study site covered more with pervious or impervious surfaces?

Prediction: _____

B. What is the volume (m³) of potential runoff of water from the study site?

Prediction: _____ m³

1. **Take measurements of your study site. Map the site on graph paper.**

2. **Calculate the area of the study site:** (The example below assumes a rectangular-shaped study site)

Length of study site: _____ Width of study site: _____ Study site area (length x width): _____

3. **Calculate the total area of impervious surface on the study site:**
Measure the dimensions of each impervious surface in order to calculate the area. Impervious surfaces include buildings, paved areas, sidewalks, etc.

Description of Impervious Surfaces	Length	Width	Area
#1:			
#2:			
#3:			
#4:			
Total area of all impervious surfaces =			

4. **Calculate the % of impervious surface on the study site:** _____

% impervious surfaces = sum of the areas of all the impervious surface X 100
                         total area of the site

Is the study site covered more with pervious or impervious surfaces? Provide percentages in your explanation:

_____

5. **Calculate the volume of rainfall on the study site.** Volume = Area of study site x depth of rain per day/month/or year. Be careful! Make sure you convert all of your measurements to either metric units or standard units before completing calculations! **Volume = _____ (ft³ or m³)**

6. **Calculate the runoff potential of the study site.** Runoff potential = % impervious surfaces x the total rainfall depth. **Runoff Potential= _____ (ft³ or m³)**

7. **Record on your map your observations of the path water takes during a heavy rainstorm.**

8. **Record on your map or on the back of this sheet any other observations about water flow.**

Urban Waterway Checkup

Grade Level: Middle School

Content Areas:
Science, Language Arts, Environmental Education

Method: Students learn about indicators or "vital signs" used to gauge the health of streams and rivers, apply their knowledge in analyzing the health of a hypothetical urban waterway, and then write a "prescription" for actions that can improve the health of the waterway.

Materials: Copies of *The Life and Times of Somewhere Creek*, copies of *Stream Inhabitants*, long strip of newsprint or a large dry-erase white board, markers, masking tape

Activity Time: one or two 50-minute sessions

People Power: any size group

Setting: indoors

Conceptual Framework Topic Reference: HNIB, HNIIB, HI IIB3, HI IIB5, HI IIC2, RAIC6

Terms to Know: waterway, aquatic, nutrients, silt, invertebrate, indicator, leach, dehydrate, dissolved oxygen

Appendices: Service Learning, Using Local Resources, Agencies and Organizations, The Ecosystem and Project WILD, Climate Change

How do we do a health checkup on a waterway?

Objectives

Students will (1) identify and describe criteria used to gauge the health of a waterway, (2) analyze the health of a hypothetical urban waterway, (3) predict how human actions affect the health of a waterway, and (4) write a plan for improving the health of a waterway.

Background

A doctor can assess a person's health by checking certain vital signs like pulse and temperature. In a similar way, people can assess the health of an urban waterway by looking for specific signs such as its clarity and the number of different species that call it home. Accurately assessing the health of urban waters depends on the type of waterway being examined. A creek in Philadelphia, Pennsylvania, will have different characteristics than a bayou in Houston, Texas; a tidal river in Norfolk, Virginia; or the Santa Monica Bay in Los Angeles, California. In the activity, students read about the life history of Somewhere Creek. Although not a real waterway, Somewhere Creek is similar to many urban freshwater creeks, streams, and rivers. The information given about this creek can be used as a starting place for assessing any urban waterway, even those with seemingly different natural histories.

An assessment of an urban waterway typically begins with simple observations:

- ***Does the water look clear and clean?*** Generally, healthy waterways have clean, clear water. However, water that looks "dirty" does not necessarily indicate poor waterway health. Some healthy waterways may appear brown or otherwise discolored because of naturally occurring substances, such as tannin from leaves, that can enter the water from the surrounding soil.

- *Are there plants and animals in the water?* Organisms living in the water are usually signs of health, although a large number of any one type of organism can indicate problems. For example, nutrient pollution promotes algae overgrowth. Additionally, if the water is devoid of life but looks crystal clear, there may be a problem such as over-acidity, a condition that impairs growth of plants and animals.

- *How does it smell?* Oily or noxious smells are potential indicators of pollution and poor health. (**NOTE:** the scent of decaying vegetation may be present in some healthy aquatic ecosystems.)

- *What is the bottom like?* There is natural variation in the materials at the bottom of a waterway, but the buildup of silt often indicates problems.

- *Does the waterway show signs that people have changed it from its natural state?* Many natural waterways offer different habitat for a variety of organisms. Such waterways may have deep pools, vegetation that provides shade, downed logs that provide shelter, and shallow riffles that stir up and aerate the water. In urban areas, channelization, vegetation removal, and dredging have altered many waterways so they no longer offer a variety of habitat.

In addition to looking for the simple presence or absence of life in a stream, investigators may actually count the number of different kinds of aquatic organisms in a waterway. Healthy waterways usually support a wide range of species. Species diversity (or lack of it) may give a general indication of water quality. While there may be greater numbers of plants and animals in downstream waters—where it is likely to be warmer, slower moving, and dirtier—there are typically fewer types of plants and animals present. Some aquatic species are considered "indicators" for particular conditions such as water temperature, oxygen levels, or pollution levels. Among fish, for example, Bluegill can live in warmer, more polluted water than trout can tolerate. Some invertebrates such as crayfish and dragonfly larvae are more tolerant of polluted conditions than are others such as mayfly nymphs and caddisfly larvae.

For more specific information, investigators can use water quality test kits that measure parameters such as temperature, dissolved oxygen, turbidity, pH, and the presence of specific pollutants as described in "Waterway Vital Signs" on the following page. Investigators may examine many sites along the course of a waterway to understand its overall health and to detect potential sources of problems. They can also try to determine what effect water conditions have on the health of the local ecosystem, and they often compare data collected from one stream or river to those collected from other, similar waterways.

WILD Work

Water Quality Specialists work at agencies like the Environmental Protection Agency (EPA), the Fish and Wildlife Service, the National Park Service, or the U.S. Army Corps of Engineers, often as biologists, chemists, hydrologists, public health officers, watershed planners, or environmental health specialists. Invite a Water Quality Specialist to speak to your class, if possible one who focuses on human-made systems like drinking water treatment plants. Have the specialist speak to the class about raw water, or water in nature that is part of the water supply. What have they found about how water quality affects human health? Are there any specific cases in the area of people getting sick from drinking water that had become polluted? Are there any actions that students can take to help ameliorate the problem or to help prevent the problem in the future?

Waterway Vital Signs

The following table lists water quality parameters that investigators use to gauge the health of urban waterways.

Water Quality Parameter	Importance
Temperature	Water temperature is important because it affects the chemical reactions that sustain life such as photosynthesis and metabolic activity. Prolonged exposure to environmental temperatures outside of the optimum range can have detrimental effects on aquatic organisms.
Dissolved Oxygen (DO) the amount of oxygen found in water, expressed as a concentration of milligrams per liter or parts per million	Oxygen availability affects the growth and development of aquatic organisms and determines whether they can survive. At high altitudes and warmer temperatures, water holds less oxygen. Because it has more contact with the air, fast-moving, turbulent water contains more oxygen than slower-moving water. Brackish water holds less oxygen than freshwater.
Turbidity a measure of the relative clarity of water in which the greater the turbidity, the murkier the water	Particles (like silt) suspended in turbid waterways absorb heat from sunlight and block light penetration into the depths. These phenomena cause an increase in water temperature and a decrease in photosynthesis, both of which lead to a decrease in the dissolved oxygen available to aquatic life. Suspended particles causing high turbidity can also clog fish gills or settle to the bottom and smother eggs or insect larvae.
pH a measure of acid or alkaline conditions in water	The pH of freshwater in the U.S. is usually between 6.5 and 8.5. Most organisms have a narrow range of tolerance for variations in pH and may die if it changes even slightly. Immature stages of aquatic insects and young fish are particularly sensitive. Acidic water can also cause heavy metals such as copper and aluminum to be released into the water from soils. These metals can accumulate in the gills of fish and cause deformities in young fish.
Pollutants	The presence of excessive nutrients such as nitrogen or phosphorus, heavy metals, petroleum, chemicals, and other pollutants can make the aquatic environment toxic for organisms.
Salinity concentration of dissolved salts in the water	Aquatic organisms are adapted to and vary in their tolerance for certain salinity ranges. High concentrations of dissolved salts dehydrate organisms that do not have mechanisms for regulating water loss under these conditions.

Procedures

1. Ask students to think about the last time they went to a doctor for a checkup. What did the doctor look at to determine the student's state of health? What kinds of questions did the doctor ask? Write the list on the board.

2. Tell students that, just like people, waterways such as streams, lakes, rivers, and bays can be healthy or unhealthy. Which waterway characteristics might scientists or other interested citizens examine to determine the waterway's state of health? Write students' ideas on the board. Tell students that they will be learning how people do a "waterway checkup" in this activity.

3. Give students copies of *The Life and Times of Somewhere Creek*, and have them read it individually, in small groups, or as a class. As they read, have each student jot down characteristics that Cecelia and Tómas could use as "clues" to determine the health of Somewhere Creek at different points along its course. Scientists sometimes refer to these characteristics as "indicators" of health.

4. Ask students for the "clues" they found in the story that indicate the health of Somewhere Creek. Record the ideas on the board or on large sheets of newsprint. Discuss each "clue" and introduce students to water quality parameters detailed in the "Background" section. Which parameters would students want to test to verify the health of Somewhere Creek? What would they expect the relative measurements to be at different points along the creek?

5. Tell students that the variety of organisms found in the stream is another very important indicator used by scientists to determine the health of a waterway. Healthy streams tend to host a diverse community of plants and animals, including fish and invertebrates. Diversity generally declines as water conditions deteriorate. Different animals and plants have particular tolerances for variations in environmental conditions, including temperature, dissolved oxygen, turbidity, and pollution levels. The number and variety of aquatic organisms in a waterway can often be a more sensitive indicator of water quality than physical or chemical tests. This is because aquatic organisms—especially invertebrates—tend to have short life cycles, to be sensitive to changes in sediments suspended in the water or deposited on the bottom, and to vary in their tolerances to pollution.

6. Hand out copies of *Stream Inhabitants* to students. Individually, in small groups, or as a whole class, make a map of Somewhere Creek on the newsprint, showing the different sections of the creek described in *The Life and Times of Somewhere Creek*. Have students use cutouts from the *Stream*

In Step with STEM

- Do online research of biological indicators and how they are used to determine waterway health. Visit the EPA's "Biological Indicators of Watershed Health" website and look for information (including water quality data) about watersheds all over the United States. You may also visit the EPA's "Surf Your Watershed" website (go to *www.projectwild.org/aquatic* for links).

- Use spreadsheet software to record and graph data, using what students found in their online research on biological indicators or water quality. If possible, have students compare data from two urban waterways and determine which of the two is more polluted.

- Use probeware to measure pH and/or other water quality parameters of two urban waterways. Probeware refers to educational hardware and software used for real-time data acquisition, display, and analysis with a computer or calculator. Use a thermometer or other device to collect the temperature of these waterways. Compare the two sets of results. Can students use the data to determine which of the two waterways is unhealthier or is more polluted?

Healthy waterways usually support a wide range of species.

Inhabitants page or make drawings to add the aquatic life they expect to see in each section of the stream. Where possible, ask students to indicate the relative abundance of the organisms in different stream segments.

7. Discuss the map and the reasoning behind student responses. Where do they think the stream seems healthy? Unhealthy? Why? What natural variations could be behind some of the characteristics that may make a waterway seem unhealthy? For example, a shallow stream segment flowing across relatively flat ground will move more slowly, be warmer, and have less dissolved oxygen than will a segment that flows over steeper terrain. The soil through which a stream flows may affect its color and acidity.

8. Discuss human activities that might influence the health of waterways. What could community members do to improve the health of urban waterways such as Somewhere Creek? Write a "prescription" for improving the health of Somewhere Creek (or a local waterway with which students are familiar). The prescription should include specific actions students and others in the community could take. Students may need to conduct additional research to develop this prescription. For example, students may recommend that their neighborhood association stop mowing the banks of its drainage ditches and plant native plants to encourage wildlife. Recommendations could also include stream cleanups, stricter enforcement of illegal dumping, and neighborhood awareness campaigns about pollution resulting from excessive use of lawn fertilizers.

Extensions

1. Research a local waterway and develop a map that characterizes different stream segments and the species that are likely to be found in each segment. Local experts from the cooperative extension service, local or state government, a watershed organization, or university can help by providing information or speaking to the class. The experts can provide an accurate picture of healthy conditions for a specific local waterway and give examples of "real" local factors that might adversely affect the health of the waterway.

2. Visit a local urban waterway. Depending on your geographic location, the waterway might be an urban creek, storage pond, drainage ditch, river, or bay. Have students observe basic parameters and, if possible, conduct water quality tests.

3. Research local organizations working to clean up and restore local waterways. Students may discover an existing project that is waiting for an interested and energetic class to provide the "people power" needed for its completion.

Evaluation

1. Identify and discuss the importance of indicators to determining waterway health.

2. Create a map of species diversity in segments of a typical urban waterway.

3. Write a prescription for improving waterway health.

Urban Waterway Checkup
© *Council for Environmental Education (CEE)*

Educators' Key to Map of Somewhere Creek

This key represents the segments of Somewhere Creek that are described in *The Life and Times of Somewhere Creek*. It illustrates the general scheme for separating stream inhabitants into segments. Student responses may vary and should be assessed based on the soundness of student reasoning.

1. Mountain stream
- Cutthroat/Brook Trout
- Rainbow/Brown Trout, Smallmouth Bass, etc.
- Spots of algae growing on rocks
- Mayfly, caddisfly, etc.
- Crayfish, riffle beetle, etc.
- Midge/black fly larvae, etc.

2. Meandering stream flowing through the foothills
- Rainbow/Brown Trout, Smallmouth Bass, etc.
- Spots of algae growing on rocks
- Eelgrass, elodea, etc.
- Mayfly, caddisfly, etc.
- Crayfish, riffle beetle, etc.
- Midge/black fly larvae, etc.

3. Fishing hole
- Rainbow/Brown Trout, Smallmouth Bass, etc. (may be fewer during the summer)
- Spots of algae growing on rocks
- Eelgrass, elodea, etc.
- Duckweed, water lily, etc.
- Large beds and floating mats of algae (in summer)
- Crayfish, riffle beetle, etc.
- Midge/black fly larvae, etc.

4. Construction runoff area
- Rainbow/Brown Trout, Smallmouth Bass, etc. (fewer than upstream because of the silt)
- Carp, chubs, shiners, etc.
- Spots of algae growing on rocks (fewer than upstream due to silt)
- Crayfish, riffle beetle, etc. (fewer than upstream)
- Midge/black fly larvae, etc.

5. Suburban area
- Carp, chubs, shiners, etc.
- Spots of algae growing on rocks
- Midge/black fly larvae, etc.

6. Flood-control area
- Carp, chubs, shiners, etc.
- Spots of algae growing on rocks (or on concrete channel walls)
- Midge/black fly larvae, etc.

7. Tunnel below the streets
- Probably very few aquatic plants due to lack of light. Animals may hide here.

8. Downtown streamside park
- Rainbow/Brown Trout, Smallmouth Bass, etc.
- Spots of algae growing on rocks
- Eelgrass, elodea, etc.
- Crayfish, riffle beetle, etc.
- Midge/blackfly larvae, etc.

9. Industrial zone
- Carp, chubs, shiners, etc. (possibly very few, depending on pH of the water)
- Spots of algae growing on rocks (possibly very few, depending on pH of the water)
- Midge/blackfly larvae, etc.

10. Flowing into Big River to the ocean

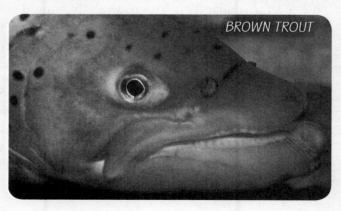
BROWN TROUT

The Life and Times of Somewhere Creek

While Somewhere Creek is not a real creek, it represents a typical urban freshwater creek, stream, or river.

Cecelia and Tómas grew up together in Someplace City. They've been friends since they were very young. Back then, their favorite thing to do was to splash around in puddles at the park in their neighborhood. Over the years their shared love of water has helped hold their friendship together. Cecelia loves math and wants to study engineering and work for the city water department when she grows up. Tómas can't understand what Cecelia finds so interesting about math, but he loves the water too. Ever since his family went rafting on Big River a few years ago, he's wanted to learn to fish and kayak. He'd like to be a river guide when he grows up.

In school, Cecelia and Tómas are studying their local watershed. Their assignment is to research water quality conditions of a body of water—a lake, stream, river, or reservoir—in their watershed. They picked Somewhere Creek, a stream that flows through their city neighborhood. Here is what they have learned so far.

Somewhere Creek begins as a fast-moving stream high in the mountains, many miles from Someplace City. A variety of fish and aquatic insects live in and around the water, and deep pools provide them shelter. Trees and shrubs along the bank also provide shade and shelter, and their roots hold the soil to the creek's banks. Shallow rocky areas of the creek (called riffles) stir up the water, and there are many small waterfalls. When Cecelia's parents took them to visit the upper reaches of Somewhere Creek, they saw many families playing and picnicking near the stream. Cecelia noticed a couple of artists who had set up their easels and were painting the beautiful scene. Tómas persuaded one of the people fly fishing in the stream to give him a casting lesson.

As the creek descends into the foothills, it naturally slows and begins to meander. Shrubs and thick grasses line the stream banks, and the water flows across the rocky bottom and through deep pools where the water is calmer and slower.

Further downstream, Somewhere Creek flows past farms and golf courses, picking up runoff that often contains fertilizers and other nutrients. Tómas has a cousin, Merced, whose family owns a farm near Tiny Town, an aptly named community along the banks of Somewhere Creek. A few times when he's visited his cousin during the summer, Tómas has noticed that the water in the local fishing hole (which is actually a small reservoir, created by a dam, that holds water used for irrigation) has turned brownish-green and has mats of algae floating near the water's edge.

Below the dam, Somewhere Creek picks up speed again, passing through an area where new homes are being built. Some of Merced's neighbors have sold parcels of their farmland to people who want to live in the country. Merced took Tómas here on their bicycles one day after a heavy rain. Tómas noticed that the stream was brown with soil that had washed into the creek from the construction sites. Merced told him that rocks at the bottom of the stream were all covered by fine silt now.

The Life and Times of Somewhere Creek

Fifty miles from its beginnings, Somewhere Creek flows into a suburban area. Tómas and Cecelia took the bus there one Saturday. They saw people walking in the park along the creek's banks with their dogs and children. Some of the children were playing in the water, turning over rocks to look for aquatic insects, but they didn't seem to be having much luck. Cecelia's grandfather told her that fishing in that part of the creek was once fantastic but that it had become mediocre at best after all the roads, parking lots, and lawns were put in. He told Cecelia that the water had always turned a little murky and green in the summer and fall when water levels dropped, but now he refused to fish there because he'd noticed an oily smell and sheen on the surface of the creek during low water.

Further downstream, where Somewhere Creek flows into the Someplace City limits, Tómas and Cecelia learned that the creek used to overflow into a flat area, especially during the spring. About thirty years ago, the county built a channel lined with concrete to contain the stream and prevent flooding. Because they were now protected against floods, people built houses in the flat area, and Somewhere Creek flows swiftly by during high water. Over the years, some silt has collected on the bottom of the channel, but most of it gets washed away during periods of high, fast water.

As the creek enters the neighborhood where Cecelia and Tómas live, its channel becomes a tunnel under the streets. Most people in this neighborhood of Someplace City don't even know the creek exists.

Once it emerges from the tunnel, Somewhere Creek flows through downtown Someplace City. About 20 years ago, the city parks department planted trees and native plants along the stream bank. Now, the trees provide plenty of shade for the slow-moving creek. When Cecelia and Tómas visited this section of the creek, they noticed that some of the trees had fallen into the water and were left there to provide shelter for fish. The water here seemed cleaner than it did in certain places upstream.

NORTH AMERICAN BEAVER

Downstream of the downtown park, Somewhere Creek flows past the city wastewater treatment plant, several manufacturing plants, and a fuel storage facility. Tómas and Cecelia talked with a local biologist who told them that the water in that part of the river was polluted with chemicals that made the water more acidic. No one knew exactly where the chemicals were coming from, but the city environmental protection department was conducting an investigation.

After flowing through Someplace City, Somewhere Creek continues its journey toward Big River, which eventually empties into the ocean.

Stream Inhabitants

Cutthroat Trout, Brook Trout

- Need very clean water with high levels of dissolved oxygen.

- Need colder water than many other fish.

Spots of algae growing on rocks

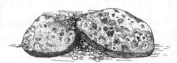

- Found in many water conditions from cold to warm, including fast-moving water.

Rainbow Trout, Brown Trout, Smallmouth Bass, suckers, whitefish

- Need relatively clean water.

- Can tolerate somewhat warmer water temperatures than cutthroat and Brook Trout.

Large beds and floating mats of algae

- Generally require slow-moving or stagnant water.

- Encouraged by high nutrient levels in the water.

Carp, chub, shiners, sunfish

- Pollution tolerant.

- Prefer warmer, slower-moving water than other types of fish.

Mayfly, caddisfly, and stonefly nymphs; gilled snails; adult riffle beetles; hellgramites (dobsonfly larvae)

- Pollution sensitive.

- Need good to excellent water quality.

Eelgrass, elodea, and other types of rooted aquatic plants

- Unlikely to grow in fast-moving water.

Crayfish, riffle beetle and cranefly larvae, dragonfly and damselfly nymphs, clams and mussels

- Somewhat pollution tolerant.

- Need fair water quality to survive.

Duckweed, water lily, and other types of floating aquatic vegetation

- Need slow-moving, sometimes even stagnant water

Midge fly and blackfly larvae, leeches, aquatic worms, lunged snails

- Pollution tolerant.

- Can survive in water of poor quality.

Urban Waterway Checkup
© Council for Environmental Education (CEE)

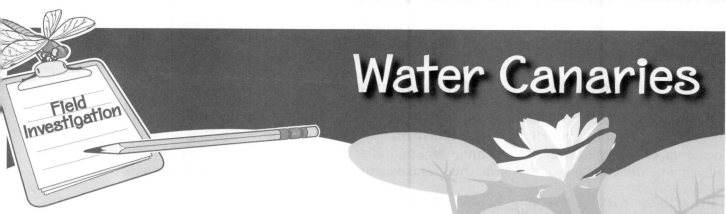

Water Canaries

What are the "water canaries" telling you about local water quality?

Objectives

Students will (1) identify several aquatic organisms, and (2) assess the relative environmental quality of a stream or pond using indicators of pH, water temperature, and the presence of a diversity of organisms.

Background

In the early days of coal mining, canaries were brought into mines to be used as indicators of the mine's air quality. Because canaries are more sensitive than humans to the presence of dangerous gases in the air, their discomfort or death indicated that the air was not safe to breathe. Although this practice no longer exists, it stands as an example of how animals have differing sensitivities to environmental factors. In streams and ponds, the presence or absence of certain organisms, called indicator species, reveals much about water quality. These creatures make up a biotic index (number of living organisms found in an ecosystem). Water with numerous aquatic species is usually a healthy environment, whereas water with just a few different species usually indicates conditions that are less than healthy. The word healthy is used to indicate an environment supportive of life. Pollution generally reduces the quality of the environment and, in turn, the diversity of life forms. In some cases, the actual biomass (the mass of living organisms) will increase because of pollution, but the diversity is compromised as a result of the limited number of types of organisms that can withstand polluted conditions.

Procedure

1. Before the activity, select a small, fairly shallow, slow-moving stream or pond near your school or organization as the sampling site for this activity. Be sensitive to the impact students may have on stream banks and beds, spawning and nesting sites, and vegetation. Have students establish ethical guidelines for their sampling activities. If the stream is not a public site, be sure to

Grade Level: Middle, High School

Content Areas: Science, Environmental Education, Language Arts

Method: Students investigate a stream or pond using sampling techniques.

Materials: Species-identification books (e.g., *The Golden Guide to Pond Life*) or mobile apps; *Student Worksheets I* and *II*; *Aquatic Conditions Fact Sheet*; sampling equipment, such as seine nets, sieves, assorted containers, white trays, magnifying lenses, eye droppers and forceps; water quality test kit (pH and dissolved oxygen), thermometer, tape measure **OPTIONAL:** stereomicroscope

Activity Time: one or two 45-minute sessions; longer if done as a field study activity

People Power: any

Setting: outdoors

Conceptual Framework Topic Reference: HNIIB

Terms to Know: indicator species, diversity, pH, biomass, biotic index

Appendix: Inventory Methods, Using Local Resources, Field Ethics, Animals in the Classroom, The Ecosystem and Project WILD

obtain permission to visit the site. Advise students in advance to dress for the setting—old shoes and shorts or jeans would be best.

NOTE: If a site visit is not possible, modify the activity to be conducted in the classroom.

2. At the sampling site, brief students on habitat courtesies, working from the students' own list of ethical guidelines for sampling activities. Instruct them on how to minimize the potential for damaging habitat, and encourage care in their collecting techniques. Emphasize that all wildlife are to be returned to their habitat unharmed. Educators may choose whether to take some organisms back to school for further study.

3. Begin the activity by observing the water. Identify organisms on the surface and below. Using sampling equipment (nets, trays, sieves, etc.), have students collect as many different forms of animal life as possible. Ask them to be alert to differing micro-habitats near rocks, in riffles, and in pools. Place the animals to be observed in the white trays for viewing and drawing. The whiteness of the trays allows detail to be seen in the animals collected. Keep an adequate amount of water in the trays, and place them in a cool, shady spot. Change the water as often as needed to keep the animals cool. This is a good time to use the microscopes, if available.

4. Using a species-identification book or mobile application (see **www.projectwild.org/aquatic** for resources), have students identify and draw on *Student Worksheet I* the animals they observed in the aquatic environment and those temporarily removed for observation in the collection containers. Ask them to fill in the number of each kind found and to describe the actual location where the animal was found. Once these observations are completed, carefully return the animals to their natural habitat.

NOTE: If you choose to take some of the animals to the classroom, be sure there is adequate water as cool as that in the natural setting. To have the entire class view the organisms, place the organisms in petri dishes or any shallow transparent dish. Then use an overhead projector, projection microscope, or video camera with projection equipment to project the images onto a screen or wall.

5. Encourage students to discuss their observations. How diverse were the aquatic organisms? Introduce the concept of diversity, and explain that a variety of different kinds of plants and animals is usually an indication of a healthy ecosystem.

6. Now it is time to test the water at the field site for other indicators of quality. Using the water quality test kit, have students determine the pH and the temperature of the water as well as the air temperature. If you choose to measure the amount of dissolved oxygen as indicated in Extension 1, include those values with water temperature and pH.

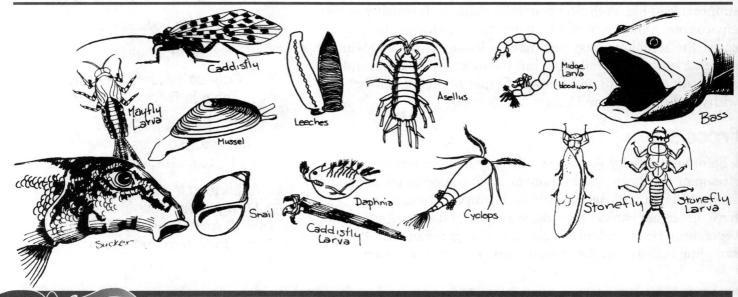

Water Canaries

NOTE: Many educators are not able to have students measure the dissolved oxygen (DO) because of the difficulty for younger students. If it is possible, measuring DO contributes greatly to the overall picture of water quality. These data need to be recorded on *Student Worksheet II*. Educators may also choose to have students measure stream velocity, which can be accomplished by timing a floating object (e.g., a ping pong ball) as it travels a known distance (e.g., 10 feet).

7. Discuss with students how the values for pH, water, and air temperature affect the diversity of life forms found in aquatic environments. Ask whether they would expect the same variety of life in other locations. Help them to understand that predictions of animal diversity can be made from measurements of pH and water temperature (see *Aquatic Conditions Fact Sheet*). Likewise, certain indicator species can also disclose information about pH and water temperature.

NOTE: A simple water quality test kit can be obtained from scientific supply houses with high school biology supplies. Often a Hydrion or Hach kit can be borrowed from a high school biology teacher. A local wastewater treatment facility may have kits that you can borrow. Local universities or wildlife agencies may also have aquatic insect kits. (See Extension 8.)

8. Ideally, this activity could be repeated at other sites with different characteristics. Biologists examine hundreds of sites in order to understand and predict what is happening in natural systems. If another site is visited, it might be useful to divide the class into two groups with one half doing worksheet I and the other half doing worksheet II. When each group is finished, students could come together and mutually predict what the other group had found.

9. Summarize the study with a re-emphasis on the fact that diversity of animals is a useful indicator of habitat quality as well as an overall indicator of environmental quality.

Extensions

1. Measure and record the dissolved oxygen for the sites visited. Look at its relationships to the values for water temperature and pH.

2. Sample the streams both above and below the local water supply.

3. Find the most diverse and least diverse streams in the area.

4. Contact local wildlife, environmental, and conservation groups to find out what their concerns are regarding water quality. Determine what can be done as an individual and as a community to improve or maintain local water quality.

WILD Work

What's the difference between a **Fisheries Biologist** and a **Conservation Biologist**? How does a **Waste Management Officer** help maintain good water quality in lakes, rivers, and wetlands? How does an **Environmental Scientist** help to protect the environment?

Start researching the answers to these questions with students by going to *www.projectwild.org/aquatic*.

In Step with STEM

Frog Populations

■ Use probeware to collect and analyze pH and/or other water quality parameters. Probeware refers to educational hardware and software used for real-time data acquisition, display, and analysis with a computer or calculator.

■ Sketch the organisms collected and, after researching online, label their anatomical features.

■ Using real macro-invertebrates or videos from the Internet, explore and compare means of locomotion for different species.

Water with numerous aquatic species is usually a healthy environment...

In streams and ponds, the presence or absence of certain organisms, called indicator species, reveals much about water quality. These creatures make up a biotic index (number of living organisms found in an ecosystem).

5. Sample streams above and below your local wastewater treatment plant.

6. What do the conditions in the stream mean for wildlife in and out of the water?

7. Research other examples of biological indicators. Determine how substances such as DDT result in bio-magnification (increased accumulation) in creatures such as birds of prey, fish, shellfish, and such.

8. Contact a local environmental agency, your state wildlife agency's aquatic education department, your state Project WILD coordinator, or the Izaak Walton League of America to see if there is an Adopt-a-Stream, river, bay, or lake monitoring project in your area (see ***www.projectwild.org/aquatic*** for resources).

Evaluation

1. Draw a simple illustration of one or more of the following organisms: Asellus (water sowbug), water strider, caddisfly larva, crayfish, scud, *Daphnia*, leech, mayfly nymph, midge larva, stonefly nymph, or dragonfly nymph. Identify each organism by writing the correct name beside the picture.

2. You found a trout in a stream with a large variety of other organisms. Predict ranges you would expect to find for pH and water temperature.

Water Canaries
© Council for Environmental Education (CEE)

Aquatic Conditions Fact Sheet

pH Ranges That Support Aquatic Life

Most Acidic ————————————— Neutral ————————————— Most Basic

| 0 | 1 | 2 | 3 | 4 | 5 | 6 | 7 | 8 | 9 | 10 | 11 | 12 | 13 | 14 |

Bacteria
1.0————————————————————————————————— 13.0

Plants (algae, rooted, etc.)   6.5 ——————————————— 13.0

Carps, suckers, catfish,   6.0 ——————— 8.5
some insects

Bass, crappie   6.0 ——————— 8.5

Snails, clams, mussels   6.5——————— 9.0

Largest variety of animals   6.0 ——————— 8.5
(trout, mayfly, stonefly, caddisfly)

Temperature Ranges (Approximate) Required for Certain Organisms

Temperature

Greater than 68 F (20 C) = Warm water

Much plant life, many fish diseases

Most bass, crappie, Bluegill, carp, catfish, caddisfly, dragonfly, mayfly, mussels

55 – 68 F (12.8 – 20 C) = Cool water

Plant life, some fish diseases

Salmon, trout, stonefly, mayfly, caddisfly, water beetles, smallmouth and rock bass, various minnows and darters, mussels

Less than 55 F (12.8 C) = Cold water

Trout, caddisfly, stonefly, mayfly, various minnows, darters, sculpins

Dissolved Oxygen (DO) Requirements for Native Fish and Other Aquatic Life (DO in parts per million [ppm])

(Below 68 F)
Cold-water organisms including salmon and trout

(Above 68 F)
Warm-water organisms including fish such as bass, crappie, catfish, and carp

6 ppm

5 ppm

Student Worksheets I and II

Student Worksheet I

Where Organism Was Found	Sketch of Organism	Number Found

Student Worksheet II

Observations	Predictions
Water Temperature _____ Air Temperature _____ pH _____ Dissolved O$_2$ _____	

Aqua Words

What words can express the wonders of water?

Objectives

Students will describe a variety of ways and reasons that water is important to people and wildlife.

Background

Water is central to all life and life activities. Plants and animals must have water to survive. Almost all plants and animals and all humans need clean water to live healthy lives. To stay healthy, humans need about two liters (about two quarts) of water each day. Water helps blood and its components transport oxygen and nutrients and removes waste through our circulatory systems. Water represents about 60–70 percent of a person's body weight. Some animals and plants contain even more water. A jellyfish is 95 percent water and a watermelon is 97 percent water. Most fish and other aquatic animals can live only when they are completely covered with water.

Water covers nearly 75 percent of the Earth's surface. Nearly everything on Earth has a direct or indirect connection with water. Rocks channel water into streams, and streams and rivers carry water across land. Ponds, lakes, marshes, and swamps often hold water in place. Trees draw water from the soil and transport it into the leaves and out again into the air. Clouds are airborne carriers of water across the sky.

Humans use water for many purposes other than drinking. Water is used for power generation, industry, and irrigating crops and lawns. Water is also a source of beauty and recreation. It is the basis of a massive global transportation system. Even the driest desert has water—and there are about 320,000,000 cubic miles of water in the oceans. Water grows our food, cools our cars, and is one of the most important substances astronauts take into space.

The major purpose of this activity is for students to increase their appreciation of the importance of water.

Grade Level: Lower Elementary, Upper Elementary

Content Areas:
Language Arts, Environmental Education

Method:
Students brainstorm water words, make word trees with those words, and write poetic statements about water.

Materials:
writing materials

Activity Time:
one or two 20- to 45-minute sessions

People Power:
any

Setting:
indoors

Conceptual Framework Topic Reference:
IDIA1, IDIIB

Terms to Know:
water habitats

Appendix:
The Ecosystem and Project WILD

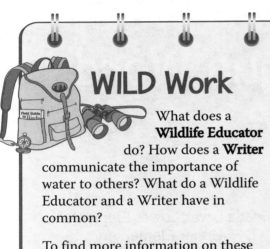

WILD Work

What does a **Wildlife Educator** do? How does a **Writer** communicate the importance of water to others? What do a Wildlife Educator and a Writer have in common?

To find more information on these careers, head to: *www.projectwild. org/aquatic.*

In Step with STEM

■ Create an eBook of the poems to share with family and other classes.

■ For younger students, find clipart to represent the words.

Plants and animals must have water to survive. Almost all plants and animals and all humans need clean water to live healthy lives. . . .Nearly everything on Earth has a direct or indirect connection with water.

Procedure

1. Have students collect pictures that show water habitats. Students can take photographs, draw pictures, or find them in magazines or on websites. Ask them to especially try to acquire images that show how organisms depend on water. Display these images, and use them as a basis for discussion.

2. Ask students to think about some of the ways they have used water today. Any pictures they collect may be used to get them started. Emphasize how all organisms are ultimately connected to water.

3. Using a long strip of paper or an empty chalkboard, ask students to list at least 100 words that have something to do with water. Ask them to think of words describing water, including how it is important to people and wildlife. Keep students expanding into new areas by suggesting examples and categories of ideas if they get bogged down.

NOTE: For younger students, use pictures or a combination of words and pictures.

4. Using the list of words, ask students to create word trees of water-related words.

Begin with a simple word tree like this:

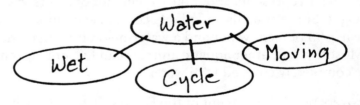

NOTE: You could give students this example for a start if they need it.

Finally, if possible, ask students to create even more complex word trees like these:

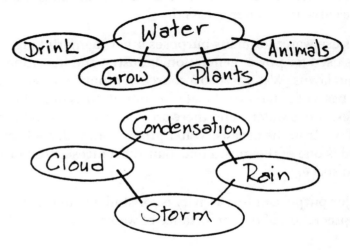

Aqua Words
© Council for Environmental Education (CEE)

5. When students have finished several word trees, have them look at what they have done and create one or two poetic definitions of water or water-related concepts. These definitions could begin "Water . . ." or "Water is . . ." For example, using the word tree of condensation-cloud-rain-storm, you might get: "Water is gray clouds condensing into a loud summer storm." Students could also simply create sentences or paragraphs about water.

6. When students have completed their poetic statements, have them write the statements onto various shades of blue, aqua, gray, white, and green construction paper cut to graphically fit the feeling of their ideas. Artistically arrange these cut-outs on a wall or window.

OPTIONAL: Examples from students have included words arranged in the shape of a stream, river, pond, lake, or ocean. Others have formed the water cycle from their words and images. Some simply have written each of their words on pieces of paper shaped like water drops.

Extension

Create a class book with each student's page included. Students write their poetic definitions at the bottom of the page and then illustrate their ideas—for example, with water colors—at the top of the page.

Evaluation

1. Explain three ways people use water.

2. Explain how plants use water.

3. Explain how animals use water.

4. Explain why water is important.

5. Write and illustrate a short story about the importance of water.

6. Use visual vocabulary techniques (see "Evaluating and Assessing Student Learning" in the Appendices) to demonstrate understanding of concepts and relationships from the activity.

Humans use water for many purposes other than drinking. Water is used for power generation, industry, and irrigating crops and lawns. Water is also a source of beauty and recreation.

Water Plant Art

Grade Level: Lower Elementary, Upper Elementary

Content Areas:
Science, Environmental Education, Expressive Arts

Method:
Students create artwork showing aquatic habitats using drawings and pressed aquatic plants.

Materials:
Seaweed, grasses, or samples of other aquatic plants; shallow pan filled with fresh water; heavy, porous, white watercolor paper; waxed paper; newspapers; several large heavy books or plant press, if available; colored pencils.
OPTIONAL: drying rack, 40-watt light bulb apparatus.

Activity Time:
one 20- to 45-minute session for discussion and construction of artwork

People Power: any

Setting:
indoors and outdoors if students help gather plant material

Conceptual Framework Topic Reference: IDIB

Terms to Know:
aquatic, ecosystem, exotic

Appendices:
Using Local Resources, Field Ethics, The Ecosystem and Project WILD

Give those animal drawings a "real" home!

Objectives

Students will identify aquatic plants as an important component of aquatic habitats and as a necessity for aquatic wildlife.

Background

Aquatic plants grow in a variety of sizes, shapes, and colors. They are essential to the web of life in any aquatic ecosystem. One benefit that aquatic plants provide is that submerged plants release oxygen into the water. The dissolved oxygen can then be used in respiration by aquatic animals.

A benefit of aquatic plants in riparian zones (e.g., river banks) is their ability to absorb excess nutrients before they hit the waterway, such as nutrients from pet waste or chemical fertilizers. Aquatic plant parts are also eaten by a variety of animals. Dead plants break down in water to form small particles of organic material called "detritus." This organic material feeds many small aquatic insects, shellfish, and small fish. These animals are then food for larger predators.

Aquatic plants benefit many aquatic animals by providing protected areas for breeding and hiding places for young. Aquatic plants also stabilize shorelines and reduce erosion. The ability of aquatic plants to perform these functions can be threatened by the introduction of exotic species. Exotics can drive out the native plants that provide oxygen, shelter, and nutrients for other organisms. When exotics disrupt the natural balance of an ecosystem, they are known as invasive species.

The major purpose of this activity is to heighten students' awareness and appreciation of the importance of aquatic plant life.

NOTE: Guides to common aquatic plants, pond life, and seashores are helpful resources that tend to be readily available. One excellent resource is *Pond Life* by George K. Reid, 2001.

Procedure

1. Discuss with students the importance of a variety of plant life in aquatic habitats. Explain how and why aquatic plants are important parts of the ecosystem. Show students pictures of different kinds of aquatic plants, animals, and ecosystems. Freshwater habitats (like streams and lakes) and marine habitats (like saltwater bays and ocean environments) can be compared. Ask students how they think the plants help the animals in each of these environments.

2. After discussing the responsible collection of plant specimens (see "Field Ethics" in the Appendix), take students to an outdoor location where they can gather small samples of aquatic plants. Seaweed from saltwater areas or grasses and algae from freshwater areas work well. Discuss with students which species are native to the area and which are exotic. If collecting plant samples is not feasible, they may be purchased from pet or aquarium stores, some plant nurseries, and science supply catalogs. Purchased aquatic plants that are left over should be disposed of in landfills.

3. Place plant samples in a pan filled with water and clean them thoroughly. If necessary, separate the plants into smaller sizes for mounting and designing artwork.

4. Distribute heavy, white, porous paper to students. (Students may work on their own, in small groups, or as a class.)

5. Using colored pencils, students should draw aquatic wildlife on the art paper. Students should not fill the entire page with art because plants will be placed on top of the art to illustrate plants in the habitat.

6. When the animal drawings are complete, gently lift the plants (still damp) and arrange them on the drawings so that they provide a habitat for the wildlife.

7. Cover the arrangement of plants and animal drawings with waxed paper.

8. Lift artwork—white paper and wax paper, too—and place it between several sheets of newspaper. (The wax paper protects the plant while the water will seep through the white paper. As the plant dries, it will adhere to the white paper.)

9. Place stack of newspapers containing the artwork on a flat surface. Stack several heavy books on top to serve as a plant press. An actual plant press is ideal, if available.

WILD Work

Botanists, or plant biologists, study all plant life, from microorganisms to giant trees. They may study how human activities near water affect aquatic plants and work toward environmental protection, or they may identify invasive and exotic plant species and evaluate how to manage or remove them.

Interpretive Guides work to increase the public's understanding, appreciation, enjoyment of, and concern for the significant historic, cultural, and natural resources of state parks and forests. They may conduct a variety of educational programs and assist with exhibit development by collecting, cataloging, organizing, and protecting park collections of photographs, specimens, and documents.

For links to more information on these occupations, see the WILD Work link at *www.projectwild.org/aquatic*.

In Step with STEM

Frog Populations

Take a fieldtrip to a local pond or stream. Have students locate, observe, and draw various aquatic plants. Diagram the key structures of the plant.

Aquatic plants grow in a variety of sizes, shapes, and colors.

(If possible, elevate the newspapers on a rack or set of bricks. Place a low (40) watt bulb under the stack. Do not let the bulb or socket rest against the stack or any potentially flammable materials. The heat from the lit bulb is just warm enough to dry the stack without damaging the plants.)

10. Drying may take from a few days to several weeks, depending on humidity.

NOTE: These plant prints can serve many purposes, for example as plant identification keys for classroom use and bulletin board artistic displays. The wax paper can be retained as protection or removed gently, leaving the plant dried flat to the paper. If the plants do not stick to the paper, use a glue stick or spray fabric glue to re-attach loose parts.

11. Display aquatic art and ask students to discuss what they learned. Speak with students again about the importance of plant life in aquatic habitats. Ask students to give examples of ways these plants are important.

Extensions

1. Identify local plants found in water. Ask students to identify the plants used in the activity. Have students research the native habitats of the plants they identify.

2. Describe how plants that grow in water can provide food and protection for animals that live in water.

3. Give reasons why it is important to have a variety of aquatic plants in aquatic ecosystems.

4. When discussing aquatic life, use a brainstorming technique to discover how plants are similar to animals. Write down common characteristics of plants and animals, or make posters.

5. Find out more about the habitat in which an aquatic plant grows. What is it like? What animals live there? What plant and animal adaptations are evident?

6. In addition to any samples collected, students can be encouraged to take photographs or make sketches of aquatic species and habitat. Images may be used to assemble a collage or to make picture ID cards.

Evaluation

1. Draw and identify two aquatic plants other than the plants pressed in the activity. What aquatic animals can be added to the pictures to show how these plants help aquatic animals?

One benefit that aquatic plants provide is that submerged plants release oxygen into the water. The dissolved oxygen can then be used in respiration by aquatic animals.

Water Plant Art
© *Council for Environmental Education (CEE)*

Marsh Munchers

Who eats whom in a salt marsh food web?

Objectives

Students will (1) identify components of a food web in a salt marsh, and (2) identify their interconnectedness in the food web.

Background

A salt marsh is an important ecosystem found between a landmass and the ocean. It is a place where freshwater and saltwater come together to form a unique habitat for wildlife. Life forms in salt marshes are often more complex and diverse than those in other habitats because of the constantly changing mixture of both freshwater and saltwater.

Salt marshes are one of the most productive ecosystems on Earth, producing up to two times as much food as the most fertile agricultural lands. The main producer for this important ecosystem is salt marsh grass, which grows and thrives in the nutrient-rich waters of estuaries where saltwater from the ocean mixes with freshwater from land drainage. A salt marsh is always producing new grass as old grass dies. Bacteria promote the decay of the marsh grass, which in turn produces detritus. Detritus is dead and decaying plant or animal matter. Fiddler crabs, snails, small shrimp, and fish such as minnows feed on decomposed marsh grasses. Oysters and clams filter detritus and single-celled, living plants from the water. These organisms then become food for crabs, birds, and a variety of fish. Many marine organisms and commercially valuable fish species—including flounder, Red Drum, and Striped Bass—depend on marsh ecosystems throughout their lifetimes.

Countless numbers of birds also depend on salt marshes for food and nesting areas. Ospreys, sandpipers, and members of the heron family can be seen feeding along marsh creeks during the spring and summer, while ducks and Northern Harriers are common sights in the winter months.

Other animals seen wandering through the marsh in search of food are racoons and small mammals such as shrews and mice.

Grade Level: Upper Elementary

Content Areas:
Science, Environmental Education, Expressive Arts

Method: Students use body movement and pantomime to simulate the feeding motions of marsh animals.

Materials: Timer; construction paper for tokens in five colors: white, green, yellow, blue, red; *Feeding Behavior Cards* (page 79); one envelope per student

Activity Time:
one 20- to 60-minute session

People Power: designed for 25 students (can be adapted for other groups). One-fifth of the class will be designated predators and four-fifths will be other organisms.

Setting: outdoors or large indoor playing area

Conceptual Framework Topic Reference:
IDIB, IDIIA, IDIIB, IDIIB1, IDIIB2, IDIIB2b, IDIIC

Terms to Know: salt marsh, food web, decomposer, detritus, predator, prey, producer, consumer

Appendix: The Ecosystem and Project WILD

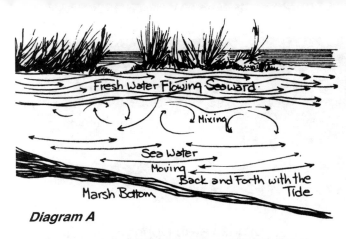

Diagram A

GREAT BLUE HERON

Table of Materials to Be Prepared and Placed in Envelopes
(One Envelope per Student Representing One Predator or Other Organism)

	Feeding-Behavior Cards	Colored Food Tokens
Predators		
1 Raccoon	1 each	
1 Blue Crab	1 each	
1 Red Drum Fish	1 each	
1 Egret	1 each	
1 Person	1 each	
Other Organisms (Detritus-Eaters)		
4 Fiddler Crabs	1 each	5 red tokens each (20 total)
4 Snails	1 each	5 blue tokens each (20 total)
4 Oysters	1 each	5 yellow tokens (20 total)
4 Juvenile Fish	1 each	5 green tokens (20 total)
4 Shrimp	1 each	5 white tokens (20 total)

Deer, grasshoppers, and geese can be seen consuming the grasses at different times of the year.

Salt marshes contribute to flood control and provide water filtration. As water flows through the marsh, much of the sediment load is filtered out to create cleaner and clearer water. Salt marsh grasses and soils also help absorb flood waters and act as natural buffers between land and ocean. These marshes protect upland ecosystems as well as billions of dollars worth of businesses and homes from storms.

Coastal development and pollution are threatening salt marsh environments. Salt marshes, like other wetlands, are destroyed or damaged when land is converted for agriculture production, filled for coastal development, dredged, or used for other purposes.

The major purpose of this activity is for students to learn about salt marshes and to reinforce their understanding of the concept of a food web.

NOTE: Because this is a simulation, some of the animals' roles are simplified. In actual salt marshes, some animals have several roles. For this activity, one dominant role for each animal has been identified.

Procedure

1. Cut appropriately colored construction paper into food tokens, according to the table (at left). Reproduce the *Feeding Behavior Cards* (5 predator cards, 20 detritus-eater cards). Place food tokens and cards into appropriate envelopes.

2. Discuss the characteristics of a salt marsh with students. Also discuss the importance of salt marshes. Emphasize its high productivity as a habitat for animals and plants. Discuss the role of detritus in the marsh food web. Mention decomposers and their importance. If appropriate, introduce the terms "predator" and "prey," and "producers" and "consumers." Show students Diagram A, and emphasize the unusual relationship between freshwater and tidal saltwater found in this habitat.

3. Give one envelope to each student. Explain to students that their creatures' identities are a secret. Each envelope contains the identity of one animal that lives in a salt marsh. The only way others will know what they are is by the way they feed. When they receive their envelopes, explain that some students will be detritus-eaters and others will be predators who prey on the detritus-eaters.

4. Instruct students to open their envelopes to see what animals they are and what feeding behaviors they use. Remind students to keep their identities a secret from the other students. Students will indicate what animals they are by the feeding behavior.

OPTIONAL: Model each behavior first, and identify it so students will know which animal does what. However, it may be more productive to allow the students to improvise.

5. Explain the rules:

- Each student represents a detritus-eater or a predator.
- Each detritus-eater has five food tokens, representing five individual marsh animals of the same species.
- The detritus-eater must give a food token to a predator when tagged.
- Each predator must acquire ten food tokens to stay alive during a tidal cycle.
- A tidal cycle is one playing period of the game.
- Each predator can acquire only one token from each organism at any one time in a tidal cycle, but needs to acquire as much prey as possible during the tidal cycle.
- Detritus-eaters continue to eat until they run out of food tokens. When they run out, they sit quietly in place decomposing in the salt marsh.
- Detritus-eaters and predators must display their feeding behaviors during the activity.
- Detritus-eaters will show their feeding behaviors from stationary, squat positions, while predators will walk as they display their behavior.

6. Establish a play area (inside or outside) and have all detritus-eaters take their envelopes with them as they spread out on the playing field and start pantomiming their feeding behaviors.

7. Tell predators to begin to pantomime their respective feeding behaviors, capture their prey, and secure a food token from the prey, placing it in their envelope.

8. Call time when appropriate (after most predators have acquired ten food tokens).

9. Tell students to hold onto their food envelopes so that they can participate in the discussions.

10. Discuss the results. Did every predator acquire ten food tokens during the tidal cycle? If not, why not? (Some animals are more selective in their feeding preferences and therefore may have a more difficult time finding food.) Discuss the different ways animals are connected to each other and to the detritus.

WILD Work

Wetlands Scientists assist in conserving, enhancing, and restoring wetlands and other habitats through research, management, and monitoring programs. They might collect field data directly from salt marshes to monitor these ecosystems.

Ecologists ask scientific questions about the relationship between organisms and their environment. For example, an ecologist might first identify one component of a food web in a marsh and then how it is connected to other parts of the food web.

For more information on these occupations, see the WILD Work link at *www.projectwild.org/aquatic.*

In Step with STEM

- For younger audiences, practice building and interpreting graphs by creating a bar chart with the tokens on a desk or table to analyze results of activity.

- Expand Evaluation #2 to create multiple food webs and illustrate them using digital presentation software.

Salt marshes are one of the most productive ecosystems on Earth...

Mention that decomposers break down plants and animals to produce the detritus. Be sure the supporting role of producers—the plants that become detritus—is not overlooked because of the more intense activity of the consumers.

11. Draw a food web based on the feeding interactions that took place during the game. Include plants that decomposers eat to produce detritus.

12. Collect the envelopes, and put the color-coded tokens back into their original envelopes.

OPTIONAL: Shuffle the envelopes, and redistribute them to the students. Replay the simulation, and draw a second food web. Compare and contrast the food webs.

13. Summarize by emphasizing the importance of salt marshes. Salt marshes are unusually productive habitats, growing large amounts of vegetation that support a variety of species of wildlife.

Extensions

1. Draw or paint a food web of a salt marsh as a mural, drawing an accurate portrait of each animal. Place each drawing in the appropriate place in the cycle. With yarn, connect each animal with what it eats.

2. If possible, visit a salt marsh.

3. Modify this activity to simulate a freshwater marsh by substituting the following freshwater animals for the previously described saltwater animals:

Detritus-Eaters	Predators
4 Crayfish	1 Raccoon
4 Clams	1 Great Blue Heron
4 Dace (small fish)	1 Bluegill
4 Scuds (shrimp-like crustacean)	1 Northern Pike
4 Mosquito larvae	1 Person

Follow the rest of the procedures as previously outlined.

Evaluation

1. Give examples of two predators and two prey species that live in salt marshes.

2. Use some of the organisms listed below, and others of your choice, to construct a food web that might be found in a salt marsh: people, raccoons, marsh grass, bacteria, snails, oysters, detritus, young fish, and egrets.

As water flows through the marsh, much of the sediment load is filtered out to create cleaner and clearer water. Salt marsh grasses and soils also help absorb flood waters and act as natural buffers between land and ocean.

Feeding Behavior Cards

Predators

Person Fishing: Student walks forward casting line, and tags prey by grasping on the shoulder.

Blue Crab: Student walks sideways, waving arms like claws and grasps prey.

Raccoon: Student walks forward washing hands and grasps prey.

Red Drum Fish: Student walks with hands held forward like a mouth, and grasps prey.

Egret: Student struts with hands on hips, so elbows are like wings. Nearing prey, arms become a beak to grasp prey.

Detritus-Eaters

Juvenile Fish: Gulps down detritus particles in the water or on the bottom. (Student puckers lips and makes sucking noises while feeding.)

Juvenile Fish: Gulps down detritus particles in the water or on the bottom. (Student puckers lips and makes sucking noises while feeding.)

Juvenile Fish: Gulps down detritus particles in the water or on the bottom. (Student puckers lips and makes sucking noises while feeding.)

Juvenile Fish: Gulps down detritus particles in the water or on the bottom. (Student puckers lips and makes sucking noises while feeding.)

Shrimp: Stirs up mud and detritus with walking legs that lift particles to mouth. (Student makes stirring motions with both arms.)

Shrimp: Stirs up mud and detritus with walking legs that lift particles to mouth. (Student makes stirring motions with both arms.)

Shrimp: Stirs up mud and detritus with walking legs that lift particles to mouth. (Student makes stirring motions with both arms.)

Shrimp: Stirs up mud and detritus with walking legs that lift particles to mouth. (Student makes stirring motions with both arms.)

Snail: Licks up detritus with specialized tongue called radula. (Student displays licking motion, using one hand as the radula.)

Snail: Licks up detritus with specialized tongue called radula. (Student displays licking motion, using one hand as the radula.)

Snail: Licks up detritus with specialized tongue called radula. (Student displays licking motion, using one hand as the radula.)

Snail: Licks up detritus with specialized tongue called radula. (Student displays licking motion, using one hand as the radula.)

Oyster: Filters detritus from water using gills. (Student waves arms back and forth in air.)

Oyster: Filters detritus from water using gills. (Student waves arms back and forth in air.)

Oyster: Filters detritus from water using gills. (Student waves arms back and forth in air.)

Oyster: Filters detritus from water using gills. (Student waves arms back and forth in air.)

Fiddler Crab: Picks detritus from sand with one or two claws. (Students pick objects from floor with thumbs and fingers acting as claws.)

Fiddler Crab: Picks detritus from sand with one or two claws. (Students pick objects from floor with thumbs and fingers acting as claws.)

Fiddler Crab: Picks detritus from sand with one or two claws. (Students pick objects from floor with thumbs and fingers acting as claws.)

Fiddler Crab: Picks detritus from sand with one or two claws. (Students pick objects from floor with thumbs and fingers acting as claws.)

Wetland Metaphors

Grade Level: Upper Elementary

Content Areas: Language Arts, Environmental Education

Method: Students are presented with a selection of objects to investigate as metaphors for the natural functions of wetlands.

Materials: A large pillowcase, bag, or box; sponge; small pillow; soap; eggbeater or mixer; small doll cradle; sieve or strainer; paper coffee filter; antacid tablets; small box of cereal or rice; 3" x 5" cards with pictures to show other wetland metaphors (a zoo represents wildlife diversity; a vegetable garden represents a wetland in which food is abundant; a vacation resort represents a resting or wintering place for migrating waterfowl) **NOTE:** A metaphoric approach such as this allows a variety of everyday objects to illustrate the basic characteristics of wetlands.

Activity Time: one or two 30- to 60-minute sessions

People Power: any

Setting: indoors or outdoors

Conceptual Framework Topic Reference: IDIA2b

Terms to Know: wetlands, metaphor

Appendices: Sustainable Seafood, The Ecosystem and Project WILD, Climate Change

Learn how soap, antacids, and doll cradles represent the functions of wetlands.

Objectives

Students will (1) describe the characteristics of wetlands, and (2) evaluate the importance of wetlands to wildlife and humans.

Background

Wetlands are many different things to many different people. Some people have never heard of or thought about wetlands. Others are working actively to protect wetlands because of their importance.

Wetlands include areas such as freshwater and saltwater marshes, wet meadows, swamps, lagoons, bogs, and prairie potholes. All wetlands, whether coastal or inland, provide special habitats that serve areas far beyond their boundaries. Wetlands are especially important to plants, animals, humans, and the total environment because of the abundance of food, vegetative cover (shelter), and water found there. Most wetlands are rich with diverse wildlife species. Coastal and inland marshes, for example, provide breeding, resting, and wintering habitats for thousands of migratory birds—including ducks, geese, swans, cranes, and shorebirds.

Wetlands are often referred to as "nurseries" because they provide critical breeding and rearing habitats for countless numbers and species of wildlife. Many species of fish that are important for commercial and personal use by humans reproduce and spend part, or all, of their life cycles in fertile wetlands adjacent to larger, more open bodies of water. These fish species include bass, salmon, walleye, perch, and pickerel. A wide variety of reptiles, amphibians, insects, and crustaceans also breed and live in wetlands. Frogs and toads, turtles of all kinds, salamanders, snakes, dragonflies, water striders, clams, and crayfish flourish in wetland habitats. Many mammals—from muskrats and beavers to White-tailed Deer and moose—also depend on wetland areas.

Wetlands also have the unique ability to purify the environment. They act as natural filtering systems and have been shown to be extremely effective. For example, they can trap and neutralize sewage waste, allow silt to settle, and promote the decomposition of many toxic substances.

The importance of vegetation associated with wetlands cannot be overlooked. Plants absorb nutrients and help cycle them through food webs. Plants also help keep nutrient concentrations from reaching toxic levels. Plants slow down water flow, causing silt to settle out. Through photosynthesis, plants add oxygen to the system and provide food to other life forms.

Of great importance to humans are the flood-control characteristics of wetlands. When runoff from rains and spring thaws is high, wetland areas absorb excess water until it gradually drains away down streams and rivers and through the soil. Acting as buffers, healthy wetlands prevent flooding and erosion. In dryer periods, wetlands hold precious moisture after open bodies of water have disappeared. The many activities that take place in wetlands make them among the most productive ecosystems in the world.

As remarkable and resilient as wetlands are, these unique areas have limits. Their destruction or abuse can have devastating effects on wildlife, humans, and overall environmental quality.

Many of the major attributes of wetlands can be explored through the use of metaphors. To use a metaphor is to apply a word or phrase to an object or concept that the word or phrase does not literally denote in order to suggest a comparison between the two. A metaphor represents a concept or idea through another concept or idea. "A tree is a home" and "books are windows of thought" are two examples. In this activity, a variety of everyday objects can be used to represent the natural functions of wetlands. For example:

Object	Metaphoric Function
sponge	absorbs excess water caused by runoff; retains moisture for a time even if standing water dries up (e.g., sponge placed in a small puddle of water absorbs water until saturated, then stays wet after standing water has evaporated)
pillow or bed	provides a resting place for migratory birds
mixer or eggbeater	mixes nutrients and oxygen in the water
cradle	provides a nursery that shelters, protects, and feeds young wildlife
sieve or strainer	strains silt and debris from water
filter	filters smaller impurities from water
antacid	neutralizes toxic substances
cereal or rice	provides nutrient-rich foods (rice is grown in wetland areas)
soap	helps cleanse the environment (as wetlands do)

Wetland habitats are being converted to other uses (agriculture, roadways, housing developments) or otherwise being altered (drained for pest control or polluted) at the average rate of about 14,000 acres per year in the United States (Source: U.S. Fish and Wildlife Service, 2004–2009 National Wetlands Inventory). Although many wetlands are protected by federal and state laws, there still appears to be a significant need to create a greater understanding of the importance of wetlands as ecosystems and as wildlife habitat.

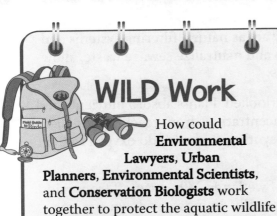

WILD Work

How could **Environmental Lawyers**, **Urban Planners**, **Environmental Scientists**, and **Conservation Biologists** work together to protect the aquatic wildlife living within a wetland and conserve the wetlands themselves?

To find more information and view videos on these careers, head to: *www.projectwild.org/aquatic*.

In Step with STEM

■ Use the "Wetlands Mapper" provided by the U.S. Fish and Wildlife Service to locate nearby wetlands or identify types of wetlands in your region. See *www.fws.gov/wetlands/Data/Mapper.html*.

■ In groups, build models of a wetland using various materials such as carpet, cloth, or sponges to test flow and absorption rates of each material.

Wetlands include areas such as freshwater and saltwater marshes, wet meadows, swamps, lagoons, bogs, and prairie potholes.

The major purpose of this activity is for students to develop an appreciation and understanding of wetlands through the power of metaphor, linking the characteristics and natural functions of wetlands to the familiar realm of everyday life.

Procedure

1. Prepare a "Mystery Metaphor Container" (pillowcase, bag, or box). It should be possible for students to put their hands into the container and pull out an object without being able to see inside the container. Educators may want to collect as many as one metaphoric object per student, but at least have enough for one per group of four students. Put the container aside to use later.

2. Discuss the variety of wetlands found in your local area, state, country, and elsewhere. Then invite students to sit quietly and close their eyes. Ask them to picture a wetland. Have them examine what it looks like and look carefully at the plants and animals, including insects and small creatures. What does the air feel like? How does it smell?

3. Invite students to share what they imagined. Compile a list of their offerings. Encourage discussion and mutual sharing.

4. With their lists as a point of reference, help students identify which plants and animals are most likely to be found in a wetland. If possible, have them classify the plants and animals according to the kind of wetland in which they would be found. State or federal wildlife officials and representatives of private conservation or nature-related organizations can be helpful.

5. Next, provide students with background information to serve as an overview of the basic ecological activities that characterize the wetland habitat. For example, educators might include:

■ **sponge effect:** absorbs runoff

■ **filter effect:** takes out silt, toxins, wastes, and such

■ **nutrient control:** absorbs nutrients from fertilizers and other sources that may cause contamination downstream

■ **natural nursery:** provides protection and nourishment for newborn wildlife

Suggest that these functions and many more students could probably think of are taking place in wetlands all the time.

6. Now bring out the "Mystery Metaphor Container." Tell students that everything in the container has something to do with a wetland. Have students divide into groups of four. Announce that when it is a team's turn, a representative from the group will draw an object from the container. Then, as a group, they must figure out how the object could represent what a wetland is or does.

Wetland Metaphors
© Council for Environmental Education (CEE)

7. Have the designated student reach into the container and withdraw one object. When each group has an object, ask them to work as a team to identify and describe the relationships between their metaphoric object and wetlands. Encourage students to build on each other's ideas. You can also assist by strengthening their connections.

NOTE: Allow students time to discuss their ideas within their groups before doing so in front of the entire class.

8. Ask each group to report its ideas to the class.

9. Following discussion and review of the functions represented by each metaphor, ask students to summarize the major roles that wetlands perform in contributing to habitat for wildlife. List the ways in which wetlands are important to humans. Why do humans convert wetlands to other uses? Ask students if their own attitudes about wetlands are different now. If yes, how? If not, why not?

10. For the final part of this activity, encourage students' understanding of how wetlands' conditions depends on each of us. Many kinds of wildlife depend on wetlands. Our own well-being requires wetland ecosystems. Strengthen students' understanding of how humans are connected to wetlands. Recreation, aesthetics, utilitarian use, environmental quality, and nature study are but a few of the connections we each have with wetlands.

Extensions

1. Visit a wetland to verify the appropriateness of the metaphors explored in the classroom.

Identify and discuss any limitations to the appropriateness of those metaphors. Identify what seem to be the most compelling attributes of the metaphors in helping you understand the characteristics and nature of the wetland. Expand on your understanding of those metaphors. Identify new and appropriate metaphors.

2. Investigate local, county, state, and federal regulations and laws that govern uses of wetlands.

Evaluation

1. Explain why wetlands are among the world's most productive ecosystems.

2. Wetlands are important to a range of organisms in the animal kingdom, from zooplankton to humans. Select five species of animals, and describe how wetlands are important to each.

> *All wetlands, whether coastal or inland, provide special habitats that serve areas far beyond their boundaries.*

Additional Resources

www.fws.gov/wetlands

http://water.epa.gov/type/wetlands/

Hooks and Ladders

Grade Level: Middle School

Content Areas:
Social Studies, Science, Environmental Education, Expressive Arts

Method: Students simulate the migration of and the hazards faced by Pacific salmon to illustrate their life cycle.

Materials: 500 feet of rope or string or six traffic cones for marking boundaries (masking tape if area is indoors); two cardboard boxes; 100 tokens (3" x 5" cards, poker chips; macaroni, etc.); jump rope

Activity Time:
one 30- to 60-minute session

People Power:
20 to 30 students or more

Setting:
Large playing area (100 feet x 50 feet), outdoors or indoors

Conceptual Framework Topic Reference: IDIIB

Terms to Know:
life cycle, limiting factors, population, migration, spawn, estuaries

Appendices: Let's Go Fishing!, Using Local Resources, Sustainable Seafood, Agencies and Organizations, The Ecosystem and Project WILD, Climate Change

Get ready to embark on the amazing life journey of the Pacific salmon.

Objectives

Students will (1) describe how some fish migrate as part of their life cycles, (2) identify the stages of the life cycle of one kind of fish, (3) describe limiting factors affecting Pacific salmon as they complete their life cycles, and (4) generalize that limiting factors affect all populations of animals.

Background

Many fish migrate from one habitat to another during their lives. Both the Atlantic and Pacific salmon are examples of fish that endure a spectacular migration.

The life cycle for Pacific salmon begins when the female deposits 1,000 to 5,000 eggs in her freshwater spawn. The eggs are deposited in a shallow gravel depression that she digs by flapping her tail from side to side. Once the eggs are deposited, the male fertilizes them; then both fish nudge the gravel back over the eggs to offer as much protection as possible. The eggs are susceptible to factors such as predation or oxygen deprivation. Within a few days, both the male and female salmon have completed their reproduction cycle and soon die.

Newly hatched salmon, called "alevins," live in the gravel and survive by absorbing proteins from their yolk sacs. After a few weeks, the yolk sacs are gone and the small fish, known as "fry," move into deeper water to find food on their own. Salmon remain in freshwater streams feeding and growing for many months or even years before migrating downstream to the ocean. These small ocean-bound salmon are now called "smolts." These salmon will feed in estuaries where fresh and saltwater mix. After a few weeks of adjusting to the brackish water, the young salmon swim into the ocean.

In the ocean, salmon grow rapidly by feeding on a rich food supply that includes other fish, shrimp, and crustaceans. Young salmon may encounter many limiting factors, including sharks, Killer Whales, other marine mammals, and humans who are fishing salmon for commercial and personal uses.

After two to five years in the ocean, Pacific salmon begin the journey that guides them to their own hatching sites. Pacific salmon spawn only once in their lives. Salmon have an inherent ability to return to their original streams. Juvenile salmon imprint or memorize the unique odors of their home streams. As returning adults, scientists hypothesize that salmon use their senses of smell to detect those odors and guide them upstream to where they were hatched. Once there, the salmon spawn and then die.

Salmon face a variety of limiting factors in the completion of their life cycles. A limiting factor is a reason or cause that reduces the population of an organism. Some limiting factors are natural, and some result from human intervention into natural systems. Natural limiting factors include drought, floods, predators, and inadequate food supply.

High human demand for salmon in recent years has inadvertently led to the problem of domestic salmon stock interfering with wild salmon stock. Salmon are farmed in open net pens, and every year millions of these domesticated salmon escape and enter surrounding marine environments or coastal rivers all over the world. The escape of domestic salmon results in numerous limiting factors for wild salmon: interbreeding with escaped domestic salmon, which is believed to result in maladaptive genetic variation; competition for food, habitat, and mates; and the transmittance of pathogens.

Throughout their lives, salmon depend on a habitat that provides plants to shade streams and deep pools of cool, clear water for spawning and resting. Incorrect logging, grazing, mining, road building, and development practices often destroy streamside vegetation, erode land, and fill streams with silt that covers gravel beds.

Life Cycle of the Pacific Salmon

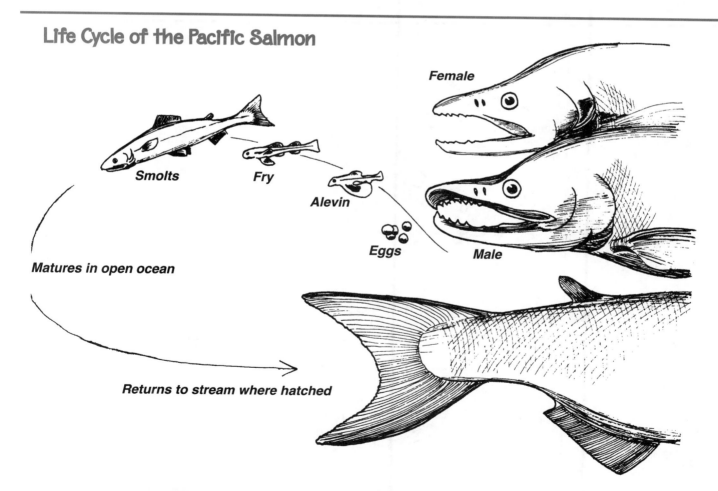

Smolts

Fry

Alevin

Eggs

Female

Male

Matures in open ocean

Returns to stream where hatched

Dams are another limiting factor that block or slow migration to and from the ocean. Salmon become disoriented by the reservoirs formed by dams and become exposed to unhealthy conditions like high water temperatures and predators. Fish ladders can be installed to help salmon through the dams. Fish ladders can be water-filled staircases that allow migrating fish to swim around the dam.

Another threat to salmon is overfishing. Overfishing, combined with habitat destruction, is viewed by biologists as a cause for the decline of salmon populations.

NOTE: All possible conditions are not covered by the design of this activity. However, the activity does serve to illustrate three important concepts: life cycle, migration, and limiting factors.

Procedure

1. Ask students what they know about the life cycles of fish that live in their area. Do any local fish migrate to spawn? If yes, which ones? (Mullet, shad, Lake Trout, Striped Bass, suckers, carp, and salmon are examples of fish that migrate to spawn.)

2. Set up a playing field as shown in Diagram A, including spawning grounds, reservoir, downstream, upstream, and ocean. The area must be at least 100 feet by 50 feet. Assign roles to each of the students. Some will be wild salmon; others will be potential limiting factors to the salmon. Assign the students roles as follows:

- Choose two students to be the turbine team. They will operate the jump rope, which represents the turbines in hydroelectric dams. Later in the simulation, when all salmon have passed the turbine going downstream, those students move to the upstream side to become the waterfall-broad jump monitors. (See diagram.)

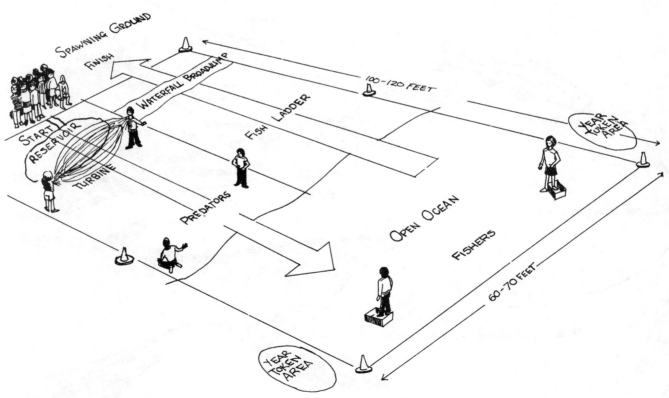

Diagram A

Hooks and Ladders
© *Council for Environmental Education (CEE)*

- Choose two students to be predatory wildlife. At the start of the simulation, predators will be stationed in the reservoir above the turbines to catch the salmon fry as they try to find their way out of the reservoir and move downstream. Then they will move to below the turbines where they catch salmon headed downstream. Later in the activity, when all the salmon are in the sea, these same two predators will patrol the area above the "broad jump" waterfalls. There they will feed on salmon just before they enter the spawning ground. (See diagram.)

- Choose two students to be domestic salmon that have escaped from a salmon farm. These students can replace or be in addition to the two students acting as predatory wildlife.

- Choose two students to be humans in fishing boats catching salmon in the open ocean. The students in fishing boats must keep one foot in a cardboard box to reduce their speed and maneuverability.

- All remaining students are wild salmon.

NOTE: These figures are based on a class size of 25 to 30. If the group is larger or smaller, adjust the number of people who are fishing and predatory wildlife accordingly.

3. Begin the activity with all salmon in the spawning ground. Salmon first move into the reservoir above the dam. They must stay in the reservoir while they count to 30. This pause simulates the disorientation that salmon face because of a lack of current in the lake to direct them on their journey. During this time, predators may catch salmon and escort them one at a time to become part of the fish ladder. The salmon then start their journey downstream. The first major limiting factor that salmon encounter is the turbines at the dam. At most dams, escape weirs guide migrating salmon past the turbines. The student salmon cannot go around the jump-rope swingers, but they can slip under the swingers' arms if they do not get touched while doing so. A salmon dies if the turbine (jump rope) hits it. The turbine operators may change the speed at which they swing the jump rope. Any salmon that "dies" at any time in this activity must immediately become part of the fish ladder. The student is no longer a fish, but becomes part of the physical structure of the human-made fish ladders now used by migrating salmon to get past barriers such as dams. The students who are in the fish ladder kneel on the ground, with one body space between them, as shown on the following page.

4. Once past the turbines, the salmon must pass some predatory wildlife or domestic salmon infected with a pathogen. These students, who have moved from the reservoir area to the area below the turbine, must catch the wild salmon with both hands—tagging isn't enough. Dead salmon are escorted by the

WILD Work

A **Fisheries Biologist** carries out a wide range of duties related to fish conservation, including monitoring populations of fish and other aquatic species, restoring habitat, controlling nuisance aquatic species, developing fishery management plans, and evaluating the impact of proposed construction projects. Education requirements to become a biologist typically include a Bachelor's degree in fisheries science or a related biological science; many positions require a graduate degree and field experience. A Fisheries Biologist must be comfortable working outdoors in all weather conditions.

To find more information and view videos on this occupation, visit *www. projectwild.org/aquatic*.

In Step with STEM

Frog Populations

Have students advise on how to adjust the playing field based on the outcomes after conducting a few trials of the activity. Students should try to maintain balance between fish populations, predator needs, and human needs (represented by the anglers). Students may adjust, for example, the speed at which the turbine (the rope) turns, the optimum distance between various parts of the playing field, the number of predators, the number of humans, or the distance required to jump across the waterfall. Relate these modifications to actions wildlife conservation professionals and engineers might make when balancing the needs of wildlife and people.

Many fish migrate from one habitat to another during their lives. Both the Atlantic and Pacific salmon are examples of fish that endure a spectacular migration.

A fish ladder may be a water-filled "staircase" that allows fish to swim around a dam.

predator to become part of the fish ladder. Later, the salmon that survive life in the open ocean will pass through the fish ladder to return to the spawning ground. **NOTE:** Both the predatory wildlife/domestic salmon in the downstream area and the people fishing in the open ocean must take dead salmon to the fish ladder site. This action moves the predators/domestic salmon and fishing boats off the field regularly, helping to provide a more realistic survival ratio.

5. Once in the open ocean, salmon can be caught by fishing boats. Salmon must move back and forth across the ocean area in order to gather four tokens. Each token represents one year of growth. Once a fish has four tokens (four years' growth), that fish can begin migration upstream. The year tokens can be picked up only one at a time on each crossing. Remember, the salmon must cross the entire open ocean area to get a token. The "four years" that these trips take make the salmon more vulnerable; thus they are more readily caught by the fishing boats. For this simulation, the impact of this limiting factor creates a more realistic survival ratio of the population before the salmon begin the return migration upstream.

6. When four of the tokens have been gathered, the salmon can start upstream. The salmon must walk through the entire pattern of the fish ladder. This enforced trip through the fish ladder gives students a hint of how restricting and tedious the upstream journey can be. In the fish ladder, predators/domestic salmon may not harm the wild salmon.

7. Once through the ladder, the salmon face the broad-jump waterfall. The waterfall represents one of the natural barriers salmon face going upstream. Be sure the jumping distance is challenging but realistic. The two former turbine students will monitor the jump. Salmon must jump the entire breadth of the waterfall to be able to continue. If a salmon fails to make the jump, then it must return to the bottom of the fish ladder and come through again. **NOTE:** When playing indoors, the broad-jump waterfall may be changed into a stepping-stone jump defined by masking tape squares on hard floors.

8. Above the falls, the two predators who started the simulation as predators below the turbines have now become the last set of limiting factors faced by salmon. They represent bears—one example of predatory wildlife. Again, remember that predators must catch salmon with both hands. If they catch a salmon, they must then take the student to become part of the structure of the fish ladder.

9. The activity ends when all salmon are gone before the spawning ground is reached—or when all surviving salmon reach the spawning ground.

Hooks and Ladders

10. Next, engage students in a discussion. Explore topics such as:

- the apparent survival or mortality ratio of salmon;
- the role of the barriers;
- the role of predatory wildlife and the people fishing;
- where the losses were greatest;
- where the losses were least;
- what the consequences would be if all the eggs deposited made the journey successfully; and
- what seemed realistic about this simulation and what did not.

Salmon eggs are deposited in shallow gravel depressions in streams such as this one.

11. Ask students to summarize what they have learned about the life cycle of salmon, the salmon's migration, and limiting factors that affect salmon. Make sure students have a clear working definition of limiting factors. Encourage students to make the generalization that all animals—not just Pacific salmon—are affected by limiting factors. Ask students to give examples of limiting factors. They might mention the availability of suitable food, water, shelter, and space; disease; weather; predation; and changes in land use and other human activities.

Variation: Atlantic Salmon

This activity can be easily adapted to feature Atlantic salmon. The most significant difference between Pacific and Atlantic salmon is that Atlantic salmon can spawn more than once. Many Atlantic salmon make their complete migratory journey and spawn two or more times. All Pacific salmon die after spawning only once. To adapt this activity for Atlantic salmon, students are to make as many complete migratory trips as possible. After the activity is finished, ask students to report how many times they successfully completed the migratory cycle. Graph the data. Have students explain how age influences mortality rates and susceptibility to limiting factors.

Variation: Striped Bass

This activity can also be adapted to feature Striped Bass rather than salmon. The Striped Bass is more widely distributed along United States' coastlines than either the Atlantic or Pacific salmon. Like the salmon, Striped Bass reproduce in freshwater and migrate to and mature in saltwater. They must also face the same limiting factors described in this activity.

Extensions

1. Write a report on the life history of one species of salmon (e.g., Chinook or King, Chum or Dog, Pink or Humpback, Coho or Silver, Sockeye or Red, Atlantic). Create a mural showing the life cycle of this salmon.

2. Research and illustrate the life cycle of any local fish. If possible, look for one that migrates.

3. Compare how the life cycle of a Pacific salmon is similar to and different from the life cycle of one or more local fish.

4. Investigate similarities and differences in the migration and life cycles of an Atlantic and a Pacific salmon. Investigate the life cycle of salmon in the Great Lakes region of the United States.

Sockeye Salmon leap over a waterfall as they migrate upstream.

5. Visit fish hatcheries that work with migratory species and investigate how they function.

6. Explore ways that dams can be modified to let fish safely pass downstream and upstream. Design the "perfect" fish ladder.

7. Investigate and discuss commercial fishing for salmon. Investigate and discuss personal, including recreational, fishing for salmon.

8. Find out about laws protecting migratory species, including fish.

9. Consider the following approach, and try the activity again:

In the past 100 years, salmon have experienced many new limiting factors resulting from human activities. Dams, commercial fishing, timber harvest, road construction, and the presence of escaped domestic salmon have had a tremendous impact on wild salmon populations. In 1991, the Snake River Sockeye Salmon was placed on the federal endangered species list. In the past, tens of thousands of Sockeyes would make the 900-mile return trip from the sea to Idaho's mountain streams and lakes. There they spawned and died. Their offspring hatched and began their early development in freshwater. The actual migration to the Pacific Ocean could be completed in as few as nine days. Today, that trip takes more than 60 days. In 1991, only four Snake River Sockeye Salmon returned to their spawning grounds. In 2011, the number of salmon that returned to their spawning grounds was 1,118. Despite this significant increase from 1991, the endangered status of the Snake River Sockeye Salmon was reaffirmed in 2011.

To simulate these increases in salmon limiting factors, play several rounds of "Hooks and Ladders." Allow each round to represent the passage of 25 years. Start in 1850. In that year, do not include dams or commercial fishing operations in the scenario. As time passes, add the commercial fishing operations. Build dams (jump ropes) and add domestic salmon as the scenario progresses into the 21st century.

Describe some of the possible effects on salmon from increased limiting factors as a result of human activities and interventions. Discuss possible positive and negative effects on both people and salmon from these increases in limiting factors affecting salmon. When the activity reaches "the present," predict what might happen to salmon in the future. Recognizing the complexity of the dilemma, discuss possible actions, if any, that might be taken to benefit both people and salmon.

10. Find out if salmon exist in your state. If so, are they native or were they introduced?

Evaluation

1. List, describe, and illustrate the major stages in a Pacific salmon's life cycle.

2. Identify and describe some of the limiting factors that affect salmon as they complete their life cycles.

3. Identify and describe some limiting factors that might affect other animal populations.

Micro Odyssey

Capture the microscopic aquatic world through art and imagination.

Objectives

Students will (1) identify forms of microscopic life that live in water, and (2) describe how various aquatic organisms are interrelated.

Background

When Anton Van Leeuwenhoek and Robert Hooke, the inventors of the first microscope, looked into the micro-world of stream and pond water, they were surprised to find life forms. As time went by and more researchers gazed into this world, it became clear that thousands of tiny organisms made their homes in water. Research has shown that without these microscopic life forms the entire aquatic ecosystem could not function. Microorganisms are vital in the food supplies of fish, aquatic birds, reptiles, amphibians, and mammals—including humans.

The major purpose of this activity is to provide students with ways of becoming familiar with various microscopic life forms and their roles in larger-scale habitats and ecosystems.

Procedure

1. Collect samples of pond water that contain abundant microorganisms. One or two gallons (or about 4–7 liters) should be adequate.

NOTE: Some educators may want to start a small aquarium. This phase can be done by the educator or as a field trip. Obtain enough pond water to stock a small aquarium and collect pond bottom materials such as soil and detritus. Aquatic plants can be transplanted into the aquarium. Certain aquatic insects, like diving beetles and water striders, may be placed in the aquarium. See page 356 of the Appendices for additional information about preparing classroom aquaria.

Grade Level: Upper Elementary, Middle School

Content Areas: Science, Environmental Education

Method: Students will examine, draw, paint, and identify microorganisms in pond water.

Materials: Pond water; hand lens; magnifiers; nets (fine mesh); microscopes, slides, cover slips, eyedroppers; writing materials; art supplies (paints, poster paper, mural paper, tape)

Activity Time: three 45-minute sessions, additional time if field trip to pond is included

People Power: any

Setting: outdoors and indoors

Conceptual Framework Topic Reference: IDIB, IDIIB2, IDIIC

Terms to Know: microorganism, pond, habitat, predator, prey, food web, detritus, producer, consumer

Appendices: Inventory Methods, Field Ethics, Benefits of a Classroom Aquarium, The Ecosystem and Project WILD

Microorganisms are vital in the food supplies of fish, aquatic birds, reptiles, amphibians, and mammals—including humans.

2. Invite students to remove a tablespoon (about 14 ml) of pond water from the container. Remember to tell them to get the water from within the container and not just at the surface. Have them examine the water with hand lenses and microscopes. Tell them to make sketches of the living things they find. They should note how the organisms move and how they interact. Do some seem to be predators? Which of the other life forms do the predators prey upon?

3. After they have sketched several organisms, encourage students to choose life forms to portray in a painting. The students should strive for detail and accuracy in portraying the organisms. Next, have students identify the organisms they painted. Ask them to write a short paragraph about the habits and habitat of the organisms. Some common pond microorganisms are shown in Diagram A. *Pond Life: Revised and Updated* (Reid, George K., 2001, St. Martin's Press, NY) can assist with identifying common microscopic organisms. Because there may be microorganisms that are difficult to identify, you may have students give those organisms temporary names. Locate additional reference materials to identify the species.

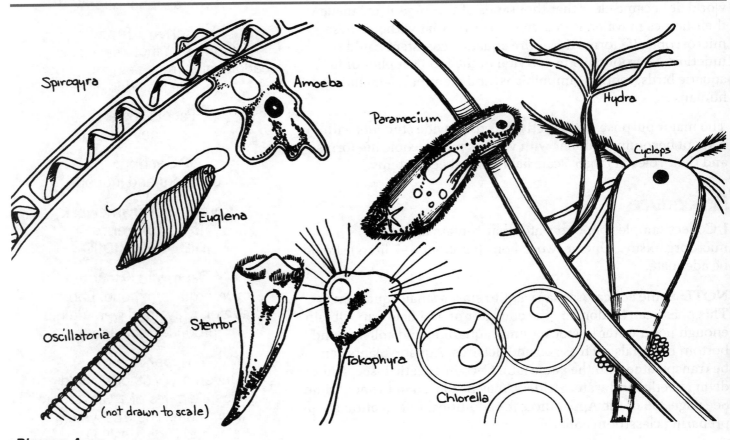

Spiroqyra · Amoeba · Paramecium · Hydra · Euglena · Cyclops · Oscillatoria · Stentor · Tokophyra · Chlorella · (not drawn to scale)

Diagram A

4. Create a class mural of a pond and its aquatic environment. The paintings done in Step 3 could be added to the mural at appropriate locations. Written reports could be displayed near the mural. Which animals should be shown preying on others? Which are decomposers? Which are producers? Which are consumers? Where should plants be placed? Each student could do additional research to discover more about his or her organism, its role in the aquatic system, and other items of interest. If possible, return the water to the pond when it is no longer needed in the classroom for instruction.

Extensions

1. What natural or unnatural events in the pond or stream could be major disasters to all the inhabitants?

2. Divide the class into crews, and have each crew create a log of an imaginary journey through their micro-world. They are to act as if they were micro-sized. The logs should be filled with written descriptions and illustrations. Students might make maps, plotting their journeys and noting places where they had adventures. The crews should then exchange logs with other crews. Using the logs, maps, and drawings, the crew members should decide how to prepare themselves and their craft for a future micro-journey.

3. Find examples of maps, drawings, and writings made in the past by famous explorers. Old World maps drawn at the time of Columbus, accounts written by explorers, and drawings of animals made by these explorers can be interesting introductions to this micro-world journey activity.

4. Read examples of great mythical voyages, such as those of Ulysses. Find old bestiaries (fables about mythical creatures popular in the Middle Ages) and read about mermaids, unicorns, and sea monsters. With these fables for inspiration, along with your writings and paintings of pond life, create a 20th-century bestiary.

Evaluation

1. Draw a simple illustration of one or more of the following pond organisms: *Daphnia, Euglena, Hydra, Spirogyra,* rotifer, water mite. Label your drawing and add information about the characteristics of the organism and its habitat.

2. Identify each of the organisms in the list above, plus sulfur bacteria, as a producer (P), consumer (C), or decomposer (D).

3. Use at least three of the organisms listed above, plus others, to construct an aquatic food web that might be found in a pond.

WILD Work

What's the difference between a **Marine Biologist** and a **Microbiologist**?

How does a **Microbiologist** determine the health of a water source?

How could a **Photographer** or **Videographer** capture microscopic life that lives in water and share it with others?

Start researching the answers to these questions with students by going to *www.projectwild.org/aquatic*.

In Step with STEM

Frog Populations

■ Add detail to sketches of organisms by identifying and labeling their anatomical features. Refer to websites or textbooks to research the anatomy of microorganisms.

■ For a link to a photo gallery of microbes, visit *www.projectwild. org/aquatic*. Then, view electron micrograph images and compare photos to specimens found in pond water.

■ Obtain several sterile agar dishes from a lab supply company. Divide students into small groups and have each group cultivate a sample of bacteria swabbed from the pond water.

Blue Ribbon Niche

Grade Level: Upper Elementary, Middle School

Content Areas:
Science, Language Arts, Environmental Education

Method: Students create a variety of representations of wildlife that can be found in riparian zones. **NOTE:** To foster imagination and develop conceptualization skills, consider conducting the Aquatic WILD activity "Riparian Retreat" as a preliminary language lesson.

Materials: A variety of art materials (e.g., paints, clay, glue, wire, string, brushes); papier mâché; construction paper; **OPTIONAL:** Nature magazines for photos, reference books about riparian habitats and wildlife

Activity Time: two or three 30- to 45-minute sessions, may be longer if field trip is involved

People Power: any, designed for classroom-sized group

Setting: outdoors and indoors (outdoors is recommended)

Conceptual Framework Topic Reference: IDIIB

Terms to Know:
niche, predator, prey, producer, consumer, decomposer, riparian, ecosystem, habitat, alluvial

Appendices: Using Local Resources, Field Ethics, The Ecosystem and Project WILD

See why riparian zones rock!

Objectives

Students will (1) identify different organisms that live in riparian areas, (2) describe the ecological role of some organisms in riparian zones, (3) describe some basic characteristics of riparian zones, and (4) evaluate potential positive and negative effects from changes in riparian zones.

Background

The role of an animal in its community—including its preferences for food, shelter, and space—is known as a niche. Different species cannot live in the same niche, because they would compete for resources and living space until one is forced out of the niche. As a metaphor, if niche is an animal's "occupation," then habitat is its "address." This activity is designed to focus on riparian niches and habitats.

Riparian zones are found wherever streams or rivers at least occasionally cause flooding beyond their channels. These zones are an important and valuable habitat that support a variety of plant and animal life. Each plant and animal has an important niche in the riparian zone. Some are predators, some are prey. Producers, consumers, and decomposers are all examples of riparian zone niches. Some work as herbivores, some carnivores, and some omnivores. The plants and animals in the riparian zone are interdependent, with each species contributing to the well-being of the overall system.

Many animals living in riparian zones cannot survive without the special conditions the zones provide. Riparian zones often provide a wide variety and great abundance of vegetation, along with a higher percentage of shade, high humidity, and high diversity in animals and plants. Riparian zones can be as broad as alluvial valleys dozens of miles wide or a narrow strip of a stream bank. The width of a riparian zone depends on factors such as the amount of available water, soil types, minerals, the water table, and geologic structures.

Riparian zones include both aquatic and terrestrial habitat areas and are characterized by a diversity of life forms. For example, frogs are commonly found in areas of calm waters in riparian zones. Frogs are predators after they mature beyond their algae-eating tadpole stages. They need moisture, sunlight, and grasses or other vegetative shelter. Their eggs must be deposited in water that is permanent enough to allow a lengthy gestation period, growth into gilled tadpoles, and finally transformation into predatory, air-breathing frogs. Both tadpoles and frogs affect other animals' niches. Fish and wading birds prey on both. Raccoons, foxes, and other animals eat both tadpoles and frogs as well as fish. What is important is how the "occupations" and "addresses" are interrelated and contribute to the uniqueness and beauty of riparian zones.

Riparian zones are easily affected by natural and human-influenced changes. For example, spring flooding and flash floods dramatically affect vegetation and wildlife. Excessive use of riparian zones by humans, livestock, and wildlife can greatly modify riparian vegetation and destabilize the stream or riverbanks, causing increased rates of erosion. Development and recreational pressures also jeopardize these unique habitats. Riparian zones have aesthetic, ecological, scientific, social, economic, recreational, and intrinsic value.

Procedure

NOTE: This activity is designed to involve a visit to an actual stream site. If that is not possible, see the "Variation" section for an alternative approach.

1. Using local maps, select a body of water to use as a study site for this activity. Discuss with students the dozens of different animals and plants that live in, around, above, and below this area. Ask students to generate a list of animals that they think inhabit the water and the nearby environment. Consider the water and adjacent land of the riparian zone.

2. Assist students in verifying which animals actually live in the region and might live in this riparian zone. The list may be obvious, making it possible for educators and students to quickly decide. However, some animals may be in question, and educators may want students to consult reference materials. Also, without additional research, many animals that live in the area may not be identified.

3. Once the list is verified, have students choose an organism from the list. Ask each student to express the animal through art. Students can use drawing, painting, collage, sculpture, magazine images, or any other art form of their choice. Be sure to ask students to make their work durable enough to be displayed outside. Each art piece needs to include a hook, string, or other support to allow it to be hung on branches, placed in the soil, or put on a solid surface.

4. Students need to research how the organisms they have chosen depend on other animals and which organisms depend on their animal. Discuss the concepts of niche and habitat with students at this point for emphasis. Again, habitat is the animal's "address." Niche is the animal's "occupation" at that address. Add terms such as predator, prey, consumer, producer, decomposer, herbivore, carnivore, omnivore, and food web.

5. Visit the local stream or body of water that was selected in the first step of this activity. Emphasize personal safety and regard for the habitat. Select a central place to which everyone can gather for discussion.

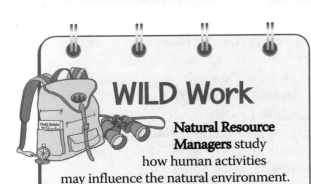

WILD Work

Natural Resource Managers study how human activities may influence the natural environment.

Park Rangers are responsible for protecting natural resources, ensuring visitor safety, enforcing laws and park rules, and leading visitor programs at state parks.

Ecologists study the relationships between organisms and their environments. By studying the niche of an organism, Ecologists can accurately understand the services and role that species provides to the ecosystem.

Illustrators, Writers, Dancers, Poets, and other artists use their work to inform and educate the public about the natural world. Through sketches, journals, photography, music, interpretive dance, sculpture, and more, artists can convey factual as well as persuasive environmental messages.

For links to more information on these occupations, see WILD Work at *www.projectwild.org/aquatic.*

The role of an animal in its community—including its preferences for food, shelter, and space—is known as a niche.

6. Ask students to place their animal art where respective species may be found within the habitat. Afterward, have students return to the central gathering place.

7. Based on his or her previous research, ask each student to present a three-minute report on the characteristics, habitat, and niche of his or her animal. Make sure all students can hear and see one another clearly during this process.

8. When presentations are complete, discuss the concepts of niche and habitat, as well as how organisms are interrelated in any ecosystem. Describe effects that water has on the surrounding area. Emphasize the word "riparian" in the discussion. Have students identify and discuss the characteristics of riparian zones.

9. Now ask students to consider things that might change this riparian zone and affect the habitat for the animals. Here are examples of potential changes that could take place in some areas:

- draining to expand acres under cultivation on nearby farms;
- removing shade-producing trees or shrubs along the bank of a flowing stream;
- introducing an exotic plant;
- harvesting a slope of trees above a stream, thus producing more silt from increased runoff;
- straightening or channelization of a stream, thereby increasing the speed of water flow;
- introducing livestock or people wading or hiking in streams, thereby disturbing fish spawning beds;
- planting vegetative cover on a previously bare slope above a riparian zone; and
- using the area in ways that compact soil and create erosion problems.

Identify and describe changes that would have negative consequences for one or more kinds of animals. Identify and describe changes that would have positive consequences for one or more kinds of animals.

10. Have one or two students demonstrate and evaluate the consequences of a change that would damage the habitat for one or more of the animals found in the riparian zone. To illustrate, students could remove the animal art form that would be immediately affected by the change. For example, severe pollution would affect aquatic dwellers—fish, frogs, mosquitoes, etc. Ask students to discuss the possible effects on the remaining animals in the area when animals are removed. Repeat with a different change, such as fire, development, damming, or stream diversion.

Blue Ribbon Niche
© *Council for Environmental Education (CEE)*

OPTIONAL: Invite students to work in small teams to investigate the area for evidence and observation of actual animal life in this riparian zone. List and quantify any species they observe. Ask students to compare similarities and differences between the diversity of animals they actually find evidence for and the diversity they represented in their drawings of animals.

11. Ask students to summarize what they have learned about niche, habitat, and riparian environments. Ask students to gather their animal art and return to class.

Variation

There is no substitute for the quality of experience gained from an actual site visit. If, however, a site visit is impossible, these alternatives are suggested:

1. Create a simulated riparian zone in an outdoor setting using chalk, paper cutouts, and other materials. (An example is shown in Diagram A.)

2. Limit the scale of a simulated riparian zone to the size of a room or even a tabletop.

Extensions

1. Identify some basic niches found in all environments, such as those of producers, consumers, and decomposers. Divide the consumer category into predator and prey groupings. Identify examples of predator and prey animals in local riparian and other aquatic habitats.

2. Investigate the kind of restoration that can be done to riparian zones after extensive damage has occurred. If it seems useful and appropriate, explore the possibility of a riparian restoration team working in your community to reinstate the health of any riparian zones that have been degraded. Consult wildlife and conservation groups for advice.

Evaluation

1. Identify and describe the habitat and niche of each of these organisms: raccoon, frog, fish, heron, and mosquito.

2. Identify three other animals that are common in riparian ecosystems in your area. What is the niche of each?

3. Describe two things that could have a positive effect on a riparian habitat.

4. A large stand of trees in a riparian zone is being evaluated for its economic potential. What other values would you ask the owners to consider before making a decision whether or not to harvest the trees? Explain.

In Step with STEM

- Conduct a *line intercept sampling* to catalog organisms and to develop an understanding of random sampling. Have students measure out a length of rope stretching from the water's edge to a designated stopping point. Record the various organisms and plants that intersect the line. Alternatively, conduct a *plot sampling* by measuring out a square area or by using a hula-hoop.

- Take a virtual river trip. See *www. projectwild.org/aquatic* for links to aerial photos that allow you to follow a local river corridor from headwaters to the sea.

Riparian zones include both aquatic and terrestrial habitat areas and are characterized by a diversity of life forms.

Diagram A

Fashion a Fish

Thousands of years of adaptations can be used to design the perfect fish.

Grade Level: Lower Elementary, Upper Elementary

Content Areas:
Science, Expressive Arts, Environmental Education

Method: Students design a fish adapted for various aquatic habitats.

Materials:
Lower Elementary: Body shape and coloration are the only *Fish Adaptation Cards* needed (masters provided at the end of this activity). The first three steps in this activity are optional. Steps 4–7 can include adaptation cards for body shape and coloration; reproduction and mouth cards are optional.

Upper Elementary: Art materials; paper; *Fish Adaptation Cards*: mouth, body shape, coloration, reproduction

Activity Time: one or two 20-minute sessions for younger students, two 30- to 45-minute sessions for older students

People Power: any; groups of four students each

Setting: indoors or outdoors

Conceptual Framework Topic Reference: CAIIA1b, CAIIA1c, CAIIB

Terms to Know: adaptation, coloration, camouflage, habitat

Appendix: Let's Go Fishing!

Objectives

Lower Elementary

Students will classify fish according to body shape and coloration.

Upper Elementary

Students will (1) describe adaptations of fish to their environments, (2) describe how adaptations can help fish survive in their habitats, and (3) interpret the importance of adaptation in animals.

Background

Aquatic animals are the products of countless adaptations over long periods of time. Those adaptations, for the most part, are features that increase the animals' likelihood of surviving in their habitat.

When a habitat changes, either slowly or catastrophically, the species of animals that have adaptations that provide for fluctuations in their environment are the ones most likely to survive. Some species have adapted to such a narrow range of habitat conditions they are extremely vulnerable to change. These species are usually more susceptible than other animals to death or extinction.

In this activity, students design a fish. Students choose the adaptations that their fish will have; each choice would actually take countless years to develop. As these adaptations become part of the fish's design, the fish becomes better suited to the habitat in which it lives. Because of the variety of conditions within each habitat, many different fish can live together and flourish. Some adaptations of fish are shown on pages 101–102.

Procedure

1. Assign students to find a picture or make a drawing of a species of animal that has a special adaptation. For example, giraffes have long necks for reaching vegetation in tall trees, while owls have large eyes that gather light and aid with night vision.

2. Conduct a class discussion on the value of different kinds of adaptations to animals. As a part of the discussion, ask students to identify different kinds of adaptations in humans.

3. Collect the students' pictures or drawings of adaptations. Categorize them into the following groups:

- protective coloration and camouflage,
- body shape or form,
- mouth type or feeding behavior,
- reproduction or behavior, and
- other (one or more categories students establish, in addition to the four above that will be needed for the rest of the activity).

4. Divide *Fish Adaptation Cards* into five groups of four cards each: one for coloration, mouth type, body shape, and reproduction.

5. Pass one complete set of cards to each group of students. There might be five groups with four to six students in each group. If the class size is larger than about 30 students, make additional sets of adaptation cards.

6. Ask students to "fashion a fish" from the characteristics of the cards in the set they receive. Each group could:

- create an art form that represents their fish,
- name the fish, and
- describe and draw the habitat for their fish.

7. Ask each group to report on the attributes of the fish they have designed, including identifying and describing its adaptations. Ask students to describe how this kind of fish is adapted for survival.

Upper Elementary

Ask students to make inferences about the importance of adaptations in fish and other animals.

Extensions

1. Take an adaptation card from any category, and find a real fish with that adaptation. **NOTE:** A collection of books about fish is useful. Do not be as concerned about reading level as much as the accuracy of the illustrations.

WILD Work

For information on the related careers of **Hatchery Manager,** **Fisheries Technician/Culturist,** and **Fisheries Biologist,** head to: *www.projectwild.org/aquatic.*

Explore this information with students, or have students do a guided exploration on their own.

In Step with STEM

- Diagram the anatomy and internal organs of a fish. Consider dissecting a fish specimen. See *www.projectwild.org/aquatic* for a video link to a fish dissection.

- See *www.projectwild.org/aquatic* for web links that allow you to build a fish electronically.

When a habitat changes, either slowly or catastrophically, the species of animals that have adaptations that provide for fluctuations in their environment are the ones most likely to survive.

2 Look at examples of actual fish. Describe the fish and speculate on its habitat by examining its coloration, body shape, and mouth.

Evaluation

Lower Elementary

Circle the fish with vertical stripes. Circle the fish with the horizontal, flat shape. Circle the fish that would be difficult to see from above. (Use the masters provided for drawings of fish.)

Upper Elementary

1. Name two fish adaptations in each of the following categories: mouth and feeding, shape, coloration, and reproduction. Then describe the advantages of each of these adaptations to the survival of fish in their habitats.

2. Invent an animal that would be adapted to live in your community. Consider mouth, shape, coloration, reproduction, food, shelter, and other characteristics. Draw and describe your animal.

Adaptation	Advantage	Examples
Mouth		
Sucker-shaped mouth	Feeds on very small plants and animals	Sucker, carp
Elongated upper jaw	Feeds on prey it looks down on	Spoonbill, sturgeon
Elongated lower jaw	Feeds on prey it sees above	Barracuda, snook
Duckbill jaws	Grasps prey	Muskellunge, pike
Extremely large jaws	Surrounds prey	Bass, grouper
Body Shape		
Torpedo shape	Fast moving	Trout, salmon, tuna
Flat bellied	Bottom feeder	Catfish, sucker
Vertical disk	Feeds above and below	Butterfish, Bluegill
Horizontal disk	Bottom dweller	Flounder, halibut
Hump backed	Stable in fast-moving water	Sockeye Salmon, chub, razorback
Coloration		
Light-colored belly	Predators have difficulty seeing it from below	Most minnows, perch, tuna, mackerel
Dark upper side	Predators have difficulty seeing it from above	Bluegill, crappie, barracuda, flounder
Vertical stripes	Can hide in vegetation	Muskellunge, pickerel, Bluegill
Horizontal stripes	Can hide in vegetation	Yellow and White Bass, snook
Mottled coloration	Can hide in rocks and on bottom	Trout, grouper, Rock Bass, hogsucker
Reproduction		
Eggs deposited in bottom	Hidden from predators	Trout, salmon, most minnows
Eggs deposited in nests	Protected by adults	Bass, stickelback
Floating eggs	Dispersed in high numbers	Striped Bass
Eggs attached to vegetation	Stable until hatched	Perch, Northern Pike, carp
Live bearers	High survival rate	Guppies

Fashion a Fish
© *Council for Environmental Education (CEE)*

Fish Adaptation Cards

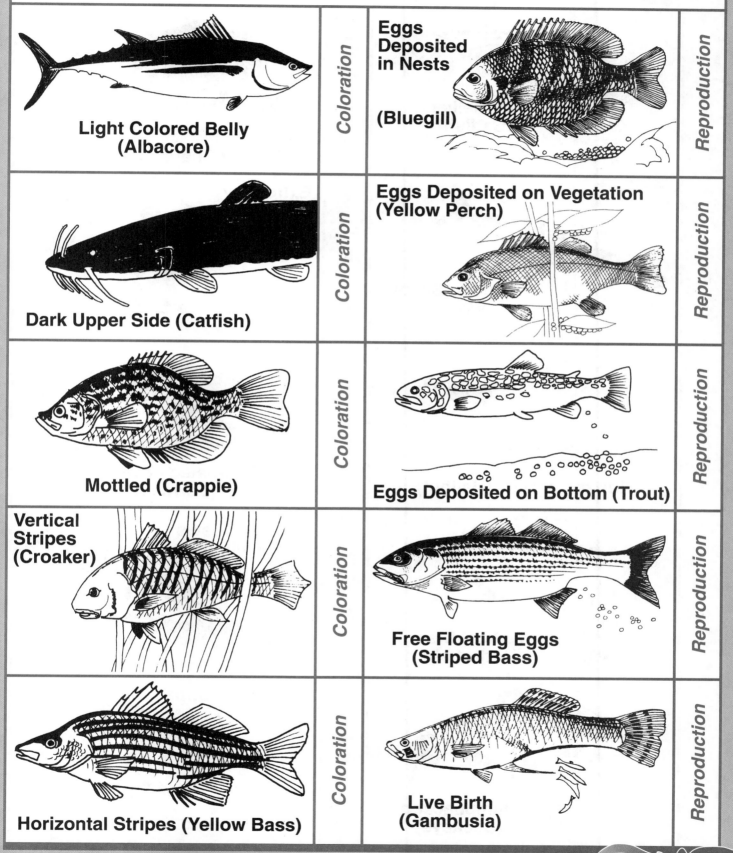

Light Colored Belly (Albacore)

Coloration

Eggs Deposited in Nests (Bluegill)

Reproduction

Dark Upper Side (Catfish)

Coloration

Eggs Deposited on Vegetation (Yellow Perch)

Reproduction

Mottled (Crappie)

Coloration

Eggs Deposited on Bottom (Trout)

Reproduction

Vertical Stripes (Croaker)

Coloration

Free Floating Eggs (Striped Bass)

Reproduction

Horizontal Stripes (Yellow Bass)

Coloration

Live Birth (Gambusia)

Reproduction

Fish Adaptation Cards

Shape	**Flat Bellied (Catfish)**	*Mouth/Feeding*	**Sucker Shaped Jaw (Sucker)**
Shape	**Torpedo Shape (Wahoo)**	*Mouth/Feeding*	**Extremely Large Jaws (Grouper)**
Shape	**Horizontal Disc (Halibut)**	*Mouth/Feeding*	**Elongated Lower Jaw (Barracuda)**
Shape	**Vertical Disc (Butterfish)**	*Mouth/Feeding*	**Duckbill Jaws (Muskellunge)**
Shape	**Humpbacked (Sockeye)**	*Mouth/Feeding*	**Elongated Upper Jaw (Cod)**

Fashion a Fish
© Council for Environmental Education (CEE)

Sockeye Scents

Could you find your way home with only your nose to guide you?

Objectives

Students will (1) trace and label the migratory route that Sockeye Salmon take from the ocean to an upstream lake, (2) describe one theory about how a salmon can find its birth stream, and (3) explain how adaptations enable some species to survive and maintain their populations.

Background

Salmon begin life as eggs in the gravel of a stream or (in the case of some Sockeye) lakeshore. They migrate down rivers and spend several years in the ocean. Then, at a certain time, the salmon swim back to their "home" rivers and migrate upstream to their exact birthplaces to spawn.

Scientists hypothesize that salmon migrate back to their home streams by sensing their orientation to the Earth's magnetic field and receiving clues from the sun's position in the sky. They also hypothesize that scent plays a major part in salmon's ability to find home. This adaptation is important for salmon to reproduce and survive. Students might give some thought to how well they would find their own homes if they had to rely only on smell.

The purpose of this activity is to demonstrate that organisms exhibit adaptations to the environment in which they live and that these adaptations maximize the survival of the species. This activity is specific to salmon of the Columbia River in Oregon; however, it can easily be adapted to any anadromous or catadromous animal found in coastal systems. Anadromous species, such as salmon, shad, bass, and others, migrate from the ocean to a stream to spawn. Catadromous species, such as eels, begin life in the ocean, migrate upstream where they spend much of their life, and then return to the ocean to reproduce.

NOTE: For more information on salmon, see the activity "Hooks and Ladders" on page 84 or "Where Have All the Salmon Gone?" on page 254. Check with your state's fish and wildlife agency for examples of life histories of migrating aquatic organisms.

Grade Level: Upper Elementary

Content Areas:
Social Studies, Science, Expressive Arts, Language Arts, Environmental Education

Method:
Students participate in map and simulation exercises that help them understand the migration of the Sockeye Salmon.

Materials:
Copies of map on page 107 (or local maps); pencils, crayons, and markers; 40 paper cups; paper towels; 40 rubber bands; 25 (if indoors) to 75 (if outdoors) yards of blue ribbon or chalk; four sample scents such as garlic, mint, chocolate, and anise; cotton balls

Activity Time:
2 hours

People Power:
small groups of four students

Setting:
indoors or outdoors

Conceptual Framework Topic Reference:
CAIIA, CAIIA1, CAIIA1c

Terms to Know: migration, spawning, anadromous, catadromous

Appendices: Let's Go Fishing!, Using Local Resources, Climate Change

Procedure

Before the activity, prepare the scent samples. Choose four scents such as garlic, mint, chocolate, and anise. Place two drops of each scent on two cotton balls, and put each cotton ball in its own cup (eight cups will be used). Cover each cup with a paper towel held in place by a rubber band. Number the cups one through eight, and make a note of which scent is in which numbered cup. Prepare 30 additional cups to be placed on the "river" system shown in Diagram A on this page.

Lay out the river system as shown in Diagram A. Either ribbon or chalk may be used. Establish two correct "spawning routes" by placing scents in the correct order at each fork in the migration path. (One route follows the odd-numbered order of scents; one route follows the even-numbered order of scents.) Be sure to note the two correct routes.

Mix up the scents for the remaining routes.

1. Ensure that students are familiar with the life cycle of the Sockeye Salmon, especially the spawning migration. (If time is limited, educators can convey the information through a discussion, guest speaker, or individual reading assignment. If time is available, educators may allow students to construct their own diagram of the life cycle.)

Diagram A

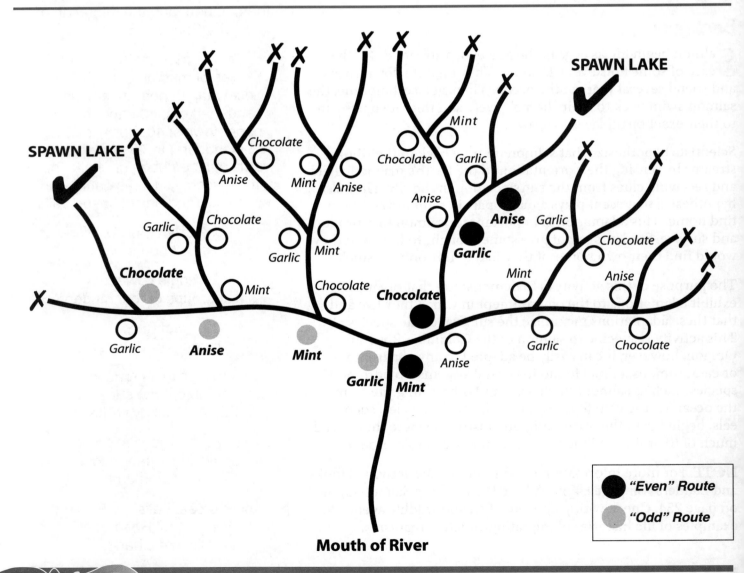

Sockeye Scents
© *Council for Environmental Education (CEE)*

Diagram B

2. Divide students into groups of four. Give each group a map of the Columbia River drainage system, and ask them to trace the route of the Sockeye Salmon from the ocean to a specific spawning lake. They need to locate and label the following: ocean, states, dams, rivers, streams, lakes, and reservoirs.

3. Display maps and discuss each group's findings. Come to consensus on the route and the major features described in Step 2.

4. Enlist four "migration helpers." Give each helper two different scents in paper cups. (See Diagram B.) Line up the four helpers near the exit door for the classroom, facing the students.

5. Ask the remaining students to line up and count off in twos. The "twos" will sniff the even-numbered cup being held by each helper; the "ones" will sniff the odd-numbered cup. Make sure all students understand that they are to move in a line from left to right (as shown in Diagram B), stopping in front of each helper and sniffing from just one of the cups each helper holds. As soon as each student completes sniffing the four cups, he or she can move to the river system.

6. When all "salmon" have completed their scent imprinting, gather them at the "mouth" of the river system. Explain that they will "migrate" in single file. They must find their way to their spawning site by following the scents they smelled in the same order.

7. Allow students to proceed. Make sure they do not discuss their decisions with each other and that all students make their decisions based on scent and not just by following another student.

8. Once all the salmon have reached what they think are their spawning grounds, reveal the two correct spawning routes. The students who chose the correct migration routes are the successful salmon for this year's spawning run. They will be able to lay eggs to produce young salmon.

9. After they complete the spawning migration, discuss what students (Sockeye Salmon) experienced, and brainstorm and discuss the many other obstacles (dams, pollution, fishing pressure, bears, etc.) that salmon encounter along the route to their spawning grounds. Discuss what might happen to salmon that make mistakes in their return journey. Do they spawn? Would they try to retrace their route? How do the salmon's special abilities (adaptations) help it survive?

WILD Work

How do a **Geographic Information System (GIS) Specialist**, a **Computer Professional**, and a **Cartographer** work together to create a map of a river system?

To find more information on these careers, head to: *www.projectwild.org/aquatic*.

In Step with STEM

Search for online sources of distribution maps and migration routes of various salmon species. Compare the locations and movements of these species.

Extensions

1. To increase the challenge of this activity and to add learning opportunities, educators may wish to have students choose their method of learning about the life cycle of Sockeye. For example, one group could decide to interview a fisheries biologist or to look for information on the Internet. Allow a specific time for this phase, and then set aside a period for groups to share their information with each other. Have the entire class contribute to a large drawing that shows the life cycle.

2. Ask students to create either visual images or a piece of creative writing that describes the life of the Sockeye.

3. Ask each group to choose another species of salmon and investigate its life cycle and migration.

4. Ask each group to choose another animal that migrates (Bald Eagle, Yellow-rumped Warbler, Monarch butterfly, elk, etc.) and to develop a class presentation (verbal or visual) describing that migration.

Evaluation

1. Participation in the closing discussion can serve as an evaluation.

2. Have groups collectively create a spawning migration map for Sockeye Salmon that shows obstacles they might encounter.

3. Invite another class to participate in the migration maze; have students lead discussions and the migration.

SOCKEYE SALMON

Sockeye Scents
© *Council for Environmental Education (CEE)*

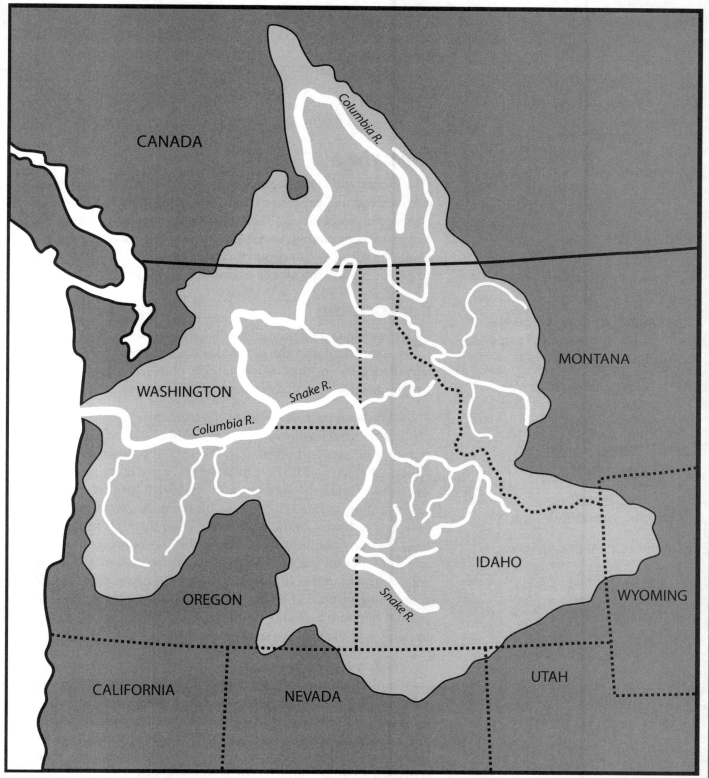

Adapted from WILD About Salmon, Idaho Department of Fish and Game, 1999.

Pond Succession

Grade Level: Middle School

Content Areas:
Science, Social Studies, Environmental Education, Expressive Arts

Method:
Students create murals showing three major stages of pond succession.

Materials:
Long pieces of drawing paper for murals, tape for securing paper to walls, drawing materials

Activity Time:
one or two 30-minute sessions or longer

People Power:
any

Setting:
indoors (outdoors optional)

Conceptual Framework Topic Reference:
CAIA, CAIB, CAIB1

Terms to Know: succession, sediment, pond, seral, vernal, climax community

Appendices:
The Ecosystem and Project WILD, Climate Change

Students capture the changes in a natural setting spanning 800 years.

Objectives

Students will (1) recognize that natural environments are involved in a process of continual change, (2) discuss the concept of succession, (3) describe succession as an example of the process of change in natural environments, and (4) apply understanding of the concept of succession by drawing a series of pictures showing stages in pond succession.

Background

Succession is a term used to describe the ever-changing environment and the gradual process by which one habitat is replaced by another. While largely undetectable to the human eye, habitats are actually in a constant state of change.

One thousand years is a short time in relation to Earth's clock, but in this time frame a shallow pond may advance to stages of marsh, wetland, and ultimately, forest. Windblown or waterborne spores of algae are the first inhabitants. Eggs of flying insects are deposited. Small fish and amphibians arrive through the inlet. Surrounding sediments begin to fill the pond, some transported by wash-out from rainfall, some entering through the pond's inlet. Marshy plants growing along the shoreline spread inward as sediments fill the pond. Land plants also spread inward and replace the marsh plants as the ground is consolidated. As more plants and animals enter the system, more opportunities for habitat become available to others. Changes from ponds to forest are only one example of succession.

Succession is generally thought of as an orderly process in which plant communities change over time in an environment. Primary succession occurs in areas that previously did not support organic life and includes the development of soil to the area. Secondary succession is the type most readily seen, in which only the plant communities present change over time. This often can be found in urban lots or yards that have not been maintained. Seral or early successional plants are generally short-lived, thrive in sunlight, colonize rapidly, and spread their seeds far and wide. Roadsides, recent burns, clear-cuts, and other areas of recent disturbance are good places to find examples of early succession.

The first plants change the environment by adding nutrients to the soil from fallen leaves and other plant parts and by providing shade to the soil. These changes allow other plants to grow. The presence of newer plants changes the environment to allow even later stage successional plants to develop. Climax or late successional plants usually thrive in shade, live a long time, and reproduce more slowly. Old growth forests are good examples of a climax stage of succession. Even within climax communities, succession is constantly at work. Events like forest fires, severe weather, and human interference will alter the path of succession.

Succession influences what kinds of animals live in an area. As the plants in an area change, the habitat available to animals changes. Therefore, the kinds of animals that live in the area are associated with the area's stage of succession.

Procedure

1. Review with students the idea of succession, a process that is generally an orderly, gradual, and continual replacement of one community of organisms in an environment with another.

2. Start the activity by talking about a pond. How many people have seen a pond? What did it look like? After a description of ponds, ask students to imagine what a pond would look like from a side view if you could see under the water and show the nearby environment. For example,

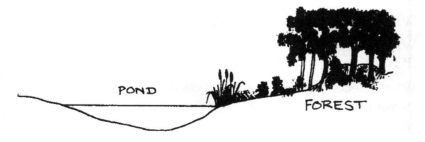

POND

FOREST

3. Explain to students that they will be drawing a series of three views of a pond over a period of about 800 years. The first (left-hand) section will show the pond as it is today; the middle section will show how it might look 500 years later after natural changes; and the third (right-hand) will show how the pond could look in 800 years. (These time periods are approximate and can vary greatly.)

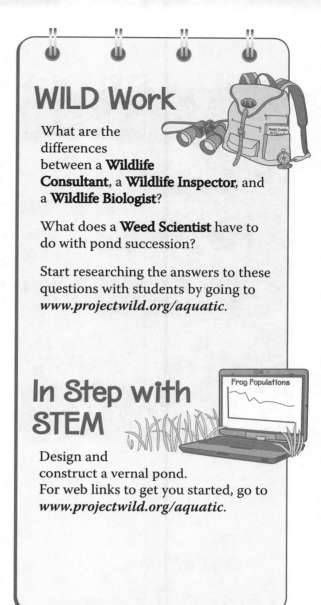

WILD Work

What are the differences between a **Wildlife Consultant**, a **Wildlife Inspector**, and a **Wildlife Biologist**?

What does a **Weed Scientist** have to do with pond succession?

Start researching the answers to these questions with students by going to *www.projectwild.org/aquatic*.

In Step with STEM

Frog Populations

Design and construct a vernal pond. For web links to get you started, go to *www.projectwild.org/aquatic*.

Succession influences what kinds of animals live in an area. As the plants in an area change, the habitat available to animals changes.

Succession in aquatic environments usually begins with grasses and small shrubs.

Even within climax communities, succession is constantly at work. Events like forest fires, severe weather, and human interference will alter the path of succession.

4. Discuss with students the possibilities of plant and animal life in the first section. What kinds of plants and animals live

- in the water,
- along the shoreline, and
- in the surrounding area?

5. Then give each group a piece of paper that members will divide into three equal sections (by folding or drawing). Instruct students to fill in the first section with their drawing of the pond and the surrounding area. Set a specific time frame for the students to draw (about ten minutes).

6. Bring the class together again for a discussion of the second section, which will be labeled "500 Years Later." Consider the following items:

- What changes have taken place in the environment?
- How will the pond look now?
- What lives and grows in the water now that it is smaller and more shallow?
- What lives and grows around the shoreline, which is now more marsh-like? (Marsh animals and plants, perhaps some willow bushes.)
- What lives and grows in the surrounding area? (Larger trees, same types of animals.) Have each group complete the second section of their mural, labeling it "500 Years Later."

7. Repeat the process for the third section, labeling it "800 Years Later," and discuss the following topics:

- By this time, the pond is almost totally filled with sediment, leaving only a small marshy area with perhaps a stream running through. What changes have taken place?
- What lives and grows in the environment?
- What lives and grows where the shoreline used to be? (Bushes, small trees.)
- What effects does the pond succession have on the surrounding area? (Different animals, trees requiring less water.)

8. After the murals are completed, students should sign them. Display the murals in the classroom so that all students can see and discuss differences and similarities. Ask students to summarize what they have learned, including how succession is one example of the ongoing process of change in natural environments.

Pond Succession
© Council for Environmental Education (CEE)

Variation

Use a stream table filled with standard soil to illustrate three-dimensionally the processes of succession. Fill the table with soil. Make an indentation in the center to represent the pond. Run water into the table to represent rainfall, streams feeding the pond, and so forth. Finally, watch the pond fill as sedimentation takes place. This demonstration illustrates the possible succession activity within a pond ecosystem. Add replicas of plants and animals during successional stages for even more interest.

Extension

1. What might happen to your model of succession if an intense forest fire burned the trees surrounding the pond? Would the pond silt in faster? Would there be a source for tree seeds to colonize the pond site? Would there be differences if the fire were not as hot? How might fires affect the species that live there? Describe some possible differences in environments where fire affects succession and where it does not.

2. Locate and visit the nearest pond and evaluate its successional stage. Interview local residents who have seen changes over time in this pond or area.

Evaluation

1. Draw a picture, with explanations, to show stages in pond succession.

2. Select a field, vacant lot, park, or other area in your community. Make a sketch and write a paragraph to describe the area as it appears today. Make a sketch and write a paragraph to describe what the area might look like in 100 or 500 years from now if a gradual process of succession took place.

Over time, this environment could see less water and heavier vegetation.

Eat and Glow

Grade Level: High School

Content Areas:
Science, Mathematics, Environmental Education

Method:
Students conduct an experiment using *Daphnia* and brine shrimp to demonstrate adaptations to environmental change by organisms.

Materials:
This activity requires special materials. Please refer to page 113 for a complete list.

Activity Time:
one 45-minute session each for activity #1 and #2, and two 45-minute sessions with preparation time in between for activity #3.

People Power:
about 28 students

Setting:
Indoors

Conceptual Framework Topic Reference:
CAIA, CAIC, CAIIA, CAIIA1, CAIIA2, CAIIC

Terms to Know:
pH, tolerance, toxic, variable, control, isolated ecosystem

Watch firsthand how water conditions can affect wildlife behavior.

Objectives

Students will (1) observe, demonstrate, and describe how life forms are affected by changes in their habitats; (2) observe, demonstrate, and describe how species differ in their abilities to adjust to changes in their habitat; and (3) observe, demonstrate, and describe how isolated ecosystems are more vulnerable to environmental changes.

Background

NOTE: See the Aquatic WILD activity "Water Canaries."

Variations and changes occur in terrestrial and aquatic ecosystems. Those changes can either be natural to the system, such as changes in pH and temperature caused by weather or forest fires, or human-related, such as changes caused by pollution or acidic deposition, also known as "acid rain."

Wildlife species differ in their abilities to adapt to such changes. Some animals can withstand substantial changes in temperature, pH, or oxygen levels. Others are very sensitive and will die with only the slightest fluctuation. Aquatic organisms tend to be more fragile than terrestrial organisms because aquatic environments tend to be more constant than most terrestrial environments. For instance, the slightest temperature change of a trout stream caused by the removal of shading vegetation may severely limit the life span of young trout. If a stream continues to stay too warm to support trout, then another species of fish, more adapted to variations in temperature, may increase in its abundance and move into the habitat.

Terrestrial animals, conversely, are adapted to handle greater changes found in the environment. However, changes in soil acidity or temperature often result in changes in the microbiotic community and the associated plants living there. Those changes can be due to natural occurrences, such as forest fires, or to human-induced events, such as agricultural production, lawn care practices, or leaching from cement foundations and sidewalks. Microorganisms are crucial to the health of soil, which affects the health of plants and ultimately the health of animals.

Effects of chemical changes are often subtle. A chemical may not kill an organism directly, but may affect its ability to capture food or escape a predator. The chemical may also interfere with an organism's ability to reproduce. Chemicals that are potentially harmful to a living organism are said to be toxic. Toxicity is a relative property that depends on the concentration of the chemical, the duration of exposure, and the tolerance range of the organism. Toxicity tests are used to evaluate the adverse effects of a chemical on a living organism. In a toxicity test, organisms are typically exposed to various levels of the chemical while all other factors are held constant.

In this experiment, students will be looking for nonlethal effects resulting from pH variation, particularly the loss of the desire or ability to eat. The chemical introduced will be vinegar. Vinegar is an acid and will change the pH level enough to cause changes in the behavior of the organisms exposed. However, the level of vinegar used in the activity will not kill the *Daphnia* or the brine shrimp. Please see "Animals in the Classroom" on page 355 in the Appendices.

In these activities, *Daphnia* and brine shrimp will be used to determine the effects of small changes in habitat. *Daphnia*, commonly called water fleas, are tiny crustaceans. They reside near the bottom of many food chains in the food web, eating small plants and being eaten by larger organisms. *Daphnia* are found in most freshwater aquatic environments. Because they are sensitive to changes in the ecosystem, they are excellent indicators of the health of the ecosystem. Brine shrimp, otherwise known as sea monkeys, are also near the bottom of food chains, but live in a highly saline environment and are more tolerant to changes than *Daphnia*.

To see how the change in pH (acidity) affects the *Daphnia* and the brine shrimp differently, students will introduce a "sugar-dye" into the system. Students will then record which organisms are eating and which are not. In this compound, the sugar and dye act in such a way that the dye is not seen until it is eaten, visible through the transparent bodies of the *Daphnia* and shrimp with an ultraviolet light.

Isolated systems tend to be more vulnerable to environmental changes. For instance, a pond that has no incoming or outgoing water to help balance chemical levels or temperature changes will be a harsh environment for living organisms. In the third activity of the lesson, students will create a non-isolated

Materials

For 28 students:

- ☑ 210 Artemia (brine shrimp), 210 *Daphnia* (both available through major biological supply catalogs), 1 gram sugar-dye compound
- ☑ * 3-ml of vinegar, water from a natural source (lakes, streams, or ponds), ultraviolet light (UV) source (a black light works best)
- ☑ viewing box for light
- ☑ 42 30-ml beakers or baby food jars, seven droppers or pipettes with wide openings
- ☑ graduated cylinders (100-ml, 50-ml, and 5-ml)
- ☑ one 1-liter bottle, styrofoam trays or other soft carving material such as balsa wood
- ☑ 60 copies of the *Student Worksheet* (30 for *Daphnia*, 30 for brine shrimp) on page 118

If students prepare their own dilution series, educators will need 21 graduated cylinders—seven of each size. Educators will need one of each size if they prepare the dilution series themselves.

*The sugar-dye compound, 4-methylumbelliferyl-beta-d-galactose, may be ordered from major suppliers such as Flinn Scientific, Inc. or Sigma-Aldrich Corporation. Purchasing 250 mg is recommended for this experiment.

Isolated systems tend to be more vulnerable to environmental changes.

Aquatic organisms tend to be more fragile than terrestrial organisms...

environment for the *Daphnia* and will determine if the ability of the flea to move out of the contaminated habitat enhances its ability to survive.

The purpose of this activity is to show that (1) organisms exhibit adaptations to their environment that allow them to survive and that (2) species differ in their ability to adjust to changes in their habitat.

Procedure

Before the Activity

- Order the sugar-dye compound from a chemical supply house, and order *Daphnia* and brine shrimp from a biological supply house.

- Establish a safe black light viewing station. **SAFETY NOTE:** UV light is harmful to eyes. To view UV light safely, use a commercial viewer or construct one. Limit the light in the room and prevent students from looking directly at the UV bulb. One method is to cut a window in a cardboard box and to place the UV bulb below the window in such a way that the sample will be illuminated but students cannot view the bulb.

- Prepare the sugar-dye solution. The sugar-dye compound will come in a crystalline form. Mix 500-ml of water to 1 gram of compound in a plastic 1-liter bottle. Use water from a natural system such as a lake, stream, or pond. Do not use tap water or even bottled spring water because these will kill the organisms. Shake well, label, and store in a refrigerator. Shake well before each use.

- Prepare and label a series of solutions using the following list. Educators may choose to have students mix their own solutions.

   Vinegar solution: 3-ml of vinegar with enough lake water to make 600-ml of solution.

   Jar #C, control jar, 30-ml of lake water.

   Jar #5, add 30-ml of vinegar solution.

   Jar #4, add 16-ml of vinegar solution and fill to 30-ml with lake water.

   Jar #3, add 8-ml of vinegar solution and fill to 30-ml with lake water.

   Jar #2, add 4-ml of vinegar solution and fill to 30-ml with lake water.

   Jar #1, add 2-ml of vinegar solution and fill to 30-ml with lake water.

Activity 1: *Daphnia* and Acidity

1. Using the background information provided with this activity, introduce the idea of a toxicity test. Ask students if they can list ways that a chemical can harm a living organism.

2. Ask students how increased levels of acid might affect the *Daphnia*. What will happen as the acid level increases? (The small amount of vinegar is not expected to kill the *Daphnia*, but it may upset them enough that they lose their desire to eat for a time. This response is what students will be observing—movement and food consumption. The *Daphnia* are expected to recover.)

BRINE SHRIMP

3. Next, discuss with students how the sugar-dye will be used in this activity.

4. Divide the class into teams of four. Each team should fill and label the six baby food jars with the six treatment solutions (Jars 1–5 and Jar C). Explain that the "treatments" represent the various levels of a variable. A variable is added to an experiment to see what effect it will have on the subject. The subject in this activity is the organism, the variable is acidity (the amount of vinegar added to the water), and the different acid concentrations are the different levels of the variable. Ask students why Jar C has no acid added. Why do they think this treatment is called the "control"? Students will change the acidity in this experiment. Ask students what factors did not change for the *Daphnia*. List those factors on the board. (All *Daphnia* had the same temperature, light, water type, etc.) Let students know that the factors that did not change are known as "constants."

5. Have students add five *Daphnia* to each of the jars, including the control jar. Demonstrate how to add *Daphnia* to a solution as follows: take the *Daphnia* from a beaker in a pipette. Put the end of the pipette below the surface of the solution it is being added to, and gently squeeze the *Daphnia* out of the pipette. If a *Daphnia* is exposed to air, air will be trapped underneath its outer covering, and the *Daphnia* will float on the surface. If a *Daphnia* floats or does not move, it has been injured during the transfer and should be replaced by another.

NOTE: Remove some water used to ship the *Daphnia* and put it in a clean container to serve as a recovery tank. To avoid contamination, do not put experimental *Daphnia* back in the original water with the *Daphnia* that were not used. Educators may want to set up a recovery tank for each class that will participate in this experiment.

6. Allow the *Daphnia* to swim in the treatments and control jars for 30 minutes. Observe. Then add approximately 10 ml of sugar-dye solution to each of the six jars, and let the *Daphnia* feed for 15 minutes.

7. Observe the *Daphnia* under the UV light using a viewer, making sure students cannot look directly at the light. Count the numbers of glowing *Daphnia* (which is evidence that they are eating) in each jar. Note their activity and complete a *Daphnia Student Worksheet*. After viewing and recording, remove the *Daphnia* from their treatments and place them together in the recovery tank.

8. Have students graph their data.

9. Discuss with students the results of the experiment. Based on the data collected, did the change in the *Daphnia*'s environment affect the organisms' need to eat or ability to survive? If so, at what treatment level did students notice this effect? In the real world, what would cause this kind of pH (acidic) change? If the

Daphnia were to die as a result of a change in pH levels, how would that affect the rest of the ecosystem? If *Daphnia* live in a habitat that is isolated, meaning they cannot leave, what would their chance of survival be? If the pH level changes, why might animals living in a non-isolated ecosystem, such as a river or lake, have a better chance of survival than organisms found in an isolated environment?

NOTE: With limited mobility, *Daphnia* can move to less-contaminated parts of their environment, but they are not likely to leave altogether.

Activity 2: Brine Shrimp, Acidity, and Tolerance Differences

1. Discuss with students that changes in pH or acidity affect some organisms differently from others because some are more tolerant. Follow the same procedures for the brine shrimp as with the *Daphnia*, and observe the differences in tolerance. Discuss the results with the class.

2. Live plants and animals have the potential to disrupt natural habitats and should never be disposed of in a way that might introduce them into the environment. To clean up, add bleach to solutions then pour them down the drain. *Daphnia* and shrimp may be retained as pets in a small aquarium. **NOTE:** Many elementary classrooms would appreciate these donations.

3. Discuss differences in results with the *Daphnia*. Which organism was more tolerant of low pH levels? What is the advantage for this organism to have a wider tolerance for pH? What is the advantage to the other organism for not having such a wide tolerance range? (It requires energy output that is usually not necessary.) In what type of environment is each animal normally found? How are these two organisms adapted for their environments? How does the response of each animal to such an environmental stress, such as an increase in pH, affect its chances for survival?

Activity 3: Changing the Isolation Factor

1. Discuss the difference between isolated and non-isolated ecosystems and the varying tolerance for change as found in the "Background" section.

2. Have students work in teams to create a non-isolated environment that will allow the *Daphnia* to move between a high-acidity area and a more neutral (lake water) area. It should be set up so that the *Daphnia* are allowed to choose between the two. For example, using styrofoam trays or a piece of balsa wood, carve deep wells for the acidic and neutral areas plus a shallow channel for the *Daphnia* to move between the two areas. (See Diagram A.) Because the vinegar will soon diffuse throughout the system, have students add three to five *Daphnia* to the channel and then add the vinegar to the acidic well simultaneously. (Use approximately one drop of the prepared vinegar solution per milliliter volume of the acidic well.)

3. Have students design a chart to collect data that will show how many *Daphnia* chose the neutral environment.

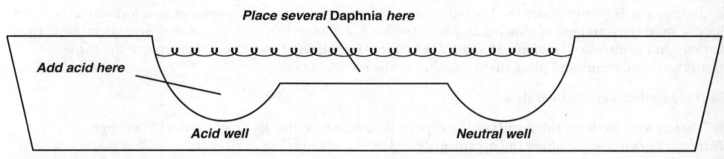

Diagram A

Eat and Glow
© Council for Environmental Education (CEE)

4. Repeat the experiment, but add the *Daphnia* to the acidic well instead. Repeat again but add the *Daphnia* to the neutral well instead. Add a new set of *Daphnia* each time, and add the same number of *Daphnia* as were added in Step 2. Were the results the same in all three cases (i.e., adding *Daphnia* to the channel, to the acidic well, and to the neutral well)? Is the experiment truly a non-isolated ecosystem?

Extensions

1. Follow the same procedures as above, but focus on temperature changes, oxygen levels, or turbidity.

2. Brine shrimp are commercially harvested from the Great Salt Lake in Utah. Research this industry and its impact on this organism. Explore how changes in the salinity of the Great Salt Lake affect brine shrimp survival.

Evaluation

Use Activity #3 as a performance-based evaluation tool.

Adapted from "A Healthy Glow," EPA/600/K-96/00, June 1997, World of Fresh Waters.

Wildlife species differ in their abilities to adapt to such changes. Some animals can withstand substantial changes in temperature, pH, or oxygen levels. Others are very sensitive and will die with only the slightest fluctuation.

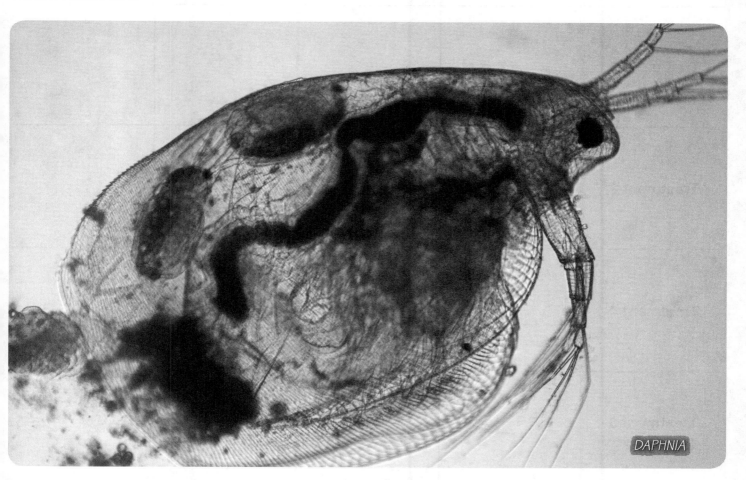

DAPHNIA

Student Worksheet

	Room Light		UV Light	
	Moving	**Not Moving**	**Glowing**	**Not Glowing (or glowing more faintly than controls)**
Control Jar				
Treatment 1 (mildest)				
Treatment 2				
Treatment 3				
Treatment 4				
Treatment 5 (strongest)				

Edge of Home

Discover the diversity of life that occurs when two habitats conjoin.

Objectives

Students will identify the characteristics of ecotones, or transitional zones, between two wildlife habitats.

Background

Ecology is the study of the interactions between living things and their environments. Ecology comes from the Greek word *oikos*, which means home. The word "ecosystem" refers to the system of interactions between living and nonliving things.

An ecotone is a special environment created by the overlap of two or more surrounding habitats. This area of overlap between two ecosystems creates a habitat edge where parts of each surrounding habitat are present. These transitional zones between ecosystems are unique habitats on their own accord, with characteristics of each of the surrounding ecosystems. (See Diagram A.)

In local communities there are abundant edges and overlaps of edges that may be accessible to the students. Playgrounds, school grounds, parking lots, stream banks, lake shores, and marsh edges can be found within walking distance for many students.

In ecotones, overlapping ecosystems are more complex than any ecosystem by itself. For example, in an overlap of forest and marsh it is common to find forest plants growing within the marsh. Often the growth of the forest plants is stunted due to the water in the marsh.

Grade Level: Upper Elementary, Middle School

Content Areas: Science, Environmental Education, Language Arts

Method: Students explore the concept of ecotones by visiting places where habitats overlap.

Materials: Pencils, paper, long rope or string for marking intervals in 1-foot segments, clipboards

Activity Time: one or two 45-minute sessions

People Power: any

Setting: outdoors and indoors

Conceptual Framework Topic Reference: BDIB4

Terms to Know: ecosystem, ecotone, edge effect

Appendices: Inventory Methods, Field Ethics, The Ecosystem and Project WILD

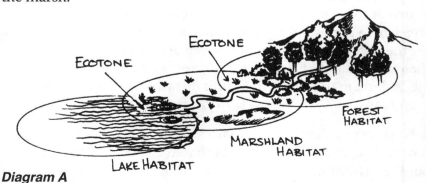

ECOTONE

ECOTONE

FOREST HABITAT

MARSHLAND HABITAT

LAKE HABITAT

Diagram A

WILD Work

For information on the related careers of **Ecologist**, **Horticulturist**, and **Botanist**, head to: *www.projectwild.org/aquatic*.

Explore this information with students, or have students do a guided exploration on their own.

In Step with STEM

■ Investigate sampling and bioassessment techniques by designating a small area with a hula hoop or string in each of the three transitional areas. Record variety and number of species found within the plot. Alternatively, conduct a line transect sampling by laying out a designated length of string and recording any organisms or plants that intersect the string. For more information on plant and wildlife inventory methods, visit *www.projectwild.org/aquatic*.

Ecology is the study

of the interactions

between living things

and their environments.

Ecology comes from

the Greek word oikos,

which means home.

Overlapping ecosystems also offer a wider diversity of wildlife because animals common to both ecosystems are brought together. Even though they may not be seen, indirect evidence of animal populations—for example, footprints, droppings, and feathers—are common.

Although ecotones play an important role in the overall landscape, it is also important to keep habitat areas (or ecosystems) from becoming too fragmented. This fragmentation can adversely affect wildlife that depends entirely on one ecosystem. The concept of maintaining ecotones and all of their components in a dynamic natural balance is defined as preserving the biodiversity of that area. The absence of diversity in ecotones is often a clue that problems may exist in the ecosystems that overlap.

Procedure

Before the activity, locate an outside study site. Choose a place where plants are invading a parking lot or the edge of a forest where it meets a meadow.

1. On the chalkboard, draw two large overlapping circles. Put a large number of small squares and triangles in one circle. Avoid the area of overlap. In the second circle draw many tiny circles and stars. Again, avoid the overlap area. Ask students to predict what kinds of things they would expect to find in the overlapping circles. Draw circles, squares, triangles, and stars in the area of overlap. Ask students where the greatest diversity exists. Label the whole area of the overlap the Ecotone (this is the area of greatest diversity). Label the original two circles as Ecosystem 1 and Ecosystem 2. Ask students to point out the "edges" of overlap. These are the places where the two ecosystems come together and interact. The process and results of this interaction are called the "edge effect."

2. Inform students that they are going to investigate a natural setting where there are habitats that overlap similar to the illustration in Diagram B. Ask them to take paper, pencils, and clipboards on which to record their observations.

3. Take students to the selected site. Ask them to work in teams of two or three to examine two different ecosystems (but not the area where the two ecosystems meet and overlap). Have students list the different species of plants and animals they observe and then tally what they find. Include direct and indirect evidence of life. Ask them to discuss the similarities and differences and to keep notes.

4. Next, ask students to carefully examine the edge. Determine how wide the ecotone or zone of shared characteristics is. Point out that while this small area is an ecotone, some ecotones can

Edge of Home
© *Council for Environmental Education (CEE)*

span great distances. Students might try to estimate the size of the ecotone as well as the diversity of species within it. Compare the diversity of plants and animals found within the ecotone to the diversity of plants and animals found in the two separate ecosystems they originally examined.

NOTE: It may help students organize more systematic observations if they stretch a length of rope or string from one ecosystem to another. Have students make and record observations every foot (or other unit of measure) along the line. It helps to mark the string or rope at these intervals.

5. After the trip, compare and interpret student findings. Based on their data collected within the three areas, have each student group identify the area which held the greatest plant and animal diversity and provide evidence to support their conclusion.

OPTIONAL: Take the class to a site in the community that has aquatic edges. Educators may be able to find a beach, a place where a stream enters or exits a lake, or other sites that might be available in the community. Once there, ask students to use the same investigating techniques, working again in teams of two or three. They should identify at least two ecosystems; list and describe the characteristic organisms in each; identify the ecotone; and list, observe, and describe the organisms in the ecotone.

An ecotone is a special environment created by the overlap of two or more surrounding habitats. This area of overlap between two ecosystems creates a habitat edge where parts of each surrounding habitat are present.

Extensions

1. Create an ecosystem map or model of your community. Indicate the location of the principal ecotones.

2. Take a simple piece of paper and measure the edges. Cut the paper into four equal pieces, and then measure the edges again. Repeat this twice again, measuring the edges each time. Support the idea that each new rectangle is a suitable habitat for some aquatic organism, and discuss how diversity is related to "edges."

3. Assess the overall health of any ecotones that seem particularly important to the quality of life for aquatic species in your community. What could be done to protect the area from being damaged, degraded, or lost?

Evaluation

1. Write a paragraph about the characteristics of ecotones. Write two additional paragraphs to describe two ecosystems and an associated ecotone.

2. Choose a species of wildlife, and write a story about its life as it utilizes several different ecosystems and ecotones. Explain how the animal's experiences are different at each of the various locations.

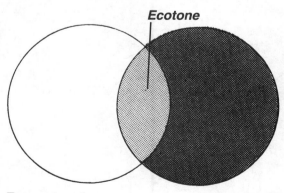

Ecotone

Ecosystem 1
Diagram B

Ecosystem 2

Social and Political Knowledge

Students examine the way human cultures, economics, and politics have affected people's attitudes toward natural resources. There are four areas of study: (1) *cultural perspectives*, addressing cultural development, expressions, and appreciation of wildlife and natural resources; (2) *economic, commercial, and recreational considerations*; (3) *historical and geographic development*, addressing the development of society and commerce as related to natural resources; and (4) *political and legislative frameworks*, both domestic and international.

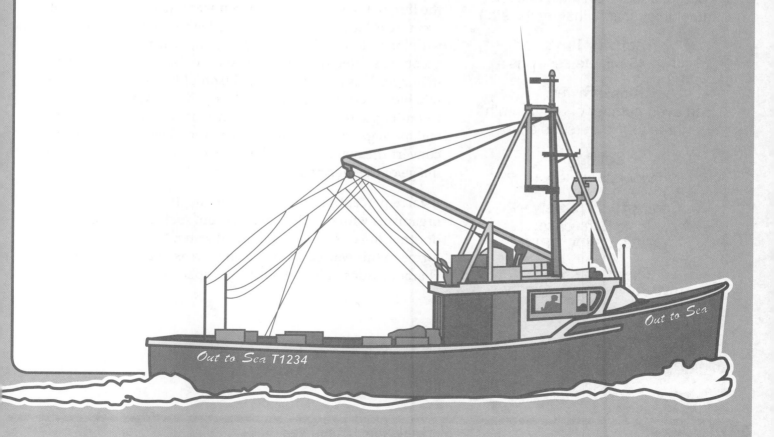

Mermaids and Manatees

Students journey through their imaginations to discern wildlife fact from fiction.

Objective

Students will (1) describe how imaginary creatures may be inspired by actual animals, (2) distinguish between mythical and actual aquatic wildlife, and (3) give examples of how wildlife can inspire myth and art.

Background

For years, wondrous and terrifying accounts of water-dwelling creatures were brought back by sailors and early explorers. These tales gave birth to belief in mermaids, sea serpents, and monsters "too terrible to mention." The Loch Ness Monster, Champy in Lake Champlain, N.Y., and the strange happenings of the Bermuda Triangle are a few contemporary examples of the lure of the sea's mysteries. But were there ever such real creatures? Early sailors claimed to have seen beautiful mermaids with long, flowing hair and undulating fish-finned tails. Later accounts shifted the mythic images to the wondrous and real manatee. This aquatic mammal (sometimes called the "sea cow") inhabits rivers, estuaries, and the open sea. Manatees bear little resemblance to the legendary mermaid. An active imagination and, perhaps, a long isolated sea voyage seem necessary to convert the manatee into the more conventionally captivating image of the mermaid.

Bizarre perceptions are possible if one describes ordinary organisms with detailed imagination, such as aquatic insects or other organisms found in pond water. Investigating such life forms in this way can provide an increased awareness of the characteristics of local habitat and species.

Grade Level:
Upper Elementary, Middle School

Content Areas:
Language Arts, Environmental Education, Social Studies, Expressive Arts

Method:
Students describe aquatic animals using a narrative style of writing that, in turn, is the basis for a drawing or painting done by other students.

Materials:
Library or Internet resources, art materials, a variety of photographs of real aquatic animals (insects, amphibians, fish, mammals, etc.)

Activity Time:
two 45-minute sessions

People Power:
an even number of groups with three to five persons each

Setting:
indoors or outdoors

Conceptual Framework Topic Reference:
CPIB1, CPIIA, CPIIC

Terms to Know:
myth, mythical, imaginary

Procedure

1. Ask students to sit quietly with their eyes closed and to try to picture a mythical creature that lives in a water environment. A mythical creature means an animal that you create in your mind and one that probably never lived outside your mind. Ask each student to picture a creature and prepare to describe it to the class.

2. Ask a few students to volunteer to describe the creature they pictured. Many of their images will likely be the result of film or television experiences.

3. Offer students an opportunity for discussion about classic myths regarding mermaids, sea serpents, and lake monsters. Explore their beliefs about whether they think such creatures were and are real or imaginary.

4. Tell students they are going on a mythic voyage where they will meet a wondrous aquatic creature. Their responsibility will be to have each crew of three to five sailors write as accurate a description of the creature as they can. The crew is to work together to produce a single written description.

5. Divide students into an even number of crews with three to five students in each crew. Provide each crew with an image of an actual aquatic animal. Be sure to select aquatic insects as well as larger animals. Some images in the Aquatic WILD activity "Are You Me?" could be helpful. Tell each crew to keep its animal a secret so that students on other crews do not see the creature.

6. Have members of the different crews find out as much as they can about their animal's actual appearance, behavior, and habitat. Allow them to use any available references or resources.

7. Once the research is finished, ask each crew to begin to develop written descriptions that will be presented to the other crews. Each student should contribute at least two or three lines to the group description. Each student could describe a different characteristic. For example,

- This creature eats fish and other things in the ocean. It has a parrot-like beak in the middle of long tubes. It swims by forcing water out of its body. It has gigantic, glistening eyes. (An octopus.)

- This is a hump-backed creature with stout, powerful wings. Its offspring live in capsules under water, where they hang onto stationary objects in flowing streams. When they grow up, the females often feed from the blood of humans. Humans attacked by these creatures develop huge, sucker-like welts that ooze fluid from their centers. Discomfort lasts for days. (A blackfly.)

WILD Work

Illustrators, Writers, Dancers, Poets, and other artists use their work to inform and educate the public about the natural world. Through sketches, journals, photography, music, interpretive dance, sculpture, and more, artists can convey factual as well as persuasive environmental messages.

Communications and Public Relations Specialists develop and manage communications programs. These programs include media outreach, public education, websites, and publicizing events. These specialists must have strong writing and editing skills, and they must be comfortable with communication of all kinds including in-person, written, and phone. For links to more information on these occupations, see the WILD Work link at *www.projectwild.org/aquatic*.

In Step with STEM

Frog Populations

- Take a virtual trip to the bottom of the ocean to explore organisms that thrive under extreme conditions away from the sun. Go to *www.projectwild.org/aquatic* for links.

- How are humans exploring what many people refer to as "the next frontier?" Research and report on advances in technology that have helped expand our knowledge of the ocean.

Early sailors claimed to have seen beautiful mermaids with long, flowing hair and undulating fish-finned tails. Later accounts shifted the mythic images to the wondrous and real manatee. . . . Manatees bear little resemblance to the legendary mermaid.

8. Once the descriptions are complete, each crew should prepare to read that group's description to another crew. Copy the descriptions so they can be exchanged in writing, as well as prepared to be read aloud.

9. Have crews pair up, and ask one crew to read aloud its description to the other crew. Provide the written descriptions at this point. The crew that receives the description then must create an image of the creature that was described. Reverse and repeat the process so that both of the paired crews have written descriptions to work with. The members of each crew must now draw or paint images of what they understood the other crew to have described. Individual drawings or paintings can be done by each student or a composite can be created by the entire crew. Limit the number of questions crews can ask of each other.

10. Once both crews have completed their images, compare written or oral descriptions with the resulting artwork. Crews can now reveal their original source photos or specimens, looking for similarities and differences.

11. Display the original source images, written descriptions, and interpretive artworks in clusters on the bulletin board or other display area.

12. Ask students to summarize and review the steps they took, analyzing where they seemed most accurate and inaccurate. Emphasize how readily descriptions can be distorted and exaggerated. Review the actual physical characteristics, habitats,

Mermaids and Manatees
© *Council for Environmental Education (CEE)*

and behaviors of all the source animals as a way to emphasize the fascinating variety of real-life wildlife. Ask students to give examples of any artwork or myths they think may be based on actual wildlife.

Extensions

1. Write a mythical story about a real aquatic creature. Show how the myth might have a basis in fact.

2. Research historical mythical creatures, and propose animals that may have provided the source for the myth.

3. Many times people see only part of an aquatic animal while the rest of the creature's body may remain unseen in dark or murky water. To simulate that experience, cover up most of a photograph of an aquatic animal. The animal's identity should not be obvious. Draw pictures of what you think the entire animal might look like. Compare your drawings with the photographs. Discuss how human perceptions form when people have only partial information.

Evaluation

Identify three mythical creatures that may have been inspired by a real animal; then identify the real animal in each case. Describe what the mythical creature is supposed to be able to do that the real animal cannot.

Bizarre perceptions are possible if one describes ordinary organisms with detailed imagination, such as aquatic insects or other organisms found in pond water. Investigating such life forms in this way can provide increased awareness of the characteristics of local habitat and species.

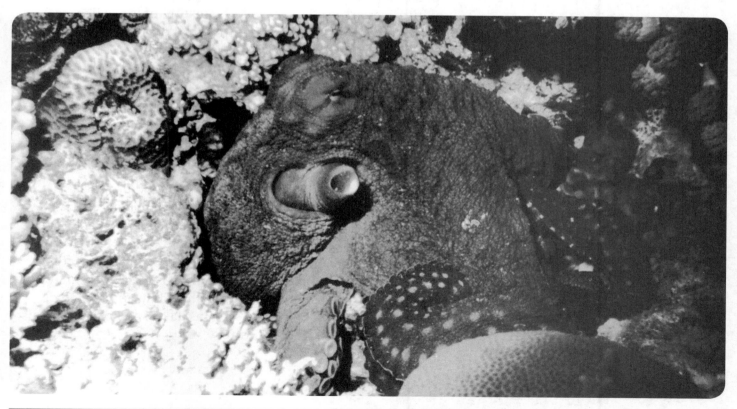

Water We Eating?

Grade Level:
Upper Elementary

Content Areas:
Social Studies, Science,
Environmental Education

Method:
Students visit a local supermarket
and compile a list of products that
originate in aquatic habitats.

Materials:
Writing materials, a world map,
magazines or newspapers
(if field trip is not possible);
OPTIONAL: clipboard

Activity Time:
one or two 20- to 60-minute
sessions; additional time
if field trip is included

People Power:
any

Setting:
indoors

**Conceptual Framework
Topic Reference:**
ECIB1, ECIB3

Terms to Know:
commercial fishing, aquaculture

Appendices:
Using Local Resources,
Sustainable Seafood

What in your supermarket can be traced back to an ocean, a river, a lake, or even a salt marsh?

Objectives

Students will (1) identify foods derived from aquatic sources and their geographic origins, and (2) describe the importance of aquatic environments as food sources.

Background

Aquatic ecosystems (oceans, estuaries, marshes, lakes, rivers, etc.) provide humans with a variety of products, including fish, shellfish, and wild and domestic rice. Other products derived from aquatic environments, such as fertilizer, soup stock, watercress, water chestnuts, and ingredients for vitamins, are not as well known. Seaweed is a source of algin, carrageenin, and agar, which are used as stabilizers, thickeners, and emulsifiers in hundreds of food products. Those seaweed derivatives are used to smooth the texture of foods like ice cream and to make them creamy. They help to keep ingredients like chocolate in suspension in chocolate milk. Certain types of seaweed, which are actually forms of algae, are consumed directly by humans. For example, nori is used in sushi, and irish moss, laver, and dulce (dulse) are used in other dishes. Yet another example, meat in oysters, is eaten directly by humans, while the shells are ground up for use as calcium supplements for humans and poultry.

Aquaculture is another source of aquatic food products. Aquaculture is an ancient form of cultivating aquatic plants, fish, and shellfish for food. In the United States, aquaculture produces perhaps as much as 99 percent of the Rainbow Trout consumed. Catfish, lobster, shrimp, oysters, crawfish, and salmon are all examples of aquatic animals raised commercially through aquaculture programs. The hatching and raising of aquatic animals for release in streams, lakes, and oceans are also considered forms of aquaculture.

NOTE: This activity does not specifically address potential ethical or environmental questions that may be raised concerning human aquaculture and mariculture practices. The activity is designed to focus on students' recognition of the role of water in the production of foods, including those from aquatic environments.

Procedure

Before the Activity:

Obtain permission from the manager of a local supermarket to bring your class or group to the store to find out how many products are derived from aquatic environments. If a field trip is not possible, educators might use the following as sources to identify aquatic products:

- Supermarket advertisements or photos from a variety of magazines or the Internet,

- Products from the pantries in students' homes, and

- A variety of products that represent the diversity of foods and other goods people use from aquatic environments.

1. Before the field trip, ask students to make a list of all the things they would expect to find in a supermarket that come directly from an aquatic environment and where in the market they can expect to be found. Be inclusive—all aquatic environments from ocean to pond and from swamp to river are appropriate. Also, design a form to record students' observations while at the supermarket. This form could be as simple as a place to record the products and what section of the market they are found in, or students can use a more detailed form that includes where the product is manufactured, its exact ingredients, and so forth.

2. Visit the supermarket and complete the observation forms.

3. After the field trip, compile a master list of aquatically derived products. Answer the following questions (some research may be needed): Where do the products come from? How are they obtained? Where and how are these products processed? How are they used?

4. On a world map, locate the country of origin of as many products as possible on the list above.

5. Ask students to draw a picture of the aquatic food products they most like to eat or to make a collage of such products from magazine pictures.

In the United States, aquaculture produces perhaps as much as 99 percent of the Rainbow Trout consumed. Catfish, lobster, shrimp, oysters, crawfish, and salmon are all examples of aquatic animals raised commercially through aquaculture programs.

WILD Work

For information on the related careers of **Farmer**, **Organic Farmer**, and **Aquaculturist**, head to *www.projectwild.org/aquatic*.

Explore this information with students, or have the students do a guided exploration on their own.

In Step with STEM

- Research the route that a food source takes from an aquatic habitat to the local grocery store. Use an online program that generates driving directions to create a map of the journey and calculate total miles traveled from harbor to supermarket.

- For younger students, purchase five to ten samples of grocery store goods derived from aquatic habitats. With students, round prices to the nearest dollar and create a bar graph. Discuss the range in prices and make inferences. Discuss the difference in prices. Why might one item be more expensive than another? Is the resource difficult to harvest?

Aquatic ecosystems provide humans with a variety of products...

6. Summarize the lesson by asking students:
- How do our lives depend on aquatic environments?
- What do aquatic environments provide for people?
- What do aquatic environments provide for wildlife?

Extensions

1. Compare aquatic products found in conventional markets in the United States with products found in markets specializing in foods from Asia (Japan, China, Philippines, Vietnam, Thailand, etc.).

2. Classify aquatic food products found in the supermarket according to the type of aquatic habitats they inhabit: saltwater (ocean, estuary, marsh, etc.) and freshwater (lake, pond, stream, river, etc.).

For Older Students:

3. Research aquacultural practices. Compare the food produced by each to the food produced through commercial fishing. What kinds of products are being produced by each? What effects, if any, are there on the environment and on populations of fish and shellfish as a result of each approach?

4. How does agriculture, and particularly irrigation, affect natural aquatic habitats?

Evaluation

1. Identify five foods derived directly from aquatic sources. List their countries or regions of origin.

2. Identify an aquatic plant or aquatic animal that you can find in a local store and that is also found growing or living in your state.

3. Have students review the world map they marked with origins of aquatically derived food products. What areas of the world dominate in using aquatic environments for food production? Have students offer explanations for their findings including proximity to water, culture, etc.

4. Describe three ways that aquatic habitats are important to humans as sources of food.

Water We Eating?
© *Council for Environmental Education (CEE)*

Net Gain, Net Effect

How do technological advances in commercial fishing affect fish populations?

Objectives

Students will (1) describe the evolution of fishing techniques, and (2) interpret the effect of changes in technology on fish populations.

Background

Throughout history, people have caught fish for food, to sell to others, for fun, and for sport. One type of fishing is subsistence fishing, in which the number of fish caught is no more than a family could consume. Commercial fishing differs from subsistence fishing because fish are caught and then sold to others. Sport fishing differs from commercial fishing because the catch is not sold for profit.

Humans have been engaged in fish gathering since prehistoric times. Research suggests that methods of catching fish began with humans wading into drying wetlands at the edges of large shallow lakes and using bare hands and clubs. As time passed, new techniques were invented. Native Americans built rock weirs or dams on streams and rivers to trap and spear the fish in holding ponds. Eventually, baskets were formed that allowed fish to swim downstream into intricately woven baffles that prevented their escape. (Source: American Sportfishing Association)

Fishing equipment has evolved over the years. Stone Age anglers used some sort of line, such as vines, and tied gorges to the end of the line. Gorges were a type of primitive hook made of bone, flint, and thorns or turtle shells. The earliest hook was made from copper about 7,000 years ago. Today, fishhooks are made from steel.

Roughly 4,000 years ago Chinese literature described wooden fishing poles with lines made from silk. Fishing lines were also made from plant fibers, human hair, cotton, and linen. Today, nylon is the most preferred material used for fishing line. Fishing rods have been made from many materials such as bamboo and steel, but today they are typically made from fiberglass.

Grade Level: Middle School

Content Areas:
Mathematics, Social Studies, Environmental Education, Science

Method: Students conduct a simulation to explore the evolution of fishing and the effects of changing technology on fish populations.

Materials: Nets of differing mesh size (see page 137): onion bags, potato bags, fruit bags, netting from hardware store, or plain cloth fabric for nets; 1-lb each of lima beans, pinto beans, black beans, lentils, and rice; writing materials; four containers that are large and deep enough to hold one-fourth of the beans and grains; *Netting Data Sheet*

Activity Time:
one 30- to 60-minute session

People Power: any size group

Setting: indoors or outdoors

Conceptual Framework Topic Reference:
ECIB, ECIIA

Terms to Know:
bycatch, depletion, commercial fishing

Appendices: Let's Go Fishing!, Using Local Resources, Sustainable Seafood, Agencies and Organizations

A tuna is ensnared in a trap.

The use of boats and rafts for fishing purposes evolved during the Stone Age. The first evolution in boat design came about when fishing boats shifted from a dugout—a narrow boat, made from hollowed trees and propelled by paddles—to sailing vessels. The development of sails allowed fishing vessels to extend their range and catch. The creation of steam and diesel-driven fishing fleets provided a method for rapid maneuver to any spot in the ocean.

The invention of the net enabled fishing to move from sustaining a family or tribe to an economic venture. Over time, the net evolved in size, design, and effectiveness. Many nets are now available for catching different fish species in a variety of situations. Gill nets, purse seines, trammel nets, and drift nets have all improved fishers' catch rates. Yet these advancements have also introduced new problems, such as the impact on other marine life, size discrimination, over-fishing, and loss of marine habitats.

Over 20 million tons of fish and other marine animals...are killed and discarded by commercial fishers each year. These discarded fishes are known as "bycatch."

Nets, combined with the range and maneuverability of steam and diesel boats, made it possible to catch larger amounts of smaller fish. Most commercial fishing companies have a specific fish species to catch, and other species that are caught inadvertently must be discarded. Over 20 million tons of fish and other marine animals, about one-fourth of the global catch, are killed and discarded by commercial fishers each year (Source: National Coalition for Marine Conservation). These discarded fishes are known as "bycatch."

Along with developments in boats and nets, changes have taken place with fishing equipment. Commercial fishers now routinely use complex sonar fish finders, radio communications, spotter aircraft, computerized navigational equipment, at-sea catch processing, and other similar sophisticated tools.

With the remarkable advances in technology and the growth in investment of fishing trawlers and factory processing ships, fisheries have become overfished and exploited. The amount of fish caught in the world's oceans grew from 19 million tons in 1950 to 88.6 million tons in 2012. As oceanic fisheries were fished at or beyond capacity, scientists saw a substantial change in the oceanic fish catch in 1989. According to the U.S. National Marine Fisheries Service, 88 fish species found off the shores of the United States have been depleted.

In the United States, the fishing industry is a $4-billion business. The largest fishing nations of the world are Japan, Russia, and China. Fish supply the main source of protein for nearly half of the more than 7 billion people on the planet. Nearly 17 million tons of sardines, herring, and anchovies are netted commercially each year, while approximately 72 million tons of other kinds of fish are caught annually.

A fisherman removes bycatch.

The high demand for seafood and the modern, technologically advanced fishing fleets have led to a modification in the world's fish species. Widespread depletion of certain ocean predators such as sharks and tunas can upset the predator-prey relationship of the oceans. Overfishing not only disrupts food webs but also can threaten marine ecosystems.

One example of a fish species on its way to recovery is the swordfish. Swordfish roam most of the world's tropical and temperate oceans. They have a large dorsal fin and a rigid, swordlike beak. Swordfish can weigh up to 1,200 pounds but average 250 pounds.

Commercial fishers use long fishing lines stretching dozens of miles and baited with hundreds of hooks to catch and kill swordfish. Since the introduction of this fishing method, there has been a decline in the weight and age of the swordfish catch. In the 1990s, the average catch size of the swordfish was 90 pounds compared to a 250-pound average in the 1960s. At 90 pounds, females have not reached a reproductive age and weight, and thus the population size declines. In 1998, plans were made to reduce the international quota for North Atlantic swordfish. The "Give Swordfish a Break" campaign, supported by chefs, grocers, and consumers, was part of a national effort that successfully restored swordfish populations to near-healthy levels. In 2002, swordfish had reached 94 percent of full recovery. This campaign is proof that focused conservation efforts can help restore ocean wildlife. (Sources: SeaWeb and the Natural Resources Defense Council)

One species of fish that was once considered endangered and now has reached a balance between catch and reproduction rates is the Striped Bass. The Striped Bass, also called rockfish, lives in estuarine waters along the Atlantic coast as a juvenile, then moves to coastal waters to feed. In spring, the mature Striped Bass returns to brackish and fresh water to spawn. The Striped Bass is a major food and sport fish on the East Coast from Maine to North Carolina. In the late 1970s, the Striped Bass population began to decline. In 1984, the Atlantic Striped Bass Conservation Act was passed to help recover this species. Effective state and federal programs to protect the Striped Bass allowed the recovery of stocks, and the species was officially recovered in 1995. By 2012, the species was at record levels. (Sources: National Oceanic and Atmospheric Administration, the Monterrey Bay Aquarium, and Sea Grant: University of Delaware)

NOTE: This activity does not address ethical questions related to the appropriateness of catching fish for human uses. This dimension may be added at the professional discretion of the educator conducting the activity.

Widespread depletion of certain ocean predators such as sharks and tunas can upset the predator-prey relationship of the oceans. Overfishing not only disrupts food webs but also can threaten marine ecosystems.

Fishermen prepare nets.

Procedure

1. Prepare the "ocean" by mixing all the beans and grains listed under "Materials," and dividing the mixture equally into four containers. These will be the four "fishing grounds."

2. For this activity, ask students to decide what species each bean will represent. Fish species can be hypothetical or can represent local fish species. On a wall chart as well as on the *Netting Data Sheet*, students can match the beans or grains with the fish they represent.

3. Divide students into four groups, and ask each group to go to the fishing grounds (the containers of beans and grains).

4. Discuss how fish are caught. Have students seen people catch fish? How were they catching fish? Could large numbers of fish be caught if all fish were caught with rods or poles? What are some ways to catch large groups of fish at one time? What are some ways people traditionally caught fish? After a general discussion on the methods people use to fish, inform students that they will now simulate the catching of fish using nets.

5. Next, distribute netting materials. The net materials must be cut into 4"x 6" squares. The number of nets needed will depend on how many students share a net. Provide one net for every three students.

6. With the coarsest netting in hand, ask students to "fish." Using only one hand, students are to hold the nets between their thumb and first finger (see Diagram A). This distance is known as the catching area. Ask students to make one pass with their nets through the fishing grounds.

For younger students, educators may want to demonstrate how to use each net. When it is the students' turn, allow them to make only one pass through the "ocean." Give each student a sheet of paper representing a boat. Instruct students to deposit their "fish" on the boat. Count the number of each species of fish caught, and record the numbers on a data sheet.

7. Next, allow students to use both hands (see Diagram B). Make one pass through the "ocean." Count the number of each species of fish caught, and record the numbers on a data sheet. Repeat this process several times.

8. Discuss the results between the one-hand and two-hand techniques. Relate those results as an improvement in technology. For example, using both hands may represent the shift from hand-powered boats with cast nets to trawlers.

Net Gain, Net Effect
© *Council for Environmental Education (CEE)*

9. Analyze the species the students have netted. The smaller lentils and rice will often slip through the netting and escape capture. The larger species—the limas and the pintos—are the most likely to have been caught. Ask students what they could do to catch more fish. Discuss possible options with them.

10. Ask students to return all fish to the ocean containers so that they can try fishing with a smaller-mesh net. Distribute a net with fine mesh (less than one-fourth inch). Again, the net needs to measure about 4" x 6". Repeat fishing attempts using one and then two hands for each type of net you are using.

11. Tabulate and discuss the results.

12. Return all the fish to the ocean.

For younger students, the activity may conclude with a discussion at this point. What happens when the different kinds of nets are used? Is it good to let the smaller fish through the net? Why or why not? What might happen if people fished from just one part of the ocean? **OPTIONAL:** Construct a bar graph to show the numbers of fish caught using the different nets and different techniques of netting.

13. Inform students that all the fish, beans through rice, are all the same species and that no fish smaller than the black bean species size can be caught. A penalty of one point will be added to the score for each of the smaller fish caught during this round. A regulatory agency responsible for monitoring fishing practices gives each team ten seconds to put the undersized fish back in the ocean after each netting. Appoint two members of each fishing team to play the regulatory agency role.

14. Instruct commercial fishers to use the fine mesh net (less than one-fourth inch mesh). Empty the net onto the table, and return the undersized fish to the ocean. At the end of ten seconds, the team must stop. The representatives of the regulatory agency will count the undersized fish that are still left on the table and fine them one point for each one.

15. Discuss the economics involved. Can the people fishing afford to return all undersized fish to the sea? What are their options? Should we release undersized fish? If yes, why? If no, why not?

16. Repeat this round with one of the larger-mesh nets. Is there an advantage to letting the smaller fish get through the net over returning them by hand? What aquatic animals might be caught in these larger nets?

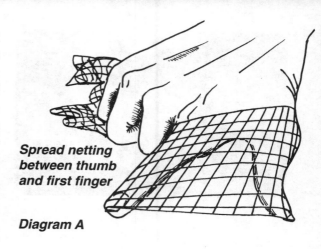

Spread netting between thumb and first finger

Diagram A

The invention of the net enabled fishing to move from sustaining a family or tribe to an economic venture. Over time, the net evolved in size, design, and effectiveness.

Diagram B

Tuna are harvested using nets or lines.

17. Ask students to summarize what they have learned. Review the general history of fishing, including how each change may have affected fish populations. Consider possible impacts on fish habitats as well. Identify some of the potential positive and negative issues related to the advancement of commercial fishing. The *Netting Worksheet* provided may be helpful.

Extensions

1. Use nets of different sizes to try to catch aquatic organisms in a local pond or stream. Observe and record any differences in what the nets catch. Be extremely careful to return any animals to their habitats unharmed. **NOTE:** Check regulations with your state's wildlife agency regarding net use; in some areas it is against the law to use nets in local waters.

The amount of fish caught in the world's oceans grew from 19 million tons in 1950 to 88.6 million tons in 2012.

2. Who "owns" the fish in the sea? In streams? In lakes? In ponds? In other aquatic habitats? Who is responsible for conserving and protecting fish species?

3. Research regulations on personal, noncommercial fishing in freshwater and marine environments.

4. Research regulations on commercial fishing in freshwater and marine environments.

5. Discuss the role of aquaculture (freshwater) and mariculture (marine) aquatic farming. How will this emerging field affect commercial fishing? What possible positive effects, if any, on fish populations and habitat might there be from a change to aquaculture? Mariculture? What possible negative effects, if any?

6. Research the fishing industry in your state. What methods are most commonly used to catch fish? What regulations apply to commercial fishing in your state? Are they different from, or similar to, the regulations for personal and recreational fishing?

7. Research international treaties and organizations dedicated to conserving and protecting oceanic habitats.

8. Create an illustrated history of the fishing net.

Evaluation

For Younger Students

1. Draw three pictures showing different ways that fish are caught. Indicate which picture shows the way most fish are caught.

For Older Students

2. Describe how fishing has changed from prehistoric times to the present. How have these changes affected fish populations?

A net is prepared for release into the water.

Net Gain, Net Effect

Netting Data Sheet

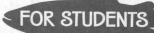

Directions: After each round of fishing, record the number of fish caught for each species.

Fish Species		Coarse Nets				Fine Nets				Comments
		Net A (most coarse)		Net B		Net C		Net D (most fine)		
Number of Hands Used →		1	2	1	2	1	2	1	2	
Name of Fish ↓										
	Species #1 Name: (example: "Lima lunker")									
	Species #2 Name:									
	Species #3 Name:									
	Species #4 Name:									
	Species #5 Name:									

Examples of Netting

Coarse — Fine

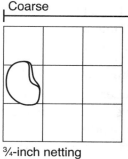

¾-inch netting
Lima Bean

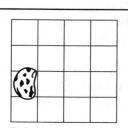

½-inch netting
Pinto Bean

¼-inch netting
Black Bean

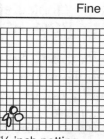

⅛-inch netting
Sunflower Seed
Rice
Lentil
Barley

Watered-Down History

Grade Level: Middle School

Content Areas: Social Studies, Environmental Education

Method: Students investigate the history of a chosen waterway through research methods, recorded personal interviews, and public records, and then display their findings on a mural.

Materials: County, city, state, regional maps or a combination; names of agencies responsible for historical records; art materials. **OPTIONAL:** names of citizens who might be interviewed, recording device

Activity Time: several class sessions, minimum of three 45-minute sessions

People Power: any size group, several small groups are recommended

Setting: indoors; a visit to an outdoor site is recommended

Conceptual Framework Topic Reference: HGIA, HGIB, HGIIB

Terms to Know: waterway, events, consequences, habitat, vegetation, geology, archaeology, culture, history, geography, navigation

Appendices: Using Local Resources, Agencies and Organizations

Students investigate the history of a waterway.

Objectives

Students will (1) describe human, plant, and animal life associated with a waterway over a period of time; (2) predict the future of the waterway; and (3) analyze correlative relationships between events and their possible effects on the waterway.

Background

Historically, waterways have provided an available path for exploration and transportation, and amenities for human settlement. Most waterways also provide a rich habitat for wildlife. Ancient fossils offer evidence that these areas were once homes for marine life, dinosaurs, and ancient mammals.

When early settlers began to immigrate into the United States, waterways provided a needed source of water prompting towns and homes to be built along shores. Waterways were used to transport logs, furs, fish, and agricultural products from one town to another. As the country has grown, waterways have been used to provide transportation, power, and irrigation to communities. Waterways such as rivers, canals, dams, and channels are used for navigation, hydropower, flood control, coastal protection, and municipal and industrial water supply. Navigable channels provide an efficient and economic corridor for moving commerce. Thousands of cities, towns, and industries rely on water supply from lakes and reservoirs. Waterways also provide recreation for people to enjoy swimming, kayaking, whitewater rafting, and fishing.

Over time, the United States' waterways have been modified. Wetlands are filled in for development, lakes and reservoirs are created by dams, and beach areas are developed for recreation. Changes in waterways have an impact on wildlife as well as on humans. Some effects may be beneficial, while others may be damaging.

Procedure

1. After introducing this activity, ask students to refer to a county, city, state, or regional map and to select one waterway that will be the focus of their research. It might be a stream, river, lake, or pond.

NOTE: If possible, students could visit the waterway as a pre-research field trip. This trip would provide an awareness of the present conditions so that historical perspectives and future recommendations would have a base in experience.

2. Once the choice has been made, divide the class into small working groups. Ask each group to choose a major topic area (e.g., geology, plants, animals, ancient people, or recent history) to establish a historical perspective. More specific topics that the students might explore include floods, dams, agriculture, recreation, fishing, irrigation, and so on.

3. Ask students to identify resources for their research. If possible, try to include living reference sources such as older citizens, members of local historical societies, and governmental professionals (geologists, water quality experts, etc.). History, science, and social studies teachers from high schools or colleges may be viable sources. Consider recording personal interviews. Old newspapers and historical archives may be available online or at local libraries and resource centers. Questions such as the following might provide guidance:

- What forms of ancient life populated these regions?
- What was life like for ancient peoples who lived here?
- How did explorers find this location?
- What were the explorers looking for?
- What kinds of wildlife did explorers and early settlers find?
- What kinds of vegetation did explorers and early settlers find?
- Are these same life forms still here?
- How has the waterway changed?

4. After the research is complete, have students create a large base map of the waterway. Each team could create artwork to illustrate the major findings of its research. The artwork could be attached temporarily to the map and removed or replaced as needed.

5. After the map is complete, have teams report in a historical sequence, beginning with the team with the earliest history and ending with the team with the most recent history. By establishing a sequence for presenting each report, each geological, archaeological, and biological topic can be addressed during its major time period. This process also creates a layering of history represented as a historical collage on the map of the waterway.

WILD Work

A **Wildlife Educator** teaches students about wildlife science and conservation including wildlife biology, ecology, toxicology, research and management techniques, and conservation policy and law.

A **Communications and Public Relations Specialist** interprets research and conservation programs to the general public. They write articles and news releases, create brochures and websites, and speak at public gatherings or through the media.

A **Research Scientist** works in a wide range of fields, performing original research in labs, for instance at universities or with governmental agencies. For links to more information, see the WILD Work link at *www.projectwild.org/aquatic*.

In Step with STEM

- Research a current and local waterway issue. Post research.
- Post research questions, discussions, and findings on a blog.
- Print a large map of a portion of a highly developed waterway. Rewrite history in reverse to design and develop the landscape back into a natural setting. How might water flow change? What would happen during a flood? What plants and animals might live in the riparian zone? For online map resources, visit *www.projectwild.org/aquatic*.

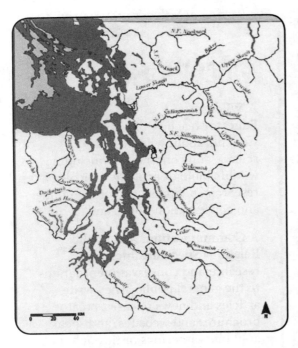

6. After reporting is complete, ask students to collectively analyze major changes involving the waterway and its associated life. Ask them to attempt to identify correlations between events and consequences of events affecting the waterway. Create a timeline, noting major events in the waterway's history.

7. Finally, have students collectively create a vision of the future for the waterway. For example, students could go back in history and undo events they believe modified the waterway in some fashion. First, they could illustrate the reversal of a change by replacing artwork they may have removed because of a historic event. Second, they could create an image of the future that they believe represents an effective ecological balance among people, wildlife, and the environment in association with this waterway. Add the future possibilities to the timeline created in Step 6. Consider having students compile a biography of their waterway to summarize the activity.

Extensions

1. Implement a project that demonstrates ecological balance between humans and wildlife in association with an aquatic environment.

2. Write a play with traditional or original music to portray the course of your waterway through time. End with possible futures being depicted, and emphasize human responsibilities for the consequences of our choices. Present the play to other groups or record it as a YouTube video.

Evaluation

1. Write at least two paragraphs describing how a waterway might have changed over a 100-year period of time—for example, from 1865 to 1965. Write another paragraph predicting what might happen between now and the year 2100.

2. Role-play the following scenario: Each student is an elected official. Mr. or Ms. Smith represents a group in favor of building a dam on a river to produce irrigation water and recreation opportunities in your area. Mr. or Ms. Jones represents another group that thinks the dam will have a damaging effect on the animals and plants in and along the river. Pick one position to support and debate the topic.

Additional Resource

Find watershed maps at *http://water.usgs.gov/outreach/*.

Changes in waterways have an impact on wildlife as well as on humans. Some effects may be beneficial, while others may be damaging.

Watered-Down History
© *Council for Environmental Education (CEE)*

A Whale of an Issue

The meeting of the International Whaling Commission is now in session.

Objectives

Students will (1) describe general characteristics and statuses of whales, (2) recognize that international alliances affect wildlife, and (3) evaluate the possible impact of wildlife issues on alliances and other relationships between and among nations.

Background

Whales are the largest animals on Earth. There are approximately 80 known species of whales, which range in size from approximately 4 to almost 100 feet in length, and from 160 pounds to 220 tons in weight. Whales are mammals, bearing live young. Some research suggests that whales and other Cetacea, including dolphins, are creatures of such intelligence that, among other things, they have unusual capacities for communication.

Out of concern for maintaining viable populations of whales, the International Whaling Commission (IWC) was established under the International Convention for the Regulation of Whaling (December 1946). The main duty of the IWC is to keep under review and revise as necessary the measures detailed in the Schedule to the Convention, which governs the conduct of whaling throughout the world. Those measures provide for the complete protection of certain whale species, designate specified areas as whale sanctuaries, set limits on the numbers and size of whales that may be taken, prescribe open and closed seasons and areas for whaling, and prohibit the capture of suckling calves and female whales accompanied by calves. The compilation of catch reports and other statistical and biological records are also required.

In addition, the Commission encourages, coordinates, and funds whale research; publishes the results of scientific research; and promotes studies into related matters. Membership in the IWC is open to any country in the world that formally adheres to the 1946 convention.

Grade Level: Middle, High School

Content Areas: Social Studies, Environmental Education

Method:
Students hold a hypothetical meeting of the International Whaling Commission.

Materials: Writing materials, research materials

Activity Time: two or three 45-minute sessions

People Power: any, excellent for large group

Setting:
indoors

Conceptual Framework Topic Reference:
PLIIA

Terms to Know:
Cetacea, alliance, regulation, commission, subsistence, sanctuary, moratorium, stock, sustainable

Appendix:
Agencies and Organizations

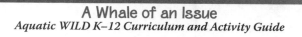

Some research suggests that whales and other Cetacea, including dolphins, are creatures of such intelligence that, among other things, they have unusual capacities for communication.

HUMPBACK WHALE

There are many stocks (geographic populations) of the twelve species of "great whales." Many of these have been depleted by over exploitation, some seriously, both in recent times and in earlier centuries. Fortunately, several species are showing signs of population increase since their protection. Whales, like any other animal population, have a natural capacity to reproduce and a natural rate of mortality. A stock remains more or less in equilibrium at its initial level because those two factors balance one another. If the number of whales in a stock is reduced, the population will begin to rebound—possibly as a result of greater food availability—by higher pregnancy rates, earlier maturation, increased survival rates, or a combination of these factors.

In 1975, a management policy for whales was adopted by the IWC to bring all stocks to levels that provide the greatest long-term harvests and set catch limits for individual stocks below their sustainable yields. However, because of uncertainties in the scientific analysis and, therefore, the precise status of various whale stocks, the IWC decided during its 1982 meeting that there should be a pause in commercial whaling on all whale stocks from 1985 to 1986 except for subsistence whaling.

Subsequently, a Revised Management Procedure (RMP) was developed by the IWC's Scientific Committee to calculate sustainable hunting levels for each stock. It was an important step in the development of wildlife resource management in that it took into account the inevitable scientific uncertainty and required relatively simple data to obtain information (knowledge of population size, past and present catches, and stock identity). In addition, a Revised Management Scheme (RMS) was developed to record observed whale stocks for accurate population counts. The IWC endorsed the RMP/RMS in 1994 but reached an impasse in 2007 despite years of effort to implement. The Scientific Committee plans to work on alternative applications for the RMP to achieve its goal of maintaining adequate stock levels. At a 2007 meeting, the IWC determined that individual governments and agencies could implement their own RMP's but none have so far.

The pause in commercial whaling does not affect aboriginal subsistence whaling, which is permitted from Denmark (Greenland—Fin and Minke whales), the Russian Federation (Siberia—Gray and Bowhead whales), St. Vincent and the Grenadines (Bequia—Humpback whales), and the United States (Alaska—Bowhead and Gray whales). Subsistence whaling is defined as harvesting whales to provide food and necessary resources to one's family and not for commercial profit.

A Whale of an Issue

As part of their response to the decision for a pause in commercial whaling, some member governments have implemented major research programs that may include the sampling of whales caught under special permits the convention allows them to grant.

The Commission also sponsors and promotes international research. A major undertaking in 1978 was a series of global ship surveys of Antarctic Minke whale stocks. This series was successfully expanded into a Southern Hemisphere research program called SOWER which concluded in 2009. Currently, Gray and Right whales are two critically endangered species receiving special attention by the IWC Conservation Committee to create sanctuaries and bring stock levels up to sustainable levels. Other funded research includes work on developing and improving new techniques such as photo-identification studies, acoustic and satellite/ radio tracking of whales, and genetic analysis of populations.

The Scientific Committee continues to work on the RMP and other environmental threats affecting whale populations such as global warming, pollution, collisions with marine vessels, and safe whale-watching procedures. The moratorium on commercial whaling has yet to be officially lifted until a clear strategy for sustainably harvesting whales can be approved and adopted.

The Commission has no enforcement powers. Beyond economic sanctions and national laws by members, the Commission relies on voluntary adherence to its rules. World public opinion is an important force on the Commission and its member nations to make and enforce responsible conservation decisions.

Procedure

1. Divide students into six research groups outlined below. Half the groups will focus on the International Whaling Commission while the other half will research whales and various interest groups that influence IWC decision making.

2. Ask each group to conduct library and online research. Possible questions for each group might include the following:

International Whaling Commission

What is the International Whaling Commission? When, why, and how was it established? Who are its members? What members are whaling nations? Are there any active whaling nations that are not members of the IWC? If so, what are their current practices affecting whales? What are the major reasons for and against continued whaling? Include economic, political, cultural, scientific, and ethical considerations.

WILD Work

How could the combined efforts of a **Whale Scientist**, an **Attorney**, an **Environmental Journalist**, and a **Wildlife Policy Analyst** support the mission of the International Whaling Commission?

To find more information on these careers, head to: *www.projectwild. org/aquatic*.

In Step with STEM

■ Research the following on a commonly hunted whale, such as the Minke whale: population size, reproduction rate (calves per year), and amount harvested per year. Compare harvest rate to calves born each year for multiple harvested species to discuss sustainability and make predictions.

■ To further integrate whale research and mathematical concepts, continue on to the *Aquatic WILD* activity "Whale of a Tail."

There are approximately 80 known species of whales, which range in size from approximately 4 to almost 100 feet in length...

There are many stocks of the twelve species of "great whales." Many of these have been depleted by over exploitation, some seriously, both in recent times and in earlier centuries. Fortunately, several species are showing signs of population increase since their protection.

What positions do member nations tend to take on issues? For what reasons? What are the accomplishments of the IWC? What problems does the IWC face? What is the role of world opinion in affecting the activities of the IWC and its member and nonmember nations? For example, a strong push from animal welfare groups led the IWC to establish a working group to identify humane killing methods for whaling nations. What recent recommendations and regulations has the IWC passed? How effective does the IWC seem to be in meeting its objectives? What other international agreements affect whales? Which countries participate in these agreements? Besides commercial and subsistence harvesting, what other factors impact whale populations?

Nonwhaling Nation Members of the IWC

Have these nations ever actively engaged in whaling? If yes, what are the historic reasons for whaling among people of their nation? For what reasons are these nations now nonwhaling nations? How did they vote on the moratorium decision of 1982? What, if any, national laws do they have involving whales?

Whaling Nation Members of the IWC

What are historic and contemporary reasons for whaling among people of their nation? What practices have they used and do they use in killing whales? What regulations, if any, do they support that affect the killing of whales? How did they vote on the moratorium decision of 1982? What, if any, national laws do they have involving whales?

Whale Conservation Groups

NOTE: Advise students to include "cetacean" as a keyword in addition to "whale" during their research.

What national and international groups exist to conserve and advocate for whales? What are the strategies and goals outlined by each group? Who are they collaborating with to reach their mission? Examples might include the government, the public, youth groups, commercial whalers, or similar coalitions. What are major current threats facing whales today? Do these groups provide services such as research, advocacy, or educational outreach for the International Whaling Commission?

Subsistence Whalers

NOTE: Certain websites may contain graphic images of harvested whales that may be disturbing to some students. To avoid this issue, provide the group with a list of pre-selected websites. For suggested sites, see links at *www.projectwild.org/aquatic*.

RIGHT WHALES

A Whale of an Issue
© *Council for Environmental Education (CEE)*

Identify villages and cultural groups around the world who rely on whaling to provide food and resources for their families. How long have they been hunting whales? What species of whales are allowed to be hunted? Are any of these species listed as endangered or threatened? Besides food, what other resources are whales hunted for?

Research Scientists

How many different kinds of whales exist today in the world? Have any whales become extinct? If yes, which? Why do you think this particular species became extinct? What are common characteristics of different whale species? What is the status of each of these species? What is the reproductive rate and success of each of these species? What population increase is possible? What food and other habitat needs do they have? What problems do they face? What species are most hunted and for what purposes, historically and in the present? Which species are most endangered and which are most abundant? How intelligent might they be? What does the future hold for whales?

World public opinion is an important force on the Commission and its member nations to make and enforce responsible conservation decisions.

3. After students have completed their research, set up the classroom to resemble a meeting hall. Hold a meeting of the IWC attended by scientific advisors and any guests, including other interest groups. Organize discussion and debate among students representing different interests from the above research. Select several topics for discussion and allow time for groups to meet and prepare a formal statement defending their position. Topics may include how to conduct proper research, exceptions to the ban on commercial whaling such as subsistence hunting, or how to regulate stock populations internationally.

4. The next task is to come up with a set of recommendations and regulations that the IWC, including its whaling and nonwhaling member nations, can agree upon. This task may be done through discussion by the whole class or by a subcommittee approach. If done by subcommittee, ask for volunteers to represent the IWC, with representatives of both whaling and nonwhaling nations. They should come up with a set of recommendations and regulations to present in written form to the rest of the class for review. Include the other interest groups as well. Note whether this approach is actually how the IWC makes decisions.

5. Discuss any final recommendations. Evaluate the possible impact of wildlife issues on relationships between and among nations.

KILLER WHALE

...measures provide for the complete protection of certain whale species, designate specified areas as whale sanctuaries, set limits on the numbers and size of whales that may be taken, prescribe open and closed seasons and areas for whaling, and prohibit the capture of suckling calves and female whales accompanied by calves.

Extension

Identify other national and international bodies that have an influence on aquatic species of wildlife. Research these groups and what issues are of concern to their organizations.

Evaluation

1. List four basic characteristics of two different species of whales.

2. Identify ten countries that are members of the International Whaling Commission. Indicate the countries that are whaling nations, and list which species of whales they harvest. Explain how each country uses its harvested whales.

3. What is the purpose of the International Whaling Commission? Describe one action within the past three years the Commission has taken to achieve its purpose. How are actions of the IWC enforced? What is your assessment of the IWC's importance and effectiveness? How would you change the IWC if given the opportunity?

4. Summarize your impressions of the impact of this issue—and other wildlife issues, if possible—on alliances and other relationships between and among nations.

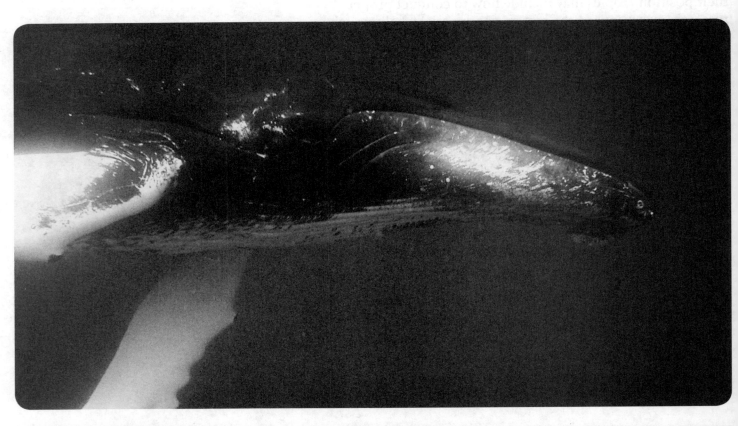

A Whale of an Issue
© *Council for Environmental Education (CEE)*

Sea Turtles International

Explore the push and pull of politics in wildlife conservation.

Objective

Students will (1) analyze the policies and philosophies that countries have relating to wildlife ownership and protection and to habitat management, (2) explain the importance of international agreements and organizations that manage species that cross national boundaries, and (3) define the difference between ownership of land and ownership of wildlife.

Background

The boundaries that exist between countries are more often political in nature than actual physical barriers and allow for the free movement of people and wildlife. Nations and their governments throughout the world vary on how they perceive the protection of wildlife and habitat. Policies are based on the country's economics and culture. For instance, countries may need to rely on all natural resources within their boundaries to sustain themselves economically—even when wildlife populations and wildlife habitat may be compromised. Even if a country has entered international agreements to protect wildlife and habitat, it may not have the funds to enforce those agreements, and its citizens may feel that the financial gain is worth the risk of breaking the law. Additionally, in some countries, land ownership includes the wildlife found on the land. In such cases, even if laws exist to protect wildlife and habitat, private landowners are exempt.

With respect to culture, the people of some countries have used wildlife products for centuries as part of their lifestyle and customs. Cultures may use ground turtle shells to treat arthritis, gall bladders to treat disease, or ground horns to improve fertility. People from such countries may have been eating rare animal parts as delicacies for generations. Wildlife products are often an integral part of cultural celebrations and ceremonies. As a result, countries may be reluctant to join international agreements banning the possession of animal products. Where usage is restricted, citizens may resort to obtaining the product illegally.

Grade Level: High School

Content Areas:
Social Studies, Environmental Education

Method:
Students simulate the political interactions of citizens from different countries who have a variety of perspectives on the conservation of wildlife and habitat.

Materials:
Copies of the *Scenario Cards* (one card per student) and the *Haves Cards*

Activity Time:
two 45-minute sessions

People Power:
at least 18 students

Setting:
indoors

Conceptual Framework Topic Reference:
PLIB, PLIC, PLIIA, PLIIB

Terms to Know:
political process, international agencies, wants, needs, entrepreneur, compliance

Appendices:
Sustainable Seafood, Agencies and Organizations

The sale of wildlife products has contributed to a decline in many populations of animals throughout the world. The Convention on International Trade in Endangered Species of Wild Flora and Fauna (CITES) was adopted on July 1, 1975, and currently has 175 member countries. These countries have agreed to ban commercial international trade of listed endangered species and require a license for trading threatened species as a way of monitoring those that may become endangered. While most countries have joined CITES and have ratified the agreements found within, not all comply stringently, as enforcement is decided by the individual country.

All species of sea turtles are either listed as endangered or threatened and are covered by CITES. Although sea turtle populations have declined, they are still being harvested for their value and ties to cultural traditions. Sea turtles are found in oceans throughout the world. Some species migrate as many as 3,000 miles in a year, often crossing one or more international boundaries. Besides being harvested in many countries, sea turtle populations are threatened by pollution and habitat loss.

The turtles' nesting grounds, found on ocean beaches, are also declining because of development. Another threat to sea turtle populations is the light from homes and businesses along beach areas. After they hatch, baby sea turtles instinctively go toward light, which is usually moonlight over water. When sea turtle eggs hatch near developed areas, the light from homes and businesses sometimes confuses the baby sea turtles and causes them to head inland instead of out to the ocean. Anglers catch sea turtles in their nets or cages. Turtle hunters around the world harvest sea turtles either legally or illegally to sell their shells, meat, or body parts to international traders. In some countries, sea turtle eggs are a delicacy and can be found in the open market.

In this activity, students will represent citizens of three different countries either trying to make a living, make a profit, enforce laws, or enforce international agreements. Each student will receive a description of their character, a list of their "wants," and a list of "haves" (items to be exchanged to obtain their "wants"). It is an understanding of this exchange of "wants" and "haves" that drives the political process and allows citizens to achieve their goals. In this activity, the characters are all connected by chains of need, and certain players are key to moving the solutions forward: the CITES representative who supports the judge, the judge who then issues a judicial order allowing the government employee to permit critical developments, and the sea turtle advocate who supplies needed funding.

The purpose of this activity is to show that governments and societies develop different programs and policies relating to wildlife ownership and protection and to wildlife management. The movement of wildlife species across national boundaries often necessitates the adoption of international agreements and the formation of international organizations to ensure the protection and management of these species.

Procedure

1. Review the background information with students.

2. Hand out a *Scenario Card* to each student. This will be the student's "character." If more than 18 students are in the class, ask students to team up. Then, direct students to identify which country they live in based on their card and group themselves accordingly. There should be one group for each country: Chumas, Pargimo, and the Republic of United Peoples.

3. Describe each country using the background information on page 151. Briefly describe the various characters from each of the countries. Discuss probable economic and cultural issues found within each country that would affect the safety of sea turtles. Also, review any vocabulary that may be unfamiliar to the students, such as "entrepreneur" and "compliance."

4. Give students time to review their own characters. Tell them that the objective of the activity is to collect one *Haves Card* for each Want listed in their scenario. They will get these *Haves Cards* from other students during the activity.

5. Pass out the *Haves Cards* by matching up the country and character to the *Scenario Cards* for each student. Tell students they will be keeping their scenario information, but they will distribute the *Haves Cards*. During the activity, they will (1) give away their initial *Haves Cards* to classmates who request them and (2) obtain the new cards they want. To find their cards, each student must first determine who the other characters are and who has the cards they want. Cards are obtained simply by asking for them. No direct trading is required. However, sometimes the initial holder of the card may not be permitted to give the card away until certain conditions specified on the card are met (i.e. other cards have already passed hands). Students should pay attention to and follow these conditions.

6. Begin the activity by letting the students move around the room to meet the other characters and fulfill their goals. Allow students time to work through their scenarios. Tell students to write on the cards the name of the character from whom they received the card. This information will help the class track the interactions during discussion later.

7. When all characters have fulfilled their needs by obtaining the necessary *Haves Cards*, tell students to return to their country (group). Have students describe their characters, what they wanted, and where they got the item they needed.

8. Discuss as a class the reactions and interactions that came about from the scenario. Did all characters fulfill their wants? Which characters had their wants fulfilled by a character outside

All species of sea turtles are either listed as endangered or threatened and are covered by CITES. Although sea turtle populations have declined, they are still being harvested for their value and ties to cultural traditions.

Leatherback Sea Turtle eggs.

WILD Work

What's the difference between a **Refuge Manager** and a **Refuge Officer**?

How does a **Wildlife Inspector** protect endangered species like sea turtles?

What does a **Forensics Specialist** have to do with global wildlife conservation?

Start researching the answers to these questions with students by going to *www.projectwild.org/aquatic*.

In Step with STEM

■ Learn how satellite telemetry is used to track sea turtle migration routes. Go to *www.projectwild.org/aquatic*.

■ In small groups of two to three, choose one marine wildlife protection organization to research. Analyze based on size, influence, funding, and strategy to compile a brief report on success and potential changes to operations. Discuss fundamental goals that each group has in common versus differences in approach.

■ Continue on with the Aquatic WILD activity "Turtle Hurdles," which simulates the effects of limiting factors on sea turtle populations.

of their country? What difficulties did they find in getting their wants met? How did the international organizations and agreements facilitate the protection of sea turtles in this activity? What might have happened without their contributions? What more might be done?

9. Ask students to differentiate between ownership of land and ownership of wildlife. In the United States, who owns wildlife? Ask students if they can articulate the different policies and philosophies that these three countries had relating to wildlife ownership and protection and to habitat management. Did students think the landowner wanted poachers arrested in order to protect the turtles or to eliminate competitors? Students should support their responses.

Extensions

1. Investigate the Sea Turtle Survival League, and track a turtle's health and movement around the world. Go to *www.projectwild.org/aquatic* for a link to the Migration-Tracking Education Program.

2. Research some products that have been made from migrating animals and that can be found in the United States. Determine their worth and their economic impact on both the buyer and the seller.

3. Research the endangered or threatened species that migrate between the United States and Canada or Mexico. Determine if there are any economic, cultural, or political circumstances that may create a desire to protect or poach these animals.

4. Plan to visit a beach site at which sea turtles nest. Prior to the visit, locate the site on a map and research the natural and cultural features of the vicinity. Have students discuss and predict the potential advantages and disadvantages of this location to nesting turtles. When visiting the site, compare the predictions to any observations made on-site. Invite an expert on sea turtle conservation along to help students develop a better understanding of the site in terms of potential dangers and benefits to sea turtles.

Evaluation

Have students choose a current conflict in the world dealing with the protection of wildlife species and international borders. Have students research topography; natural features; economic, cultural, and political structures of the countries involved; and what, if anything, is being done internationally or locally to help migrating wildlife. Students should specifically address how culture, economics, and politics of selected countries determine the fate of wildlife species that cross international borders.

Country Background Information

Pargimo

- Developing country.
- Some coastal land development.
- Coastal village income is based on fishing.
- Borders the Republic of United Peoples (RUP).
- Sea turtle and sea turtle eggs are a common food.
- Sea turtles, sea turtles eggs, and products made from sea turtles have been traded internationally for centuries and were an important part of the country's and individuals' incomes.
- Sea turtles migrate from the RUP coast to the Pargimo coast to spend their nonbreeding season.
- Some of the turtles migrate from the south of Pargimo to the north where they lay their eggs on the furthest northeast shores.
- A member of CITES, but lacking financial resources for enforcement.
- Ocean pollution by industrial sources is a concern.

The Republic of United Peoples (RUP)

- Developed country.
- A very active member of CITES with active enforcement.
- Borders Pargimo.
- Sea turtles migrate from the coast of Pargimo to the coast of RUP to lay eggs.
- Coastal lobster and shrimp fishery is a large source of income for many coastal communities.
- Extensive coastal land development.

Chumas

- Developed country.
- Landlocked, therefore no sea turtles.
- Non-enforcing member of CITES.
- Culture encourages the use of sea turtles and sea turtle products as a food source, as a health aid, and for ceremonial uses.
- Black market for sea turtle products that goes unchecked by the government.

Scenario Cards

Country: Chumas

Sea turtle jewelry dealer
Because you know how valuable sea turtle jewelry is all over the world, you buy as much as you can, even though it is prohibited.

Wants:
Turtles
Money

Country: Chumas

Restaurant owner
The people of your community have been eating sea turtle eggs and sea turtles for thousands of years as a delicacy. You buy as many eggs and turtles as you can.

Wants:
Turtles
Turtle eggs
Money

Country: Chumas

Turtle trader
Middle class. You buy sea turtles from collectors in Pargimo to sell to companies in Chumas that make medicine, ceremonial products, and traditional food. Although your work has been respected and needed, it has now become illegal.

Wants:
Job

Country: Chumas

Ceremonial sea turtle buyer
You buy products made from sea turtles to sell for ceremonial uses. People in your community have been using sea turtle products for generations. Without them, the ceremonies would fail and harm would fall on the village.

Wants:
Turtles

Country: Chumas

Turtle egg trader
Middle class. You buy sea turtle eggs from collectors in Pargimo to sell to companies in Chumas that make medicine and traditional food. Although your work has been respected and needed, it has now become illegal.

Wants:
Job

Country: Pargimo

Government employee
You are interested in the agency operating efficiently. You have received a request for a special land development permit, but because of the new CITES regulations, must wait for judicial orders before you can fulfill this request.

Wants:
Judicial order for coastal building permits

Scenario Cards

Country: Pargimo

Landowner

You have extensive coastal land holdings but are cash poor and need money to rejuvenate other businesses. You believe wild animals are the property of the landowner. You want poachers arrested.

Wants:
Capital investment funds

Country: Pargimo

Judge

You are frustrated by a lack of professional recognition for community efforts. You would like to further CITES by requiring developers to set aside beach natural areas for turtle habitat when applying for building permits. You hope that ecotourism will develop. You believe wildlife belongs to the public for protection.

Wants:
Professional recognition

Country: Pargimo

Illegal collector of turtles (poacher)

You poach turtles from the beach and ocean to sell to traders in Chumas in order to support a large family. You believe wildlife should be available for public taking, but would prefer a legal job.

Wants:
Job

Country: Pargimo

Illegal collector of turtle eggs (poacher)

You poach turtle eggs from the beach and ocean to sell to traders in Chumas in order to support a large family. You believe wildlife should be available for public taking, but would prefer a legal job.

Wants:
Job

Country: Pargimo

Wildlife biologist and manager

You are frustrated by the poaching of turtles and by news of potential beach development. You would like to see the beaches protected and have a way to replenish the population of baby turtles. You believe wildlife belongs to the public.

Wants:
Beach in natural condition
Compliance by poacher
Turtle eggs

Country: Pargimo

Law officer

You are required to arrest poachers and traders of turtles or turtle products. Your position is difficult because you personally know the families that are trying to subsist through this illegal activity. You believe wildlife should be available for public taking, and you wish you did not have to arrest poachers.

Wants:
Compliance by poacher
Compliance by trader
Compliance by ceremonial sea turtle buyer

Scenario Cards

Country: The Republic of United Peoples

CITES organization head stationed in Pargimo

You are trying to ensure that the agreements of CITES are being enforced. You are well connected to government and environmental organizations in your country, and are willing to help anyone achieve recognition who facilitates compliance with CITES regulations.

Wants:
Compliance by poacher
Compliance by trader
Compliance by ceremonial sea turtle buyer

Country: The Republic of United Peoples

Sea turtle advocate

You are an advocate for the protection of endangered and threatened species. You would like to see the coastal areas left in a natural state and the citizens respecting the new laws to protect the turtles. You are well financed.

Wants:
Beach in natural condition
Compliance by poacher
Compliance by trader
Compliance by ceremonial sea turtle buyer

Country: The Republic of United Peoples

Wealthy developer

Because of increased demands for isolated vacation sites, your company plans to buy land on the southeast coast of Pargimo—natural areas that are prime sea turtle egg laying habitat. You plan to develop the area by building a hotel/lodge and to make a profit for the company and its investors.

Wants:
Money
Land
Land development permit

Country: The Republic of United Peoples

Entrepreneur

You would like to make a fresh start and move to Pargimo. The business you would like to develop is a turtle farm. Most of the turtles raised on the farm will be sold to local companies, although a set number of turtles can be donated to natural resource agencies each year if needed to maintain populations. You need a loan to begin the business.

Wants:
Start-up funds
Business operating license
Hotel

Country: The Republic of United Peoples

Tourist

You are looking for rare items (food and jewelry) to buy. You also need some experimental medicines not found in the RUP. On future trips, you would like to find a safe, comfortable hotel for your family to "get away from it all." You would also like to find out about local natural features for this next trip.

Wants:
Food   Jewelry
Medicine   Safety
Information on natural features

Country: The Republic of United Peoples

Owner of pharmaceutical company

Your company makes medicines, but the high cost of labor in the RUP is forcing you to move to Pargimo, where salaries are lower. It would also be closer to a source of turtle eggs, which contain chemicals that are ingredients in some medicines.

Wants:
Money
Turtle eggs
Business operating license

Haves Cards

To begin, distribute these cards to the students representing the character typed in bold on the card. Most characters will get several cards. Characters receiving Haves Cards will provide these cards to other characters who request them during the activity, as long as the trading conditions (as described in italics) are first met. Haves Cards are exchanged simply through one character asking another. No direct trading is required. The first card in the set of Haves Cards below is a sample.

Country: Chumas/Pargimo or The Republic of UP **(Title) The person holding the Scenario Card matching this job title should receive this card.** (Want) A listing of what the holder of the card is giving away. *(Restrictions) Conditions that must be met before the card can be given away.*	Country: Pargimo **Collector of turtles (poacher)** Compliance to laws *May not be given until you've received a job.*
Country: Chumas **Sea turtle jewelry dealer** Jewelry *May not be sold until you've received turtles.*	Country: Chumas **Restaurant owner** Food *May not be sold until you've received turtles.*
Country: Chumas **Turtle trader** Compliance to laws *May not be given until you've received a job.*	Country: Chumas **Ceremonial sea turtle buyer** Compliance to laws *May not be given until you've received a job.*
Country: Chumas **Turtle trader** Compliance to laws *May not be given until you've received a job.*	Country: Chumas **Ceremonial sea turtle buyer** Compliance to laws *May not be given until you've received a job.*
Country: Chumas **Turtle trader** Compliance to laws *May not be given until you've received a job.*	Country: Chumas **Ceremonial sea turtle buyer** Compliance to laws *May not be given until you've received a job.*
Country: Chumas **Turtle egg trader** Compliance to laws *May not be given until you've received a job.*	Country: Chumas **Turtle egg trader** Compliance to laws *May not be given until you've received a job.*
Country: Chumas **Turtle egg trader** Compliance to laws *May not be given until you've received a job.*	Country: Pargimo **Landowner** Beach in natural condition *May not be given until shown a judicial order setting aside this land.*
Country: Pargimo **Landowner** Land *May not sell until notified that developer has received a land development permit.*	Country: Pargimo **Landowner** Beach in natural condition *May not be given until shown a judicial order setting aside this land.*

Country: Pargimo **Judge** Judicial order (to set aside habitat) *Will not be issued until you've received professional recognition from CITES.*	Country: The Republic of United Peoples **Wealthy developer** Hotel *May not be given until a land development permit is received.*
Country: Pargimo **Collector of turtles (poacher)** Compliance to laws *May not be given until you've received a job.*	Country: Pargimo **Collector of turtle eggs (poacher)** Compliance to laws *May not be given until you've received a job.*
Country: Pargimo **Collector of turtles (poacher)** Compliance to laws *May not be given until you've received a job.*	Country: Pargimo **Collector of turtle eggs (poacher)** Compliance to laws *May not be given until you've received a job.*
Country: Pargimo **Collector of turtles (poacher)** Compliance to laws *May not be given until you've received a job.*	Country: Pargimo **Collector of turtle eggs (poacher)** Compliance to laws *May not be given until you've received a job.*
Country: Pargimo **Wildlife biologist and manager** Information *May be given at any time.*	Country: Pargimo **Collector of turtle eggs (poacher)** Compliance to laws *May not be given until you've received a job.*
Country: Pargimo **Government bureaucrat** Land development permit *Cannot be given until a judicial order is received.*	Country: Pargimo **Law enforcement officer** Safety *May be given at any time.*
Country: Pargimo **Government bureaucrat** Business operating license *May be given at any time.*	Country: Pargimo **Government bureaucrat** Business operating license *May be given at any time.*
Country: The Republic of United Peoples **CITES organization head stationed in Pargimo** Professional recognition *May be given at any time.*	Country: The Republic of United Peoples **Sea turtle advocate** Start-up funds *May be given at any time.*
Country: The Republic of United Peoples **Wealthy developer** Capital investment funds *May be given at any time.*	Country: The Republic of United Peoples **Entrepreneur** Job *May not be given until start-up funds and business operating license are received.*

Haves Cards

Country: The Republic of United Peoples **Entrepreneur** Job *May not be given until start-up funds and business operating license are received.*	Country: The Republic of United Peoples **Owner of pharmaceutical company** Medicine *May not be filled until business operating license and turtle eggs are received.*
Country: The Republic of United Peoples **Entrepreneur** Turtles *May not be given until start-up funds and business operating license are received.*	Country: The Republic of United Peoples **Entrepreneur** Turtles *May not be given until start-up funds and business operating license are received.*
Country: The Republic of United Peoples **Entrepreneur** Turtles *May not be given until start-up funds and business operating license are received.*	Country: The Republic of United Peoples **Entrepreneur** Turtle eggs *May not be given until start-up funds and business operating license are received.*
Country: The Republic of United Peoples **Entrepreneur** Turtle eggs *May not be given until start-up funds and business operating license are received.*	Country: The Republic of United Peoples **Entrepreneur** Turtle eggs *May not be given until start-up funds and business operating license are received.*
Country: The Republic of United Peoples **Tourist** Money *To be exchanged directly for item on "Wants" list only.*	Country: The Republic of United Peoples **Tourist** Money *To be exchanged directly for item on "Wants" list only.*
Country: The Republic of United Peoples **Tourist** Money *To be exchanged directly for item on "Wants" list only.*	Country: The Republic of United Peoples **Tourist** Money *To be exchanged directly for item on "Wants" list only.*
Country: The Republic of United Peoples **Owner of pharmaceutical company** Job *May not be filled until business operating license and turtle eggs are received.*	Country: The Republic of United Peoples **Owner of pharmaceutical company** Job *May not be filled until business operating license and turtle eggs are received.*

Sustaining Fish and Wildlife Resources

The activities in this section are designed to encourage students to recognize, evaluate, and make responsible choices in their own lives regarding natural resources while reflecting on the knowledge and skills they have acquired in earlier activities. There are five areas of study: (1) attitudes and awareness, including human perspectives and values; (2) human impacts, both positive and negative; (3) issues and trends in global perspectives, land use, consumptive and nonconsumptive uses of wildlife, and wildlife populations; (4) wildlife management, addressing basic concepts related to management considerations and practices; and (5) responsible action and service, focusing on how students and others can take action on behalf of wildlife and the environment.

Water Wings

Grade Level: Upper Elementary, Middle School

Content Areas:
Environmental Education, Expressive Arts, Language Arts

Method: Students will visualize a simulated field trip and then create artwork and poetry.

Materials: Music, water sounds, or "ecosystem" recordings of an aquatic habitat; art materials (water-based paints such as acrylics, water color, or poster paints; brushes, paper, containers for water); writing materials

Activity Time:
one or two 30- to 60-minute sessions

People Power:
any

Setting:
indoors, outdoors for first part of activity if site is available

Conceptual Framework Topic Reference:
AAIA

Terms to Know:
water cycle, planet, ocean, precipitation, condensation, evaporation, transpiration, groundwater, watershed

Imagine where water can take you.

Objectives

Students will (1) illustrate the water cycle; (2) describe the interrelatedness of the world's waters; and (3) state the importance of water to people, plants, and animals.

Background

There is, in a sense, only one body of water on Earth. Its rivers reach out in sinuous paths from the hearts of every continent. All water, everywhere, is somehow connected. Almost everyone can easily see and sometimes physically touch this universal body of water in some form—perhaps by turning on a water faucet or by looking at clouds moving high in the sky. Lakes, ponds, and inland seas are webbed together by waters flowing across the surface of the land or in the seeping flow of groundwater. The continuous circulation of water through evaporation, transpiration, condensation, precipitation, and runoff is called the water cycle. The concept of the water cycle is a way to view the moving connectedness of water in its many forms (see figure on the next page).

People seldom think of the waters of the world as being connected into one body. Maps emphasize the continents and political boundaries on land. Geographers have named dozens of seas, which in reality cannot be delineated from each other—similar to the way that territorial boundaries on land tend to be more political than geographical.

Human beings are linked to the planet's watery world. Our bodies are approximately 60–70 percent water. Each molecule within us has been part of the oceanic realm in times past. Molecules of our bodies' water may have flowed in streams, lofted in air, or been locked in glacial ice. Other animals and plants are also tied to the planet's waters—directly and indirectly. Plants are an especially active part of the water cycle in many ways, including transpiration (a process by which plants lose moisture through their leaves by evaporation). Living things are partly made of water; all life depends on water in some way.

The Water Cycle

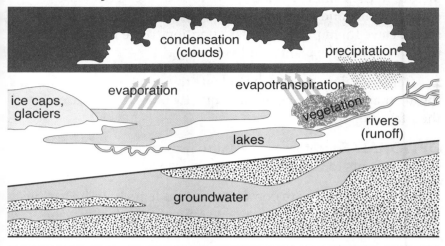

condensation (clouds) · **precipitation** · **evaporation** · **evapotranspiration** · **vegetation** · **ice caps, glaciers** · **lakes** · **rivers (runoff)** · **groundwater**

There is, in a sense, only one body of water on Earth. Its rivers reach out in sinuous paths from the hearts of every continent. All water, everywhere, is somehow connected.

Procedure

1. If at all possible, students should visit a real stream, pond, lake, river, or beach. Try to choose a location where human-made sounds are minimized. If possible and not dangerous, allow students to touch water during the simulated field trip portion of this activity. Consider taking a device on the field trip to record some of the natural sounds students experience so you can later play it back in the classroom.

If the outdoor field trip is not possible, try to use recordings of natural ecosystems. The sounds of oceans, rivers, streams, swamps, or brooks are often available through smartphone applications or online bookstores, music stores, and shops that specialize in nature. A number of selections of contemporary music are excellent. You can also make your own recordings.

2. Ask students to sit or rest quietly in a comfortable position. If water is available, invite students to relax and listen carefully to the water. If not, play recordings. These sounds are simply background for the ideas you are going to ask them to visualize in their minds. Read the "Simulated Field Trip" at the end of this activity.

NOTE: Educators may want to modify the water images in the simulated field trip text for local regions.

3. Once the visualization is complete, ask students to open their eyes. Explain that each student had his or her own private journey even though all students heard the same words. Explain that in a moment you will ask them to close their eyes again and find one place on the journey through the world's waters that was their favorite—and you will ask them to try to remember what that picture was like.

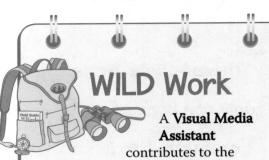

WILD Work

A **Visual Media Assistant** contributes to the development of visual media projects, such as those at a national park. He or she is responsible for filming, editing, and preparing video; recording, editing, and preparing audio for short movies to be used online and in programs for the public; digital design for print projects such as brochures, posters, and flyers; and photographing, editing, and preparing images for use in print and web media. Education requirements often include one year of graduate study in the field of fine arts, art history, visual communication, or a related field. To find more information on this occupation, visit *www.projectwild.org/aquatic*.

In Step with STEM

To expand students' understanding of the water cycle and systems models, construct open system and closed system models of the water cycle. For an open system, materials can include a heat source, frying pans, heat-resistant gloves, ice, and water. For a closed system, materials can include large plastic or glass jars with tops, duct tape, sand, water, and rocks. This activity is adapted from "Water Models" in the *WET in the City Curriculum and Activity Guide*, © Council for Environmental Education.

4. Ask them to relax again and have them try to recreate the picture in their minds. Tell them to look at the detail—the colors, plants, and animals—and to try to capture it all in one scene. Have them pay particular attention to the role of water in the lives of people, plants, and animals.

5. After several minutes, ask students to open their eyes. Provide the art materials and ask them to quietly paint the picture of their favorite place.

OPTIONAL: Educators may want to provide an opportunity for some students to talk briefly about their favorite places.

6. Once the pictures are complete, ask students to write various short forms of poetry that express some of their feelings about water and its importance. Here are a few examples of poetic forms that can be used.

Haiku: Haiku, a Japanese lyric verse form having three unrhymed lines of five, seven, and five syllables, traditionally invokes an aspect of nature or the seasons. Traditionally and ideally, a haiku presents a pair of contrasting images: one suggestive of time and place, the other a vivid but fleeting observation. Working together, they evoke mood and emotion. The emphasis is syllabic, not rhyming. For example,

> The fish swam by me
> Nothing left in the shimmer
> My heart beat faster

Cinquain: The word "cinquain" is derived from the French and Spanish words for five. The cinquain is a poetic form, originated by the American poet Adelaide Crapsey (1878–1914), comprising five unrhyming lines of, respectively, two, four, six, eight, and two syllables. Each line has a mandatory purpose and number of syllables or words. These are (1) the title in two syllables (or words); (2) a description of the title in four syllables (or words); (3) a description of action in six syllables (or words); (4) a description of a feeling in eight syllables (or words); and (5) another word for the title in two syllables (or words). Here are two examples, the first using syllables and the second using words:

> **Osprey**
> Fishing eagle
> Moves above dark water
> With graceful strength it finds its meal
> Seeker

> **Sea Otter**
> Mammal of living waters
> Swimming, sleeping, eating, diving, basking, playing
> Sensitive indicator of the quality of continuing life
> Still here

Diamante: Diamante is a poem shaped in the form of a diamond. It can be used to show that words are related through shades of meaning from one extreme to an opposite extreme, following a pattern of parts of speech like this:

noun
adjective adjective
participle participle participle
noun noun noun noun
participle participle participle
adjective adjective
noun

For example,

Stream
Small, clear
Rippling, moving, growing
Life, plants, animals, people
Rushing, sustaining, cleansing
Connected, universal
Ocean

Free verse: Free verse is poetry in which the author is free to invent its form. It may or may not rhyme. For example:

Water strider
I watch you stand on glass
that bursts apart to my gentlest touch.
You dash, you dart and exhaust the eyes
that try to follow.
I think you are teaching me something
I will know
on some day like this—
but in a time long after
you are gone.

OPTIONAL: Display the pictures and poetry in a circle around a world map. With yarn, connect the pictures that students painted of their favorite places to the sites where they appear on the map.

7. Discuss the "one body of water" metaphor. Emphasize the concept that all the waters of the world are interrelated and connected. Help students see that the atmosphere is also part of that connection. It is the atmosphere that carries water back to the rivers from the sea. Point out that a watershed is an area of land that catches precipitation and drains the water to a particular river or lake. Talk about the importance of water to people, plants, and animals.

8. End the activity with a description of the water cycle. Ask students to describe how their favorite places, which they illustrated in their paintings, are a part of the water cycle.

Plants are an especially active part of the water cycle in many ways, including transpiration (a process by which plants lose moisture through their leaves by evaporation). Living things are partly made of water; all life depends on water in some way.

OSPREY

Human beings are linked to the planet's watery world. Our bodies are approximately 60–70 percent water. Each molecule within us has been part of the oceanic realm in times past. Molecules of our bodies' water may have flowed in streams, lofted in air, or been locked in glacial ice.

You might want to point out that the water they used in their paintings has evaporated from the pictures and is back in the water cycle again!

Extensions

1. Find out the annual rainfall and climate in the area that you chose to paint.

2. Trace the migratory path of a salmon, tuna, or whale. Describe its water journey and the water environment it is dependent upon.

3. Choose a body of freshwater near you and trace its path to the sea.

Evaluation

1. Describe the water cycle. Illustrate your description.

2. Describe how all of Earth's water is connected and interrelated.

3. List at least ten ways you use water every day.

4. Describe a world without water.

5. Draw a picture showing how one drop of water can connect with a whale, a school, and a cactus.

Water Wings

Simulated Field Trip

"Try to imagine the things you will hear me describing. Sit comfortably and close your eyes…. Relax, and do your best to picture what I am describing…. You are sitting on the edge of a stream (lake, ocean, etc.)…. Your bare feet are swinging in clean, clear water…. The water feels good, but it is cool…. You feel a current washing over your feet, pulling at them…. Think about the water flowing past your feet until it reaches a larger stream…. The water connects you with the larger stream…. Feel its more powerful flow…. See the green ribbon of trees and plant life on the banks…. The larger stream carries the water past flat farmlands, cities, factories, and forests until it eventually reaches the sea…. Through your feet and the continuous currents of water you can sense the sea…. Now stretch your mind and realize that you interconnect with all the world's oceans…. You are now touching one single body of water that stretches all around the world…. Your own body contains water that is part of this system…. Your water laps against the shores of the Pacific Ocean; it flows under the Golden Gate Bridge in San Francisco Bay; it leaps and plunges around oil drilling platforms in the North Atlantic…. It pours from the sky as a storm rages, dark and gray…. It drenches an Alaskan native who shivers on the Arctic shores before her parka begins to warm her. It glistens on the back of a Greek boy who tugs fiercely on fishing nets in the warm Mediterranean Sea…. Water connects your feet with every stream flowing into the oceans around the world…. You can reach up the rivers to the hearts of continents…. You can feel the tremor of the hippopotamus that just dove into an African river…. You can feel an alligator

Holgate Beach, New Jersey

Colorado River,
Grand Canyon National Park

silently sliding toward a heron in the Florida Everglades…. You can feel beavers busily building a dam on a stream in Europe…. You can see water, thousands of tons of it, in great drifting fleets of heavy white clouds…. Your reach embraces all the whales, all the porpoises, all the sharks…. You are connected with the mythical creatures that live only in the minds of people in the past—mermaids, citizens of Atlantis, and the mythical monsters that swim in Loch Ness…. Your feet feel the flow of the current of the miles-wide Amazon River in South America, the ancient Nile River pushing north through Africa, the Colorado River thundering with a boatful of river rafters through the Grand Canyon…. Your watery embrace wraps all around the Earth…. And, of course, the water flowing over your feet connects you with everyone else who is now sitting, with feet dangling in a stream, wondering where the water goes…. It is time to come back…. Bring the limits of your senses back from the world's rivers and oceans…. back to the surfaces of your feet…. back to where you are…. When you feel ready, you may open your eyes."

Puddle Wonders

Field Investigation

Grade Level: Middle School

Content Areas: Mathematics, Science, Environmental Education, Language Arts

Method: Students measure and record the depth, area, and volume of puddles; look for evidence of wildlife using the puddles; and graph and interpret data.

Materials: pencils; science notebooks; one copy per student of: *What's My Question* (page 388), *Conclusions and Next Steps* (page 389), and *Puddle Wonders Data Sheet* (page 174); measuring instruments (yardsticks, meter sticks, or tape measures); string (for making measurements); map of the school/study site (or students can make a map of the site). **OPTIONAL:** digital cameras; hand lenses

Activity Time: three 30- to 45-minute sessions

People Power: small groups of three to five

Setting: outdoor study site (ideally before and after a rainstorm) and indoors

Conceptual Framework Topic Reference: AAIA

Terms to Know: puddle, runoff, vernal pool, wildlife, area, depth, volume

Appendices: Inventory Methods, Field Ethics, Metric Conversion Chart

Be careful stomping in that puddle; it's a habitat!

Objectives

Students will (1) predict where and why puddles will form, (2) observe and describe organisms that live in or near puddles, (3) measure and record the amount of water in puddles, and (4) make inferences about what types of organisms occupy puddles.

Study Site

Determine where you will conduct this field investigation activity. In many cases, an outdoor school site will work because students are investigating puddles that form after a rain. If the school site is not appropriate, arrange for permission to use a nearby site. In arid areas, small puddles may be created using buckets or water hoses. Outdoor areas with temporary pools or retention ponds that fill during rainfall are also ideal.

Background

When water flows down a hill, it sometimes stops flowing and collects in a puddle, pool, or pond. Puddles form in low spots or depressions in the land's surface. Depending on the size of the puddle, water may be trapped for some time. If puddles or small pools last for several days, there is a strong possibility they will be visited by wildlife.

Vernal pools—which are isolated and temporary puddles or ponds—can provide essential habitat for certain animals. One-celled animals, aquatic insects, and amphibians may use temporary puddles and ponds for reproduction. The eggs and larvae of these species must be capable of developing rapidly and must be ready to move onto land before the pool of water dries up.

The spadefoot toad is one example of a species that goes through rapid development to cope with the short life span of puddles. Spadefoot toads spend most of their adult lives underground, thus requiring access to soil they can burrow into. They emerge at night during warm weather to feed on insects and other invertebrates. In extreme cold or hot weather, these toads stay hidden. Immediately after the first heavy rains of summer, spadefoots emerge to mate. The female lays between 300 and 500 eggs in temporary puddles and ponds. The male goes into the puddle or pond and externally fertilizes the eggs. The eggs hatch and the tadpoles complete their development over 10 to 12 days before the water dries up.

Salamanders also rely on temporary puddles and ponds for reproduction. They spend most of their lives in burrows and under rocks on the forest floor and nearby streams. Mole Salamanders are one species that gather in vernal pools after early spring rains for mating and laying eggs. The eggs develop in the pool, and by the time the pool dries up, the young have emerged to begin their lives as terrestrial animals.

Many species of flying insects—such as butterflies, wasps, and flies—visit puddles. They sip the water on the banks of the puddles where they can get salts and other vital minerals from the mud. Some species of swallows and mud dauber wasps visit puddles for mud-building materials for their nests. Other animals may visit the puddle to bathe or drink.

An advantage of temporary pools is that many species that prey on amphibians or compete with them for food cannot live in this type of habitat. Predators such as fish cannot survive in temporary puddles or ponds because of the periodic drying.

Aquatic biologists study the life forms in ponds, vernal pools, and lakes. Students examining puddles can replicate some techniques these biologists use. Simple observations and measurements can determine size, depth, volume, cause of accumulation, and identity of transient animal life.

Introducing the Field Investigation

1. Begin with a discussion about rainfall and runoff. How much annual rainfall does your region receive? Do students know what runoff is? (Runoff is water that drains or flows off the surface of the land.) When it rains, do students know where the water around their school or home goes? Tell students that the class will be conducting a field investigation to study the smallest body of water formed as rainwater flows across the land—the puddle! Explain that puddles form when water ceases to run off a surface.

2. Tell students about the study site—location, description, etc. Show students an aerial photograph (available on sites such as Google Maps or Google Earth) and/or map of the area. Have students prepare a simple base map of their site in their science notebooks (see Guidelines for Mapping in the "Aquatic WILD Field Investigations" portion of this guide).

Questions to Investigate

Questions could include . . .

- Where and how many puddles will form on the study site after a rainfall?

- What will be the size (area and volume) of the puddles or pools?

- What natural features will cause puddles to form (slope of the land, depressions in the ground, lack of plants, etc.)?

- How do humans contribute to puddle formations (downspouts from buildings, grading the land, removing or adding plants/grass, erosion, etc.)?

- What animal life is found on the study site before the rainstorm compared to after the rainstorm?

- What transient animal life will be found in and near the puddles? (See background information.)

If puddles or small pools last for several days, there is a strong possibility they will be visited by wildlife.

3. Discuss the importance of investigating water at the study site. What do students think they can learn by studying puddles? How could knowledge about the flow and accumulation of water at the site enable students to better understand the ecosystem? What wildlife (animals and insects) do students predict would use puddles or temporary pools on the site after a rain? How would those species benefit from the puddle or pool? Have students record their predictions in their science notebooks.

4. Discuss good field ethics the students should model during the field investigation; for example, they should disturb the area as little as possible and try not to harm any animals (see "Aquatic WILD Field Investigations" [page xiv] and "Field Ethics" [page 354] for more information). Also discuss safety concerns—keeping within the study site, staying out of deep water, and avoiding poisonous plants and animals.

Forming the Question

1. Before a rainstorm, take students to the study site with their science notebooks, pencils, map (or paper for mapping the site), and digital cameras (optional). Students should spend some time looking for animals and signs of them. Look for birds, insects, mammals, worms, amphibians, reptiles, and other organisms. Ask students to look beyond direct observation and to find indirect evidence of wildlife, such as tracks, scat (droppings), slug trails, feathers, nests, ant hills, and eggs. They should also note on their maps where they think puddles or small pools will form. Keep the maps and wildlife lists for later use following the rainstorm. Students may want to photograph evidence of wildlife and locations where water might accumulate. Ask students what they observed, and get them thinking about researchable questions by brainstorming a list of observable/measureable variables that could be recorded at the sites.

2. Ask students what researchable questions they might be able to answer by observing, taking measurements of, and collecting data about puddles and pools. Divide the class into teams of three to five students. Have teams brainstorm ideas and then come back together to compare notes. Students should write several field investigation questions in their science notebooks. See "Questions to Investigate" in the sidebar for potential student questions.

3. Back in the classroom, discuss students' questions. What type of observations will students need to make in order to answer the questions? Help students refine their questions to ensure the investigative questions are researchable—that is, questions students can answer based on their own observations at the site. Students can record their questions on the *What's My Question?* page. Select a question for students to investigate or allow students to choose an appropriate, researchable question.

Conducting the Field Investigation

1. Discuss with students the best way to gather data. What attributes or characteristics at the study site will they need to measure? How will measurements be taken and recorded? Why is it important for all students to take measurements the same way? Similarly, why is it important to take measurements the same way when collecting data at different times or locations? Are all of the data collection methods safe?

2. Have students write a plan for conducting the investigation, including:

    a) A prediction or hypothesis about what they will find or how their question will be answered;

    b) Materials they will need to conduct the investigation; and

    c) Each step they will take, with enough detail so others could read the steps to conduct the same experiment.

3. Review with students the *Puddle Wonders Data Sheet*. They will need one data sheet for each puddle they observe. You may want to work with students to customize a data sheet based on their research question(s). Make sure there is space to record any other pertinent data that will help address their investigative question(s).

4. After a big rainstorm, gather materials and send teams outside to the study site to make observations, take measurements, and record data on their *Puddle Wonders Data Sheet*, in their science notebooks, and on their maps of the site. Teams will be comparing data, so it is helpful for all teams to take all the measurements and record their own observations. Start by having students record data for the study site in its entirety. Have teams map the location and approximate dimensions of each puddle or pool. Student teams should make a comprehensive list of all animals seen on the site and in or near the puddles or pools. Students may want to take photographs of puddle locations and wildlife observed.

5. Students should then be assigned one or more puddles or pools for their teams to study closely. Data to be recorded by individual teams include the measurements of the puddles or pools, observations of any associated wildlife, and any other measurable variables you have identified in your discussions. For observing wildlife, consider how to maximize observations by watching puddles or pools from a distance, watching through a window, or sitting still and quietly for extended time at a site so as not to scare away animals. Students should use one *Puddle Wonders Data Sheet* for each puddle observed.

Vernal pools—which are isolated and temporary puddles or ponds—can provide essential habitat for certain animals. One-celled animals, aquatic insects, frogs, and salamanders may use temporary puddles and ponds for reproduction.

6. Explain to students how to find the area, volume, and depth of the puddles and pools. Diagrams A and B show students how to calculate the area of a puddle. Although pools may be more difficult to measure due to their size, students may be able to estimate the radius or determine the circumference of pools by taking measurements along the edges. (Note: the radius of a circle can be determined by the formula $r = c \div 2\Pi$, in which c is the circumference).

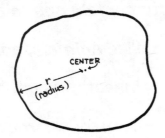

Diagram A

Round Puddles
Area = $\Pi r2$
(Π = 3.14; it is a mathematical constant)
Area = 3.14 x r x r

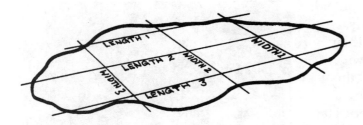

Diagram B

Oval puddles
Area = Length (average) x Width (average)
Average Length (La) = $\dfrac{L1 + L2 + L3}{3}$ (a= average)

(3 is the number of measurements)

Average Width (Wa) = $\dfrac{W1 + W2 + W3}{3}$

Area = La x Wa

Students should determine the volume of water in the puddles. Before that number can be calculated, the average depth of the puddle must be measured. There are many ways to determine the average depth. Either of two methods shown can be used:

Method 1 (Diagram C)

- Establish a grid on the surface of the puddle (lengths of string tied to rocks or nails pushed into the soil to anchor the strings).

- Measure the depth at every place the strings cross (see the small arrows on the drawing).

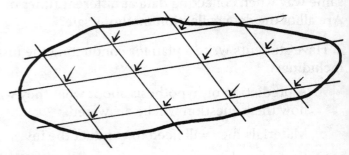

Diagram C

Method 2 (Diagram D)

- Imagine a grid on the surface of the puddle. This approach can be used for puddles on concrete, stone, brick, or other surfaces that are too hard for nails to penetrate.

- Measure the depth every place the imaginary lines come together.

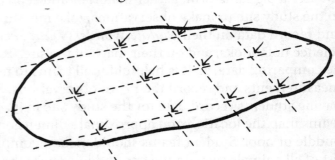

Diagram D

Use the following formula for average depth (Da). There are ten measurements of depth shown in the example above.

Da (average) =
$\dfrac{D1 + D2 + D3 + D4 + D5 + D6 + D7 + D8 + D9 + D10}{10 \text{ (the number of measurements)}}$

Now the volume can be calculated:

Volume = La x Wa x Da

7. Once all the measurements have been taken for each puddle—or during the time while at a puddle—students should make observations about wildlife. Each team should list any species of animal for which there is direct or indirect evidence of using the puddle in some way. Written observations in their notebooks should include:

- species name or description of species if name is unknown
- evidence
- apparent uses of puddle by species
- estimated number of animals of each species using the puddle

Organizing and Analyzing the Data

In the classroom, ask each team to report back to the other teams and discuss their observations. If possible, students can enter data into a spreadsheet program to help them analyze their findings. Teams should organize, analyze, and present their results in graphic and/or written reports, using tools such as charts, bar graphs, and maps. Consider having students use presentation software to develop their reports.

Drawing Conclusions

1. Discuss conclusions and questions that can be derived from the data. Students can complete the *Conclusions and Next Steps* page.

- Review similarities and differences in the teams' findings. Have students discuss why these differences might exist. What conclusions can students draw about the accuracy of their findings?

- Discuss with students how their early predictions about the puddles and wildlife compare with their actual findings.

- Ask students if the data summaries answer their investigative questions. Which particular observations were most useful? What other data might they have collected?

- What additional research questions do students have? (Their additional questions could lead to further comparative and correlative field investigations.)

2. If students did not include the following points in their conclusions, review them so they will understand the critical role of puddles and vernal pools to many species of wildlife:

- Puddles provide essential water for wildlife, including birds, small mammals, toads, frogs, salamanders, and butterflies and other insects.

WILD Work

Field Biologists study animals to determine what they need to survive and factors that affect them. For example, they might study how drought could affect animals that depend on puddles for part of their life cycle or try to predict the effects of global climate change on habitat.

Civil Engineers design drainage systems, bridges, roads, and sidewalks. Without them, you would be walking in and driving through puddles! For more information on these occupations, see *www.projectwild.org/aquatic*.

In Step with STEM

Frog Populations

- Ask students if any puddles are located in places that are undesirable—for example, where students walk to get into school. Can they think of designs/actions that could alleviate the problem, such as filling in depressions, creating better drainage systems, fixing slanted sidewalks, moving downspouts, or collecting rainwater from roofs into a rain barrel?

- Students can use an electronic level to predict where puddles will form. Laser distance sensors can be used to measure distances across larger pools.

- Students can contact a landscape architect for tips on designing vernal pools to enhance habitat for wildlife at your school or site.

Many species of flying insects—such as butterflies, wasps, and flies—visit puddles. They sip the water on the banks of the puddles where they can get salts and other vital minerals from the mud. Some species of swallows and mud dauber wasps visit puddles for mud building materials for their nests.

■ Vernal pools are critical to the lifecycle of many species; for example, frogs and salamanders may rely on these temporary, oversized puddles for breeding.

■ Wildlife, such as birds and squirrels, use puddles for drinking water.

■ Many species of butterflies and other flying insects depend on the mud around puddles to obtain essential nutrients.

■ Some species of swallows and mud dauber wasps gather mud from puddles to build their nests.

■ Some animals, such as turtles, snails, and snakes, feed on microorganisms, vegetation, insects, and small animals that are found in or near puddles and vernal pools.

Students should now have a clear understanding of what causes puddles to form, how to measure them, the importance of puddles and vernal pools to wildlife, and the inherently fascinating nature of the under-appreciated puddle!

Extensions

1. Keep a record of these areas of water accumulation over the seasons. What similarities occur? What differences? Ask students to calculate how much water is "caught" each year by the puddle they studied.

2. Biologists sometimes need to know where a pond is shallow and where it is deep. They use the same grid work approach used in the procedures above; the difference is that they keep a record of the change in depth along a straight line (see Diagram E).

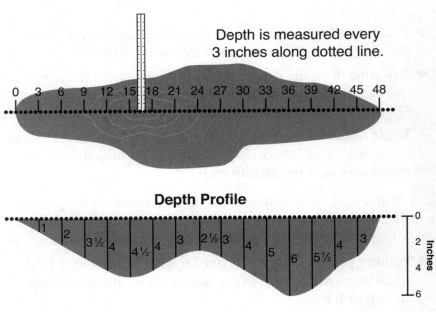

Diagram E

Puddle Wonders
© *Council for Environmental Education (CEE)*

A good approximation of the shape of the puddle bottom can be achieved when this procedure is accomplished on all the lines. How can knowledge of underwater terrain benefit efforts to manage wildlife species?

3. Conduct the "Puddle Wonders!" activity using both English and metric measurements.

Evaluation

1. Describe common characteristics of animals that use puddles. Explain the value of puddles to these animals.

2. What conclusions can you make in response to the field investigation question(s)?

3. How would you determine the amount of water in a puddle? Explain your method.

4. Why are vernal pools essential to many species of wildlife?

An advantage of temporary pools is that many species that prey on amphibians or compete with them for food cannot live in this type of habitat. Predators such as fish cannot survive in temporary puddles or pools because of periodic drying.

Puddle Wonders
Aquatic WILD K–12 Curriculum and Activity Guide

Puddle Wonders Data Sheet

Date: _____   **Time:** _____   **Puddle Number:** _____

Study Site Location: _____

Team Members: _____

I. Puddle Data: Sketch the puddle, record puddle measurements including units, and show calculations in the boxes below.

Sketch a Puddle:	Circumference:	Length:
	Radius:	Width:
	Area:	
	Depth:	
	Volume:	

What caused the puddle to form?

Other interesting observations and findings:

II. Wildlife Data: Note species name, signs of use, and how wildlife is using the puddle. Estimate the number of each species. Look for small organisms, birds, worms, mammals, insects, reptiles, and amphibians. If you're not sure what it is, sketch it!

Riparian Retreat

Did you know as you ramble along a river that you're experiencing a riparian zone?

Objectives

Students will (1) describe habitat characteristics of riparian areas, (2) identify animals that inhabit them, and (3) state the importance of riparian areas to wildlife and humans.

Background

Riparian zones are the green ribbons of life found on the edges of waterways (streams, lakes, ponds, etc.). Riparian areas or zones are important and valuable in many ways, including hosting whole communities of life. Conditions within the zones support plant communities that grow best when their root systems are near the level of high groundwater. These zones range in width from narrow strips in desert and mountain settings to wide bands on the plains and lowlands. Riparian areas provide space, shelter, and food for the plant and animal communities with which they are associated. For example, leaf litter and terrestrial insects that fall from vegetation into a stream are a source of detritus, providing nourishment for some aquatic life. Vegetation may also provide shade from the sun for aquatic plants and animals and land-dwelling creatures at the water's edge.

Riparian areas are also transportation corridors for animals that depend on waterways for food and shelter. The riparian plant community, especially shrubs and trees, provides shelter and food for many animals. Trees and marshy areas provide shelter for nesting birds, and the banks provide homes for burrowing animals.

The riparian zone may serve as a buffer between the uplands and the water. For example, rain falling on uplands and flowing downhill can be cleansed as it flows through a riparian zone. The banks of riparian areas store water during periods of high flow such as rainstorms or snow melt and release this water to the stream during low-flow times.

Grade Level:
Upper Elementary

Content Areas:
Art, Language Arts, Environmental Education

Method:
Awareness of a riparian zone is created through the use of a simulated field trip and artwork.

Materials:
Art materials: water colors, acrylics, poster paints, crayons

Activity Time:
one 30- to 45-minute session

People Power:
any

Setting:
outdoors or indoors

Conceptual Framework Topic Reference:
AAIA, AAIB, AAIIA

Terms to Know:
riparian, ecology, habitat, value, buffer

Appendix: The Ecosystem and Project WILD

WILD Work

A **Corporate Land Manager** is responsible for the overall operation of all corporate lands, including wetland and riparian areas. Responsibilities include meeting conservation goals by ensuring suitable habitat, providing recreation opportunities for visitors as permitted, and working with community groups to influence land use and policy decisions that might affect wetlands and wildlife. Education requirements typically include a graduate degree in natural resources, land planning, landscape design, or outdoor recreation management. Land managers work outdoors, as well as in an office environment. To find out more, visit *www.projectwild.org/aquatic.*

In Step with STEM

■ To extend a connection to the life sciences and biology, consider conducting this activity as a preliminary exercise to the "Blue Ribbon Niche" activity, which asks students to catalogue and evaluate niche and habitat characteristics of a particular riparian zone.

■ Visit *www.projectwild.org/aquatic* for links to smartphone Apps to aid in researching animals found in riparian zones. Monitor and report data on species in your area that live near or migrate to a local stream or waterbody.

Riparian vegetation also strengthens stream banks. This tends to prevent erosion and maintains the stream channel, helping to keep the water clear.

Riparian areas have aesthetic and recreational values for humans. They are used for fishing, hiking, camping, picnicking, and resting.

Procedure

1. Ask students if they have been to a stream or riverbank. What was it like? Were plants growing there? What did the area look like? Was it hot or cool? Encourage students to talk about and share descriptions of any area by a stream or riverbank they may have been to or have seen on TV or in pictures.

2. Next, tell students that the kind of area they have been describing has a special name: "riparian area." Riparian areas are important natural areas for people and wildlife. Invite students to get in a comfortable position, close their eyes, and do their best to picture what they hear.

3. Read aloud to students the *Simulated Field Trip* that begins on page 178. Consider playing a recording of flowing water (for instance, a stream) in the background to enhance students' experience of the field trip.

4. Ask students to continue to sit quietly with their eyes closed and to remember what the area looked like, how it smelled, how it sounded, and what they did there. Have them pay particular attention to their favorite images. Tell them they will be asked to describe this setting as they saw it. Invite them to open their eyes.

5. Ask students to describe their favorite images. Once each student has done this, invite all students to select art materials. Each student should draw or paint his or her favorite images on the paper provided. Once they are finished, have students tape up their artwork on a display area.

6. Ask students to identify some characteristics of riparian areas. What kinds of plants did they see? What kinds of animals? Was the environment near the water different than the environment farther away? If yes, what were some similarities and some differences? Ask students to list, describe, and discuss some of the many reasons that riparian areas are important and have intrinsic value, as well as value to wildlife and humans.

Extensions

1. Visit a riparian habitat. Look for things that you encountered on your simulated field trip. List things found there that you did not picture in your mind.

2. Develop a list of ways that would make it possible for people to visit a riparian area without damaging it.

3. Put your descriptions in writing. Combine words and pictures to convey some of the diversity in riparian areas.

4. Is a different word used in your region to describe these kinds of areas? If not riparian zone, what are they called?

Evaluation

1. What is a riparian zone?

2. Identify four animals found in a riparian zone.

3. Why are riparian zones important to wildlife? To humans? Why are riparian zones intrinsically valuable? Write a poem to explain your response.

4. Describe your position on a plan to develop a riparian habitat for recreational use by hikers, birdwatchers, and other "low-impact" users. Consider a parking area, restrooms, walkways, garbage removal, and other needs.

Riparian zones are the green ribbons of life found on the edges of waterways...These zones range in width from narrow strips in desert and mountain settings to wide bands on the plains and lowlands.

Simulated Field Trip:

"It is a hot summer day. You are walking in a meadow filled with knee-high grasses. Here and there are masses of tiny blue wildflowers…. The ground beneath your feet is uneven, but you are in no hurry as you walk slowly toward a grove of trees. As you near the trees, you notice the changing colors of green…. A breeze whispers through, showing first a shiny green, then the dull green underside of the leaves…. As you step into the grove of trees, you are surrounded with a welcome coolness…. You immediately feel the protection of the canopy of green above your head…. A tap-tap-tapping sound breaks into your thoughts. Searching about among the rough-barked trunks, your eyes finally spot a bird, black and white with a touch of red on its head, clinging to a vertical tree trunk and bobbing its head in time to the rhythmic tapping…. Your eyes fill with the beauty of the setting…. Your skin welcomes the cool…. As you breathe deeply, the very scent of green comes to you…. The aroma of earth and growing things is strong, and you detect here and there almost a memory of the sweet perfume of flowers…. Once in a while, the pungent but not unpleasant odor of wet soil and last season's decaying leaves and grasses catches your attention.

"As you explore further, you notice that the tree trunks are not as crowded and close as before…. Grass, which earlier reached to your knees, is being overshadowed by chest-high bushes. Although these bushes have no thorns, they nevertheless snag your clothing…. Your arms are lightly scratched by the twig ends. Several bushes are covered with small berries, pink and pale green, ripening into red in the warm sun. The bushes become taller…. You find yourself pulling aside thick, tangled willows taller than your head…. You carefully choose a safe path along the precarious trail beneath your feet. Suddenly, your left foot drops six inches, and looking down to examine the terrain more closely, you notice that, where you stepped, the tunnel of a burrowing animal collapsed from your weight. Moving on again you feel the whisper of an abandoned spider web touch the side of your face…. Brushing it aside, you notice the slope of the land is steeper…You pause, listening… listening. You can hear the high drone of insects…. It has come upon you so gradually, you are surprised that you didn't hear it before…. Now it seems almost frighteningly loud.

Riparian Retreat
© *Council for Environmental Education (CEE)*

"And beneath the buzzing drone, but lower in pitch and volume, is the sound of water gently spilling over rocks. Above the place where the water must be, you see thousands of tiny spots milling before your eyes, the creators of that high buzzing sound…. The spots are hundreds of swarming insects in a cloud too thick to picture…. A dragonfly flashes by with its iridescent pinks and greens, darting here, pausing, darting there, pausing, snatching dozens of the dots, relishing a meal in an unending insect buffet. You step aside, ducking beneath the swarming insects…. You smile as your eyes come to rest on the splashing waters of the stream a few feet below. As you proceed, you use your arms to open a space to walk between the graceful tan and green willows that bounce back undisturbed in your wake. As your eyes comb the scene for a place to rest, you notice a hip-high rock ahead of you—gray, warm, and not yet water-smoothed…. You pause before reaching the rock and bend toward the water, gathering a handful of pebbles from the stream bed. One leg anchors itself on the ground

between two willows while the other reaches over the water. With the pebbles in your hand, you swing up onto the dry perch of the rock. You settle down and look at the still wet pebbles—gray, pink, tan, and cool in your warm hand. After you examine them carefully, you toss the stones one at a time into the stream, listening to the pleasing plop of stone on water. Then your eyes drift downward to the waters of the stream near the base of your rock…. In an eddy you see a fish, hidden like an illusion in the stone and silt, waiting, waiting, unblinking and still, only the faint wave of a gill, a tail fin, showing any evidence of life at all.

"As you continue to look downstream, you notice all kinds of small insects dancing across and above the water…. A small ripple occurs in the water, then another and another…. You realize that fish are rising from below and feeding on the surface insects…. Birds dart in and out of the tangle of vegetation…. Some fly through. Downstream a frog begins to croak…. Much nearer, another frog offers a reply. You look around quickly to see if you can find the nearer frog. For a moment, you think you spot it, but then you realize that, unless it sings again, you may never find it. Your eyes search for a moment as more frogs telegraph their messages back and forth. But then it seems time to leave…. You take one last sweeping look all around this beautiful setting…. You slowly get up from your rock along the streamside and head back home."

How Wet Is Our Planet?

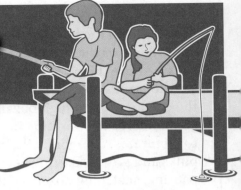

Grade Level: Middle School

Content Areas:
Mathematics, Environmental Education, Social Studies

Method:
Students calculate water volumes using percentages.

Materials:
Large display map of the world, 12-inch diameter globe (preferably one showing the ocean bottom); 5- or 10-gallon aquarium (or other container, such as a trash can); writing materials; calculators; 16-ounce plastic container; plastic cup (less than 16 ounces); tablespoon-measuring spoon; eyedroppers (1 per 3 students)

Activity Time:
one 40- to 60-minute session

People Power:
any, individual and small group work

Setting: indoors

Conceptual Framework Topic Reference:
AAIIA2

Terms to Know:
water cycle, freshwater, saltwater, groundwater, Earth, planet, potable

Appendices: Climate Change, Metric Conversion Chart

How do available freshwater resources amount to just a few drops in a bucket?

Objectives

Students will (1) describe the amount and distribution of water on Earth in oceans, rivers, lakes, groundwater, icecaps, and the atmosphere; and (2) make inferences about the importance of responsible water use.

Background

The Earth has been called the "water planet." Between two-thirds and three-fourths of its surface is water. The Earth's water can be seen in flowing rivers, ponds, lakes, and oceans, locked in the northern and southern icecaps, and drifting through the air as clouds. Water that has seeped into the Earth's crust (groundwater) is more difficult to see, yet all forms of water are part of the dynamic, interrelated flow of the water cycle.

Water is continually moving around, through, and above Earth as water vapor, liquid, and ice. The same water is continually being recycled all around the Earth.

Students tend to think of water on the planet as limitless, and yet simple calculations demonstrate the fact that the amount of water is limited. Scientists believe that all the water we will ever have is on Earth right now. Whatever amount is available to humans and wildlife depends largely on how its quality is maintained. Human beings have a responsibility to conserve water, use it wisely, and protect its quality.

Procedure

NOTE: Refer to the table on the last page of this activity for metric approximations.

1. Using a map of Earth, begin a discussion of the amount of water that covers Earth. Ask students why Earth is called the "water planet." Call their attention to the statistic that between two-thirds and three-fourths of the Earth's surface is covered with water. Following the discussion, provide students with these statistics:

Water on Earth	
Source	Percentage of Total Water (%)
Oceans (saltwater)	96.5400
Groundwater	
Saline/brackish groundwater	0.9300
Fresh groundwater	0.7600
Surface Water	
Glaciers/icecaps	1.7400
Freshwater lakes	0.0070
Saltwater lakes	0.0060
Rivers	0.0002
Other	
Ground ice/permafrost	0.0220
Atmospheric water vapor	0.0010
Marshes, wetlands (mix of fresh and saline)	0.0010
Soil moisture	0.0010
Incorporated in organisms	0.0001
Total	100.0000

NOTE: Total may not add up to 100 due to rounding.

Source: Shiklomanov, I.A. 1993. "World Fresh Water Resources." In P.H. Gleick (ed.), Water in Crisis: A Guide to the World's Fresh Water Resources. Oxford University Press, New York.

2. Discuss the relative percentages. Ask students to calculate the estimated amounts of freshwater potentially available for human use:

Freshwater Amounts Potentially Available for Human Use	
Source	Percentage of Total Water (%)
Glaciers/icecaps	1.7400
Fresh groundwater	0.7600
Freshwater lakes	0.0070
Rivers	0.0002
Total	2.5072

3. In discussing these figures, emphasize that pollution and contamination reduce the usable percentage of existing freshwater. Also, all groundwater is not available, and icecaps are not readily available. Discuss our need for usable freshwater. Introduce the term "potable," which describes water that is drinkable by humans. Ask students to consider what other life forms need both fresh and saline (salt) water.

4. Show students five gallons of water in a 5- or 10-gallon aquarium (or, a 5- or 10-gallon bucket, trash can, or other container). Provide them with the following equation: 5 gal = 1,280 Tablespoons (Tbsp).

5. Have students assume that these five gallons represent all water on Earth. Calculate, either as a class or individually, the volume of other quantities provided in the table "Water on Earth." This step will require the use of decimals. Remind students that for multiplying percentages, the decimal must be shifted two places to the left prior to multiplying, so that 96.54 percent becomes 0.9654 (e.g., $0.9654 \times 1,280$ Tbsp = 1235.71 Tbsp). The following amounts result:

5 Gallons (1,280 Tablespoons)	
Source	Tablespoons (Tbsp)
Oceans (saltwater)	1,235.7100
Groundwater	
Saline/brackish groundwater	11.9040
Fresh groundwater	9.7280
Surface water	
Glaciers/icecaps	22.2720
Freshwater lakes	0.0896
Saltwater lakes	0.0768
Rivers	0.0026
Other	
Ground ice/permafrost	0.2816
Atmospheric water vapor	0.0128
Marshes, wetlands (mix of fresh and saline)	0.0128
Soil moisture	0.0128
Incorporated in organisms	0.0013
Total	Approx. 1,280

NOTE: Total may not add to 1,280 due to rounding.

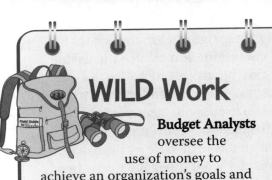

WILD Work

Budget Analysts oversee the use of money to achieve an organization's goals and accomplish its programs. They must maintain the budget as new needs arise and revenues change, similarly to maintaining the balance of water on earth as global needs and sources of water fluctuate.

Computer Professionals are engaged in a range of scientific and administrative support activities: image processing and massive data storage, information dissemination through the web, database management, and systems analysis and design activities. Computer experts often provide support in an environment that is dedicated to earth and natural resources science but dependent on computers and the people who utilize them.

For more information on these occupations, see WILD Work at *www.projectwild.org/aquatic.*

Water is continually moving around, through, and above Earth as water vapor, liquid, and ice. The same water is continually being recycled all around the Earth.

6. Once the values are obtained, ask students to calculate the volume of water, excluding ocean water and saltwater sources (approxiately 32 Tbsp). Have students, working in teams of three, put 32 Tbsp of water in the 16-ounce container. This freshwater portion represents only about 2.5 percent of all the water on Earth! (See table on "Freshwater Amounts Potentially Available for Human Use.") Furthermore, most freshwater is locked up in glaciers and icecaps covering Antarctica and Greenland or is in deep groundwater aquifers.

7. Next, from the 32 Tbsp of "freshwater," have students remove all accessible freshwater sources (fresh groundwater, rivers, and lakes—approximately 10 tbsp), and place the amount in the smaller container.

8. Since most of the fresh groundwater is located in deep aquifers and not readily available, ask students to remove from the small container the amount of water representing all freshwater lakes and rivers (0.0922 tbsp—approximately one-tenth of a tablespoon or 25 drops from a standard dropper). Have them place this amount into the tablespoon-measuring spoon. Then ask students to extract the amount represented by rivers alone (about 2 one hundred-thousandths of a tablespoon, or less than a drop). Discuss the relative proportions with students. Discuss how many species depend upon this very small percentage of freshwater for their survival.

9. Consider the fragile nature of the freshwater, wetlands, and oceans of our planet. Summarize the activity by using a globe to illustrate that if Earth were 12 inches in diameter, less than one-half cup (8 Tbsp) of water would fill all the oceans, rivers, lakes, and icecaps. And, of all the water on Earth, only 0.01% (one one-hundredth of one percent) is useable by humans!

Variation

Do this activity using the metric system. If you use the conversion factor of 1 gallon = 3.8 liters, then all water on Earth represented earlier by 5 gallons would be equivalent to 19 liters, or 19,000 milliliters.

Extensions

1. Create a mural of the water cycle that graphically includes the statistics that represent the relative amount of water in each component of the cycle.

2. Calculate the size of a model of Earth that would accommodate all the water in the aquarium used in the demonstration.

How Wet Is Our Planet?

3. Collect rain gauge samples at your school site on a weekly basis. Estimate the annual average precipitation and compare that amount with local annual precipitation data from the United States Geological Survey (USGS). Compare data from other locations and regions across the country. Make charts and graphs to represent the rainfall. For a link to USGS data, visit *www.projectwild.org/aquatic*.

Evaluation

1. Estimate the percentage of water that is distributed in each of the following areas of our planet: oceans, rivers, freshwater lakes, inland seas and saltwater lakes, groundwater, icecaps and glaciers, and the atmosphere.

2. Explain why it is important that humans use water responsibly.

Additional Resources

http://ga.water.usgs.gov/edu/

In Step with STEM

- Collect liquids with various densities such as dish soap, Karo syrup, vegetable oil, water, and honey. Construct a density column to illustrate "Chart 1: Water on Earth." With food coloring, dye each level a different color to better view the layers.

- Explore your state's surface and groundwater fluctuations throughout various seasons, and observe abnormal levels using USGS data maps found at: *http://water.usgs.gov/data/#now*

- See the activity "Where Does Water Run?" to calculate and compare the percentage of surface area covered by permeable and impermeable surfaces around your school yard.

19 Liters (19,000 Milliliters)	
Source	**Milliliters**
Oceans (saltwater)	18,342.600
Groundwater	
Saline/brackish groundwater	176.700
Fresh groundwater	44.400
Surface water	
Glaciers/icecaps	300.600
Freshwater lakes	1.330
Saltwater lakes	1.140
Rivers	0.038
Other	
Ground ice/permafrost	4.180
Atmospheric water vapor	0.190
Marshes, wetlands (mix of fresh and saline)	0.190
Soil moisture	0.190
Incorporated in organisms	0.019
Total	**Approx. 9,000**

Facts and Falsehoods

Grade Level: Middle, High School

Content Areas: Language Arts, Environmental Education

Method: Students analyze and evaluate print material according to criteria they establish for a strong presentation; as an option, they can then develop their own presentations using the same criteria.

Materials:
A collection of sample print informational brochures and publications concerning aquatic environments; sample advertisements and articles from popular tabloid publications; art materials, markers, poster paper; display boards; a display area.
OPTIONAL: video or still cameras, darkroom facilities

Activity Time: two or three 45-minute sessions

People Power: any size group; part of activity has students working in small groups

Setting: indoors

Conceptual Framework Topic Reference: AAIIA1

Terms to Know: balance, criteria, objectivity, subjectivity, bias, propaganda, accuracy

Appendices: Using Local Resources, Agencies and Organizations, Climate Change

Who is communicating the truth and nothing but the truth?

Objectives

Students will (1) develop criteria for evaluating the quality of a presentation, and (2) evaluate the balance and fairness of presentations designed to represent specific points of view about an environmental topic.

Background

People have many different points of view, particularly concerning issues they feel passionate about. At times it is difficult to discern fact from falsehood, objectivity from subjectivity, and accuracy from exaggeration. Sometimes people are knowingly selective in what information they present about a topic. Other times they do not realize that they are presenting only a narrow view of the topic.

Issues and concerns are subject to an individual's personal filters and perspective. Objectivity is one goal of science. Even in the precise world of scientific measurement, pure objectivity without some influence from the observer's part may be beyond reach. Objectivity is a goal that is difficult, if not impossible, to achieve in a pure and technical sense.

If objectivity is so difficult to achieve, how do students develop skills of objectivity? One technique is to become more discerning about balance and fairness. When a speaker is presenting information on a topic, particularly a controversial topic, ask if that person is making an effort to describe the topic as a whole. Or is the speaker selectively describing only his or her view? Does the speaker acknowledge that there are any other differing points of view? Is the speaker presenting accurate information or only opinion expressed as if it were factually based? These are some of the questions this activity is designed to address.

Information about the environment is provided in settings as varied as classrooms, national parks, government offices, reactor sites, industrial complexes, and wilderness preserves. Much information is provided through the media. In other cases, the information is given through a presentation, possibly using many media and involving audience participation. Prepared lectures, exhibits, and handouts contain ecological, recreational, scientific, and historical information.

The main goal of the organizations that prepare materials and presentations is to inform the public. The result may be a mixture of information, entertainment, and subtle justifications of policy offered in a palatable form. Sometimes the exhibits, programs, media, and materials, of various organizations, agencies, or special interest groups become fairly one-sided and possibly even closed to other options or viewpoints. This approach may not be intentional in all cases, but the effect may be more to influence than to inform or educate.

In some situations, the lack of complete information is intentional. At other times, the limitations are a reflection of emerging and conflicting perspectives about what is accurate concerning the topic. Science itself is not free from controversy. Physicists argue about whether light is a wave or particle. Biologists debate whether wolves should be reintroduced to their former habitats, or whether Inuits should be allowed to kill Bowhead Whales. Aquatic biologists are on both sides of the fence regarding the introduction of exotic fish species to North American waters from other parts of the world. Those who sponsor the construction of dams, canals, and aqueducts, as well as those who propose large-scale diking and dredging projects, must wrestle with the impact that such projects may have on the aquatic habitat and its life forms.

Procedure

Before the activity, assemble website links and collect sample informational brochures from various public or private agencies and organizations (see the "Agencies and Organizations" listing in the appendices). The websites and brochures may cover a range of topics. Make sure some address aquatic topics or issues. Examples might include freshwater inflow, water pollution, conservation, sewage treatment, or hydroelectric power. Articles concerning water issues—including water quality, the development of aquatic resources, and water use—from local news media would also be of potential use.

Obtain several links to websites or hard copies of popular, sensational tabloid publications—such as newspapers and magazines widely available in convenience stores. These publications will be used as a tool to evaluate balanced, fair, and accurate information. Articles, feature stories, and advertisements that deal

People have many different points of view, particularly concerning issues they feel passionate about. At times it is difficult to discern fact from falsehood, objectively from subjectivity, and accuracy from exaggeration.

with science, health, the environment, new products, or new inventions and discoveries are most suited to this activity. Next, prepare a list of questions similar to the ones given below. (Add others suited to the setting.)

- Does the piece cite or list facts? What are they?

- Does it make a claim? Is the claim based on or supported by facts or by some sort of evidence? Describe the claims and the supporting facts and evidence.

- Is the claim or story based in some part on science or technology? Is a scientific law or principle used as support? If so, what are they? Is a scientist or engineer cited as an authority? Who is he or she, and how is his or her expertise established? Which fields of science or engineering are touched upon?

- Is there any indication that the writer stands behind the claim's accuracy or validity? Will the publishers or editors support the claims? Will the advertisers back up their products?

- How could you go about checking or verifying the claims and facts in the article?

- Overall, how strong is the piece? Exceptionally strong? Generally strong? Somewhat strong? Generally weak? Exceptionally weak?

1. Divide the class into pairs or groups. Give each group an article from a tabloid or website and the list of questions. Ask students to review the item and to answer the questions on the sheet. Encourage students to develop any other questions they think might be useful. Discuss the students' results. What do they think about the overall quality of the articles? Do they believe each article? Would they buy the advertised products? Why or why not?

2. Next, distribute the brochures, handouts, or pamphlets related to aquatic and other environmental topics. Ask students to analyze and evaluate these materials in the same way they did the tabloid items. Provide students with another copy of the list of questions. Again, encourage them to add questions of their own. In addition, ask students to consider the following:

- Does the publication acknowledge different points of view about the topic?

- Does the material try to persuade the reader in some way, or is the reader invited to make up his or her own mind? What evidence can students find to support their viewpoints?

Facts and Falsehoods

3. Ask each group to report on its findings. Groups can summarize their findings by giving the brochure an overall rating—using the five categories from "exceptionally strong" to "exceptionally weak." Ask them to support their evaluations with evidence.

4. Now have students work as a single group to develop a checklist they can use to evaluate informational materials, exhibits, or presentations; this would be a "Checklist for a Strong Informational Presentation." What, in their view, should be the characteristics of a strong presentation? They might suggest the information to be:

- Accurate (free from error);
- Fair (does not favor one side);
- Complete (nothing essential is left out);
- Relevant (not muddled with useless facts);
- Reliable (from a credible source);
- Understandable (not burdened with unnecessary jargon and technical details);
- Up-to-date (not outdated);
- Verifiable (another researcher, using the same method, would come up with the same result);
- Other critera . . .

5. After the checklist has been drafted, open the discussion to a few more questions. For example, ask students whether it is possible to be forceful and effective in expressing one's view without becoming unfair or biased. Is it possible to separate one's own viewpoint from a publicly neutral position? To what extent do government agencies, citizens' groups, businesses, interest groups, and individual citizens have a responsibility to acknowledge other points of view concerning their policies and practices? After this discussion, see if students want to make any additional changes to the checklist, and then post the final. Provide each student with a copy of the final checklist for personal use.

OPTIONAL: Prepare a set of assignments in which groups of students are to act as the designers and developers of an informational brochure or program. Have students draw assignments at random. Each group will prepare an informational presentation that has two components:

- a verbal presentation (ten minutes maximum)
- a print brochure

WILD Work

How do **Writers**, **Editors**, **Graphic Designers**, and **Photographers** work together to create a balanced and informative publication on aquatic wildlife?

To learn more on these careers, head to: *www.projectwild.org/aquatic.*

In Step with STEM

Introduce the idea of *ecosystem services*. In simple terms, ecosystem services are the benefits people obtain from the ecosystem. Benefits include provisioning services such as supplies of food, water, and medicine; regulating services, such as carbon sequestration, erosion control, and pollination; cultural services like recreation, ecotourism, and educational and spiritual values; and supporting services like nutrient cycling and soil formation. While traditionally these services have been considered free, ecologists and economists have begun analyzing ecosystem services in terms of monetary value.

After further research on ecosystem services, students can reflect and discuss how, if at all, the environment-related informational sources they previously explored address this concept.

In each case, the remainder of the class will apply the criteria from the final checklist to the presentations. Following each presentation, the other class members will suggest improvements and changes to enhance the quality.

Extensions

1. Visit a site where environmental information is provided to the public. Evaluate the programs, exhibits, and printed materials using the established criteria.

2. Choose an aquatic wildlife issue in the students' community. Write an article for a newspaper or develop a presentation to make in informal educational settings (garden club, Kiwanis, Chamber of Commerce, etc.). Make sure your article or presentation reflects the standards compiled in the checklist.

3. What could students do to enhance the public's understanding of aquatic wildlife and habitats without using propaganda?

4. Contact a local environmental consulting firm or natural resource agency and arrange to visit a real site evaluation involving an aquatic issue. Discuss what measures are taken to ensure fairness and accuracy.

Evaluation

1. Select one of the following topics and describe the types of information that could be included in a presentation designed for students: conservation of a local aquatic species, development of a local wetland area, or harvesting of a marine mammal.

2. Why is it important or not important for informational presentations to be accurate, balanced, complete, and so on?

3. The Big City Dam Visitor Center has two informational displays. One display explains how water is taken from the basin for irrigation and for urban use. The second shows property damage from floods before the dam was constructed. What other information, if any, could be provided for visitors?

Facts and Falsehoods
© *Council for Environmental Education (CEE)*

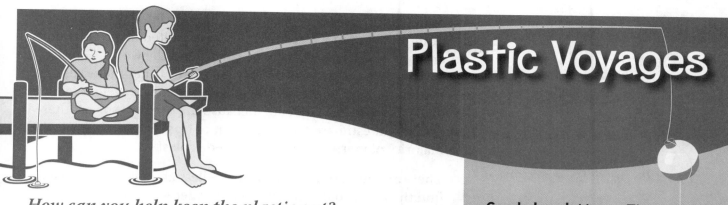

Plastic Voyages

How can you help keep the plastic out?

Objectives

Students will (1) identify and describe sources of marine debris, (2) describe the potential effects of plastic waste on aquatic wildlife and habitat, and (3) identify specific actions they can take to help remedy the problem.

Background

The United States produces over 250 million tons of trash every year, and the amount continues to increase. In 1960, Americans produced 2.68 pounds of trash a day per person, but by 2010 the amount had risen to 4.43 pounds per day *per person*! Disposing of all that waste negatively affects wildlife. Although the production of cheap and disposable plastics has made life more convenient, it causes a great deal of concern regarding litter and quantity of waste. It is not surprising that 12 percent of waste produced each year in the U.S. (30 million tons) is plastic, and only 8 percent of plastic waste (2.4 million tons) is recycled; the rest (27.6 million tons) goes to landfills or into the environment.

Before plastic even reaches our hands, the petroleum compounds (examples include polyethylene, polystyrene, and polypropylene) are refined and shaped into raw material called resin pellets. These spherical pellets range from 1 mm to 5 mm and eventually are melted down and molded into everything from water bottles to pipes used in construction projects. After being formed, the resin pellets are transported to processors for molding and can be spilled along the way. Similar to other litter, unless picked up, the pellets will be carried by rainwater to drainage systems that lead into creeks, rivers, and ultimately, the ocean.

In addition to plastic resin pellets, plastic waste is a large component of marine debris. While most of the waste produced today in the United States is recycled or deposited in landfills, this wasn't always the case. Heavily populated coastal cities often loaded trash onto barges and dumped it into the open ocean until the Clean Water Act was passed in 1972. Many

Grade Level: Upper Elementary

Content Areas: Environmental Education, Social Studies, Mathematics, Science

Method: Students monitor plastic waste in their own households, learn about its effects on marine life, and propose ways to mitigate the problem.

Materials: Plastic waste from home; a shallow tray or box (2- to 3-square feet in area) for each pair of students; enough sand (such as play sand available at home supply stores) to cover the bottom of the trays; one tablespoon of tiny beads in various sizes (1–5 mm diameter) placed in sandwich bags for each student pair; paper towels
OPTIONAL: sieve for separating sand from beads for reuse

Activity Time: one 20- to 60-minute session or longer

People Power: any

Setting: outdoors and indoors

Conceptual Framework Topic Reference: HI1A, HI11A3a, HI11A3b, HI11B5

Terms to Know: biodegradable, debris, entangled, ingest, litter, plastic, pollution

Appendices: Service Learning, Agencies and Organizations, Climate Change

12 percent of waste produced each year in the U.S. (30 million tons) is plastic, and only 8 percent of plastic waste (2.4 million tons) is recycled; the rest (27.6 million tons) goes to landfills or into the environment.

other countries still deposit waste directly into lakes and rivers or into the ocean. Over time, this has resulted in a tremendous amount of garbage in every ocean around the world. Dense garbage like metals sink quickly, but many other materials can float in the upper layers of the ocean and may travel incredible distances with the currents. Because the ocean is so vast there is no current estimate on the amount of trash it contains, but the majority of marine debris recovered is plastic.

There are numerous ways plastic pellets and plastic litter can find their way to the ocean: (1) rainwater washes plastic into streams where it is then carried out to sea; (2) the tide carries it from beaches into the water; (3) storm drains and sewage overflow systems dump litter into the ocean; (4) fishing boats, cargo ships, and oil platforms leave equipment, nets, and other debris behind; (5) trash is discarded from the side of boats; (6) waste escapes from coastal landfills; (7) industrial sites can have spills or accidents; and (8) natural disasters, like Japan's tsunami in 2011, sweep away vulnerable materials.

Plastic is especially problematic because it does not degrade (rot) like paper or food scraps. Once it reaches the ocean it is there to stay. Many people are familiar with the problem of wildlife entanglement in discarded fishing equipment like nets and lines that can kill aquatic wildlife long after they are abandoned (a phenomenon sometimes called "ghost fishing").

A gray seal is found entangled on a beach.

Plastic Voyages
© *Council for Environmental Education (CEE)*

There are many other growing concerns among scientists regarding plastic marine debris. While plastic does not rot, it will eventually break down into smaller and smaller pieces that range from a few millimeters (mm) across to microscopic in size. In warm waters, debris like shopping bags and plastic bottles can break down into small fragments in as little as one year. The problem of plastic fragments is compounded by accidental spills of the resin pellets prior to manufacturing.

Most of the trash in the ocean is a mixture of resin pellets and small plastic fragments. Several documented accounts describe plastic ingestion by wildlife, most notably by seabirds and sea turtles. Before degrading, plastic bags can be mistaken for jellyfish and consumed by sea turtles. The plastic fragments can choke animals, damage their digestive tracts, or cause false feelings of satiation (i.e., the animals feel as though they have eaten). Seabirds ingest plastic more frequently than any other animal; approximately one-quarter of all seabird species are known to ingest pellets. According to the Monterey Bay Aquarium, over 40 percent of Laysan Albatross chicks die each year from plastic debris fed to them by their parents. Some researchers believe animals may be poisoned by chemicals in the plastics they consume, but the extent of this effect is not known.

Beyond wildlife, plastic waste can negatively affect human health. People might step on sharp pieces of broken plastic hidden in sand or be sickened from bacteria or contaminated plastic medical waste. In the United States, the Environmental Protection Agency regulates marine debris through many laws including the Beaches Environmental Assessment and Coastal Health Act (BEACH), which provides grants to organizations that test for and reduce the spread of disease from waste.

One of the challenges of cleaning up ocean pollution is efficiently removing these tiny fragments without harming aquatic life. The buoyancy of these small pieces varies greatly, and as much as 70 percent of plastic debris sinks. While water may look unpolluted at the surface, plastic may be on the seafloor and suspended throughout the water column.

Another problem with plastic waste is that once it enters the ocean, it can be carried long distances by surface winds and ocean currents. Plastic has been found on shorelines in remote regions of the Arctic and on isolated South Pacific islands. Plastic debris may also serve as a "float" that carries species outside their native habitat.

Much of the plastic debris traveling the ocean becomes concentrated in large, circular ocean currents known as gyres. The largest of these, the Great Pacific Garbage Patch, is located between North America and Japan. In sections of this garbage

While most of the waste produced today in the United States is recycled or deposited in landfills, this wasn't always the case. Heavily populated coastal cities often loaded trash onto barges and dumped it into the open ocean until the Clean Water Act was passed in 1972.

LAYSAN ALBATROSS

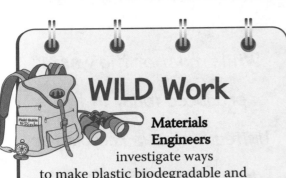

WILD Work

Materials Engineers

investigate ways to make plastic biodegradable and also develop new materials that can be used as a replacement for plastic. **Marine Meteorologists** study the effects of weather on ocean currents and processes. **Recycling Coordinators** create or manage recycling programs for municipalities, private companies, or public events and educate others on the benefits of reducing and recycling waste.

For more information on these occupations, see WILD Work resources at *www.projectwild.org/aquatic.*

Debris is found floating after the 2011 tsunami hit Japan.

patch there are as many as 300,000 items of debris per square kilometer, and there is six times as much plastic (by weight) as plankton, which produces oxygen and serves as food for many animals.

Many governments, local municipalities, and international organizations have all addressed the effects of marine debris. The International Maritime Organization created the International Convention for the Prevention of Pollution from Ships (MARPOL) in 1973 to provide laws and regulations that each participating country can enforce to control marine pollution. Currently there are six annexes which focus on different aspects such as solid waste, cargo vessels, fishing equipment, etc. Over 170 countries participate in MARPOL, but regulation and implementation can be difficult for many countries.

While the scope of plastic pollution is immense, future generations will only see a reduction in marine debris through all countries and organizations collaborating together to both prevent and clean up plastics.

Procedure:

1. Ask students to collect and save every piece of plastic waste produced in their homes for a two-day period. Ask them to share what they expect to be their most common reason for using plastic products (convenience, packaging, price, etc.). Have students ask an adult to help clean out the items, especially household cleaner containers such as ammonia or chlorine. If students cannot bring items from home, this activity can be completed using sample items collected by the instructor.

2. Have students examine the plastic items and discuss possible ways they might negatively affect aquatic animals if they are not disposed of properly. Are any of them likely to be mistaken for food? Might an animal become entangled or trapped in an item?

3. Sort items that might harm marine animals into three groups (some items will fit into more than one group):

   a) Items in which animals may become entangled.

   b) Materials that might be mistakenly eaten by animals as food.

   c) Items that might cut an animal that steps on it or attempts to eat it.

Classify the sorted items by using the following codes: **E** = entanglement hazard, **F** = mistaken as food, **C** = cutting hazard.

Examples: six-pack holders—E; plastic bags—F & E; strapping/packaging bands—E & C; plastic utensils—C; cups—F; plastic water bottle—E

4. Discuss ways in which plastic can become ocean trash. How might the plastic trash they brought from home end up in the ocean or another waterbody? How could they keep plastic from becoming aquatic debris? Ask students how people might remove plastic pollution from various aquatic environments and compare the logistics of a cleanup along a creek versus the ocean.

5. Explain to students that plastics are broken down into small pieces when directly exposed to sunlight for extended periods. Show them the beads and explain how the plastic containers they brought in, including plastic water bottles, can eventually turn into fragments this size and smaller in the environment. Ask students how these tiny pieces of plastic could affect wildlife. Do they think these small plastic pieces would be harder or easier to remove from the environment than larger debris?

6. Explain to students that small plastic fragments wash up onto beaches and become mixed in with the sand. Divide the class into pairs, and give each pair a jar or reusable cup containing a heaping tablespoon of beads and a tray of sand. Ask students to place the beads on a paper towel and to count them. Record these amounts on the board or flip chart.

7. Direct each pair of students to sprinkle the beads evenly over the sand in the tray. When all beads are in the sand, tell students to jostle their tray vigorously for 30 seconds. Emphasize that they must not lift the tray, but keep the tray on the table.

8. Next, ask students to try to find all of the beads. Allow students to look for exactly three minutes (less time for older students) and have them place the beads back on a paper towel. When the time is up, have students count their beads. Record these numbers on the paper towel and on the class data chart. Have students total the number of beads recovered by the class.

9. Discuss students' findings. Did they recover all of the beads? If not, why? What obstacles did they face? Can they suggest more efficient ways to recover the beads from the sand?

10. Discuss with students how plastic can be distributed throughout the water column and ask how they would collect the beads from an aquatic environment. How would it be different than collecting beads from sand? What obstacles might they face? How would they remove small plastic pieces from the deepest parts of the ocean? How would they remove plastics without disturbing marine wildlife?

Most of the trash in the ocean is a mixture of resin pellets and small plastic fragments. Several documented accounts describe plastic ingestion by wildlife, most notably by seabirds and sea turtles.

Garbage that has traveled with ocean currents frequently washes up on beaches.

Much of the plastic debris traveling the ocean becomes concentrated in large, circular ocean currents known as gyres. The largest of these, the Great Pacific Garbage Patch, is located between North America and Japan.

Recycle your:

- **Plastic Bottles**
  NO plastic wrappers or packaging
- **Cans**
- **Newspapers & Magazines**

Waste Aware

Volvic

11. Have students brainstorm what could be done to keep plastics out of the ocean and freshwater environments in their community. What can they do in their homes? What can they do at school? What might the government do to prevent plastic debris from entering our waters? Discuss recycling programs at home and school and why it is important to take the extra time to recycle. Discuss reducing versus recycling plastic products.

12. Have the class brainstorm actions the plastics industry might be able to take to minimize loose pellets in the environment. What actions could government take?

13. When cleaning up, separate any remaining beads from the sand (you may want to use a sieve) and store your sand and pellets in containers for future use. If you need to dispose of any sand that may still contain beads, make sure the sand is not disposed of outdoors where beads might wash into streams or other bodies of water.

14. While students are cleaning up, ask them to name any plastic products they used in this activity (beads, plastic sandwich bags, pens) and to discuss how the use of plastic could have been reduced by substituting other materials. Also make sure that students properly dispose of the materials they brought from home.

15. How else might students reduce plastic waste? (e.g., eliminating plastic grocery bags and plastic water bottles, using reusable containers, purchasing items with less packaging, and reducing overall "consumption" of products)

Extensions

1. Have students investigate the difficulty in removing the beads from a dish of water. Ask them to attempt to remove only a single color of bead to demonstrate how difficult it is to clean up ocean debris without harming wildlife like plankton, fish, and turtles.

2. Demonstrate to students how ocean currents work.

- Give each pair of students a pie tin filled with water.
- Have students sprinkle a dried herb like oregano or chili powder on top of the water.
- Have students use a straw to gently blow across the top of the water. What happens to the herbs? How do they think ocean currents affect floating plastic debris in the ocean?

3. Have students draw a map of their local watershed and trace possible pathways plastic litter might take to end up in streams, rivers, lakes, and oceans.

Plastic Voyages

4. Discuss the possible effects of entanglement on turtles, birds, and other aquatic wildlife. Have students wrap a rubber band over the top of one hand and around the thumb and pinkie fingers. Challenge them to try to pick up something with these fingers tied (similar to a bird trying to use its beak or feet). Have them try to remove the band without using their teeth or other hand to demonstrate how difficult it is for animals to disentangle themselves from fishing line, nets, and bags.

5. Take various types of plastic, including biodegradable options, and put the items outdoors where they will not be disturbed for one month. Set up an observation schedule and a means of recording the date and the changes you observe in the plastic samples. What conclusions can you draw from your observations?

6. Invite students to survey their school grounds or community for plastic litter. Look to see if and where it exists. Organize a cleanup with an after school club or as a mini fieldtrip. Trash grabber tools allow students to pick up litter without touching it and are relatively inexpensive. Students should be encouraged to use gloves. Investigate the potential negative effect of litter on animals in the community. If there is damaging plastic litter in the community, ask students to create an action plan that will increase public awareness of the problem and help mitigate it (e.g., setting up a plastic recycling depot).

Evaluation

1. List three ways plastic trash can enter a marine environment.

2. Describe the effects of plastic waste on marine animals.

3. List two things you can do to prevent harm to wildlife from plastic litter.

4. Describe what might be seen in a marine ecosystem that has been impacted by plastic pollution.

In Step with STEM

■ Assist students in calculating how much plastic trash they create. Start by asking them to count the number of items they brought in. If they collected two days' worth of trash from home, how many items would they collect from home in a month? A year? Ten years? How much would the class collect together? Use graphs to chart the increase. Have students estimate the weight of the trash generated each day in addition to the amount. Ask students to think of ways they might reduce the amount of plastic waste they create. Have them try out their ideas and record the results in a spreadsheet. They could also share their findings via an audiovisual presentation.

■ Go to *www.projectwild.org/aquatic* and access online links to up-to-date maps of ocean winds and currents. Have students use the map to track where plastic pollution might be carried from different locations. Have students look for circular currents that would trap and concentrate marine debris and also for currents that would wash debris back on shore.

One of the challenges of cleaning up ocean pollution is efficiently removing these tiny fragments without harming wildlife.

Watershed

Grade Level: Middle, High School

Content Areas:
Environmental Education, Mathematics, Language Arts

Method: Students measure the area of a local watershed, calculate the amount of water it receives each year, and discuss functions of the watershed.

Materials:
Six stakes or markers; hammer; two 50-foot (15-meter) measuring tapes; two 100-foot (30-meter) measuring tapes; writing materials; clipboards; large pad of paper for display; local maps showing bodies of water
NOTE: Twine or heavy string can be used instead of measuring tapes by marking at intervals.

Activity Time: one or more 30- to 60-minute sessions

People Power: small groups of three to five students each

Setting: outdoors and indoors

Conceptual Framework Topic Reference: HIIIB3

Terms to Know: runoff, precipitation, watershed, erosion, ridgeline

Appendices: The Ecosystem and Project WILD, Metric Conversion Chart

---

Do you know where your water flows?

Objectives

Students will (1) describe the characteristics of watersheds, (2) discuss the role of watersheds in providing wildlife habitat as well as human habitat, and (3) give examples of watershed conservation.

Background

A watershed is an area of land that allows water to flow over or under its surface into a particular body of water. The boundaries of a watershed are determined by the guiding contours of the land surrounding a stream, river, lake, or bay. Because precipitation and its runoff must flow somewhere, all land areas are a part of some watershed. Every home, school, office, business, and industry is part of a watershed.

A watershed is more than just a geological feature. It is a hydrologic system linking all living things within its boundaries. Not only does all plant and animal life depend on the water within each watershed, but also the watercourses are conduits that transport water, organisms, nutrients, and other materials within the system. What affects one watershed eventually affects other sites downstream.

One material moving through the watershed is soil. Because rivers of a watershed are constantly engaged in the gradual erosion of the highlands that contain it, suspended sediments are part of the natural dynamics. However, human activities can accelerate this process through actions such as land clearing, dam building, farming, and industrial development. Runoff carries the loose soil into the water system, which may affect watershed quality. Significantly increased turbidity (cloudiness of water due to individual particles) can interfere with sunlight transmission, fish respiration, and plant photosynthesis.

Of particular concern are contaminants in the water. Contaminants may be excessive nutrients that overload natural systems, or they may be harmful chemicals introduced into the water. Both of these problems are often related to agricultural and industrial activities that result in the release of water back into the watershed that has been altered by its use. Fertilizers and pesticides are the major sources of agricultural contamination. Industrial wastewater can contain myriad contaminants from oil to heavy metals.

Contamination of watersheds is a serious problem for humans, but it is as great or greater a problem for wildlife. Most often it is wildlife—particularly aquatic wildlife—that suffers the most directly and immediately from contaminated water. Slight changes in pH (acidity) can destroy the natural balance in a body of water. Natural food webs can be damaged for decades by a single contamination.

Water contamination, like water, does not just remain on the surface. As part of the water cycle, watersheds both feed and are fed by groundwater. Surface contamination can penetrate into the earth and contaminate water supplies. On a watershed's surface, water can move so rapidly it is often expressed in cubic feet (cubic meters) per second. Below the ground's surface, its movement might be expressed in inches (centimeters) per year. Contaminated groundwater can negatively affect a watershed's quality for centuries. Most scientists argue that it is far more economical to prevent contaminants from entering water systems than to clean up pollution after it takes place.

Another human activity that affects watershed systems is the diversion of water from the natural flow of streams, ponds, rivers, and lakes. The growth of human populations in a watershed may result in greater and greater diversion. For example, the need for water and hydroelectric power often motivates the building of dams. Dams may radically alter stream habitat, yet they do provide predictable water supplies for agriculture, domestic uses, and industry. There are obvious benefits and liabilities to consider when making decisions affecting watersheds.

Because watersheds are natural units, they represent a logical basis for managing resources. Traditionally, water quality improvements have focused on specific sources of pollution, such as sewage discharges, or on specific water resources, such as a river segment or wetland. While this approach may be successful in addressing specific problems, it often fails to address some subtle and chronic problems that might contribute to a watershed's decline. For example, pollution from a sewage treatment plant might be significantly reduced after new technology is installed. Yet the local river may still suffer if other factors in the watershed, such as habitat destruction or other sources of polluted runoff, are not also addressed. Managing the watershed unit as an integrated system provides a stronger foundation for uncovering issues that affect it, and it better equips resource managers to determine what actions are needed to protect and restore it.

A watershed is more than just a geological feature. It is a hydrologic system linking all living things within its boundaries. Not only does all plant and animal life depend on water within each watershed, but also the watercourses are conduits that transport water, organisms, nutrients, and other materials within the system.

Procedure

Before the activity, select an outdoor site approximately 100-feet (30-meters) square that resembles a small watershed. If possible, there should be a visible drainage pattern. Look around the school or in a nearby park for a site that will suffice. There needs to be enough topography so students will be able to visualize the watershed concept. **OPTIONAL:** Research the annual rainfall amounts for your area. Visit *www.projectwild.org/aquatic* for helpful web links.

1. Using local maps and local stream systems as examples, discuss the concept of a watershed. Topographical maps or raised-relief maps are valuable tools. Emphasize that the size of watersheds varies, from tiny tributaries to river systems as large as the Mississippi. Introduce the concept that a ridgeline is the border between two designated watersheds. Using local maps, show how the boundaries of a watershed can be determined by tracing the ridgelines between adjacent watersheds. To demonstrate this point, use a transparent overlay on a standard paper map, or use water-soluble marking pens on a plastic raised-relief map.

2. Explain to students that they will be going to a small watershed and will be measuring its area in much the same way large watersheds are measured. Show them the equipment you will be taking along, and explain how five of the stakes will be used to mark the top of the ridgeline of the watershed. Indicate the "control" stake that will represent the bottom of the drainage system. Educators may choose to read the rest of the procedures and illustrate the process of measuring a watershed on the chalkboard before going to the site, or they may use a large pad and markers to review the procedures visually at the site.

3. Upon reaching the site, divide students into teams of three to five. Determine the ridgeline of the watershed, and drive the stakes or markers along the upper boundary of their watershed. The ridge stakes should be 20 to 40 feet (6 to 12 meters) apart.

4. As a group, have students determine the location of the control stake at the "bottom" of the watershed. The control stake is the one from which measurements to other stakes are made. The control stake should be 60 to 100 feet (18 to 30 meters) from the ridge stakes.

5. Begin measurements that will result in a map of the watershed. Each team should draw a map of this miniature watershed. Ask students to record their results to scale on a large piece of paper (use about 1/4 or 1/8 inch [1 cm] on the map for each foot [meter] on the ground), as shown in Diagram A. The scale will depend on the size of the paper.

Watershed

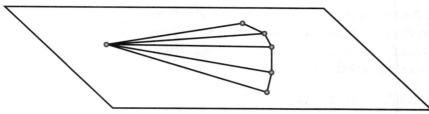

Finished Map

Diagram A

6. Have each team determine the area of the watershed, following these procedures (see Diagrams B and C):

- Turn each triangle segment into a rectangle, and then determine the area by multiplying length times width.

    L x W = Area of a rectangle
    (in square feet or square meters)

- Then divide by two because the area of the triangle will be one half the area of the rectangle.

- Repeat for each triangle.

- Add the areas of all five triangles together to get the area of the watershed (in square feet or meters).

Educators may want to use the formula for the area of a triangle: Area = ½ Base x Height

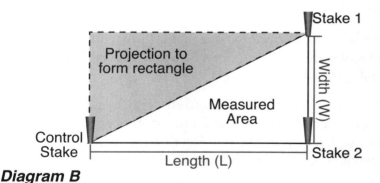

Diagram B

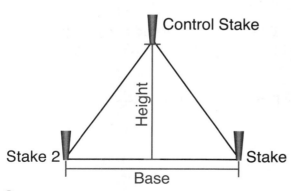

Diagram C

Most often it is wildlife—particularly aquatic wildlife—that suffers the most directly and immediately from contaminated water.

7. As an option, calculate the amount of precipitation that falls on the miniature watershed each year. This is when the value for annual rainfall is needed. The rainfall value must be expressed in feet (meters) thus:

Rainfall x Area = Volume of Rain

8. Discuss the following questions with students. How does a watershed work? How does it affect humans? How does it affect wildlife? How is groundwater affected by conditions in your watershed? What kinds of things can be done to protect, conserve, and improve watershed quality? What are some of the reasons, if any, to protect and conserve watersheds? What are some of the potential tradeoffs involved? When, if ever, might it seem inappropriate to protect and conserve a watershed?

Extensions

1. Simulate a watershed. Have students stand in a circle with quart (liter) containers of water, and empty the containers on cue toward the center of the circle. Have students trace the "natural" paths taken by the water, and see if they can trace the watersheds indicated by the diverse flow pattern.

2. Trace the watersheds of major North American rivers. Use tracing paper or acetate overlays on large scale maps.

3. On a map, locate the habitat of specific life forms in your local watershed.

4. A noted scientist once remarked that "Human activities speed up the flow of water while nature slows it down." Is this true for the watershed in which you live?

5. Explore an actual watershed where students live. Identify locations of water diversion from natural pathways, determine the use of the diverted water, and describe the condition of the water when it is returned to the natural drainage.

Evaluation

1. Describe and draw a watershed.

2. How are wildlife habitats related to watersheds? Why are watersheds important to people? Write a short essay in response to these questions.

3. Develop a plan on how to protect, conserve, or restore a watershed.

Watershed

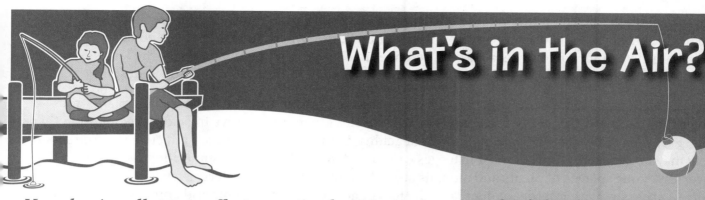

What's in the Air?

How do air pollutants affect aquatic plants?

Learning Objectives

Students will (1) describe acidic precipitation, (2) generate and test hypotheses concerning effects of acidic precipitation, and (3) make inferences about the potential effects of acidic precipitation on aquatic life.

Background

Rain and other forms of precipitation that are normally slightly acidic can become more acidic because of pollutants in the air. These pollutants, sulfur dioxide and nitrogen oxide, combine with atmospheric water to produce a mild solution of sulfuric acid and nitric acid known as acidic precipitation. Scientists have discovered that air pollution from the burning of fossil fuels is one of the major causes of acidic precipitation. Nitrogen oxide is produced by the exhaust systems of cars, while electrical plants, industries, and smelters that burn coal and other fossil fuels generate sulfur dioxide. Other causes for acidic precipitation include mining, forest fires, lightning, and volcanoes. Acidic precipitation may come in the form of rain, snow, sleet, or fog.

Acid precipitation is thought to be carried long distances by air currents and storm systems. Understanding the movement of storm systems, high and low pressure movements, and fronts can help scientists discover where acidic precipitation is coming from and where the precipitation is returning to the ground. By making projections of storm systems and air currents, researchers are also attempting to track where gases, fly ash, soot, and dust particles go.

The effects of acidic precipitation are visible in aquatic habitats. Most lakes and streams have a pH between 6.5 and 8.5 (a measure of the acidity or alkalinity of a solution, numerically equal to 7 for neutral solutions, increasing with higher alkalinity and decreasing with higher acidity). The pH scale commonly in use ranges from 0 to 14. Some lakes are naturally acidic even without the effects of acidic precipitation. Lakes and

Grade Level: Middle School

Content Areas: Science, Social Studies, Mathematics, Environmental Education

Method: Through simulations and direct measurement, students experience differing acidic conditions in aquatic habitats and explore their consequences on aquatic life.

Materials: Vinegar; distilled water; graduated cylinders; pH test kit or probe; six trays of grass seedlings in soil to be grown in the classroom (grass seed may be purchased at a plant nursery or hardware store); assorted containers

Activity Time: two 20- to 45-minute sessions, plus growing time of one or two weeks for seedlings to show effects of acidic precipitation.

People Power: any

Setting: indoors

Conceptual Framework Topic Reference: HIIIB1, HIIIB4, HIIIB5

Terms to Know: acidic precipitation

Appendix: Climate Change

streams become acidic when the water and its surrounding soil cannot buffer acidic precipitation enough to neutralize it. In areas such as the northeastern United States, where soil buffering is poor, some lakes have become even more acidic. Because of differences in emissions and wind patterns, the levels of acidic deposition are generally lower in the western United States than in the eastern United States.

As lakes and streams become more acidic, the numbers and types of fish and other aquatic plants and animals may decrease. Generally, the young of most species are more sensitive to acidic precipitation than adults. Frogs may tolerate relatively high levels of acidity, but if certain insects are affected, the frog's food supply may be reduced. At pH 5, most fish eggs cannot hatch; at other levels, some adult fish may die. Conversely, some species of plants and animals are able to tolerate acidic waters. Even so, all organisms within an ecosystem are interdependent, and the loss of acidic-sensitive plants and animals will in time affect all the organisms in the ecosystem.

Scientists believe that acidic waters dissolve nutrients and helpful minerals in the soil and then wash them away before the plants can use them to grow. At the same time, acidic precipitation causes the release of other metals such as aluminum, cadmium, and mercury into the soil. Even if the soil is well buffered, modification in plant species can occur from acidic fog and clouds that surround mountains at higher elevations. Tree leaves are frequently bathed in fog or clouds, and the leaves are damaged and cannot produce the food the tree needs to grow.

There are several methods currently used by industries and power plants to reduce the amount of pollutants released into the atmosphere. The four most commonly used technologies are smokestack scrubbers, electrostatic precipitators, fabric filters, and cyclones. Scrubbers are designed to remove various gases from emissions, while electrostatic precipitators are designed to remove the visible soot from emissions. Fabric filters are essentially "giant" vacuum cleaners that collect fine particulate matter, while cyclones are devices that separate particulates from the gas stream through aerodynamic/centrifugal forces.

The automobile industry is also working to reduce vehicle emissions. Fuel-efficient hybrid vehicles have become commonplace. Hydrogen engineering has introduced a new way to power cars, with hydrogen burned in an internal combustion engine or reacted with oxygen in a fuel cell. (If the hydrogen is retrieved from wind, solar, or nuclear sources, then the vehicle does not produce any carbon emissions.) The Corporate Average Fuel Economy (CAFE) standards released in 2012 mandate that all vehicles on the road

become much more efficient by 2025. In order to meet the CAFE requirements, automakers must increase fuel efficiency to 54.5 miles per gallon. There are other current approaches to control vehicle emissions: the development of auto inspection and maintenance programs; cleaner, high-quality fuels; the addition of vapor and particulate recovery systems; and technological advances in vehicle and engine design. For example, cleaner vehicles are being manufactured that recirculate the automobile exhaust back to the engine to burn extra nitrogen oxide.

Background Information on the Experiment

This activity uses vinegar, distilled water, and grass seedlings to simulate the reaction that might occur in nature between acidic precipitation and plants.

Vinegar does not typically get into rain and water supplies, but in this activity it is used to illustrate how something with similar characteristics—sulfuric acid—can affect plants. Students will use litmus paper to test the acidity of vinegar and distilled water. Litmus paper is treated with chemicals so that it turns different colors depending on how acidic a liquid is. The measure of acidity is calibrated into a scale called pH. High acidity is designated by a low pH number (1). Conversely, a high pH number (14) means the solution is not very acidic. Vinegar, lemon juice, and sulfuric acid all have high acidity, thus a low pH.

Acids are chemical substances that are called "electrolytes." They furnish hydrogen ions in chemical reactions that create powerful reactions with other substances. There are strong acids and weak acids. Normal rainwater is a weak acid. However, rain and other precipitation often come in contact with chemicals from pollution. When precipitation is exposed to these chemicals, it often becomes more acidic.

Using a simple experiment, this activity will aid students in identifying some potential consequences of acidic precipitation.

Procedure

Before the activity, establish six trays of 50 to 100 grass seedlings each in a sunlit area of the room. Grass seedlings are used because of their fast growth and because the single blade makes height measurements less arbitrary. Trays should have the same type of soil. Label the trays 0 percent, 1 percent, 5 percent, 10 percent, 25 percent, and 50 percent.

1. Begin by pouring a quantity of vinegar onto four or five sheets of paper towels. Place these towels around the class when students are absent. When the students return, note their discomfort with the smell with a bit of theatrical drama. Is something wrong? Solicit their descriptions of what seems to be wrong.

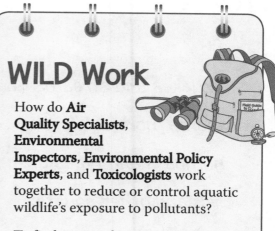

WILD Work

How do **Air Quality Specialists**, **Environmental Inspectors**, **Environmental Policy Experts**, and **Toxicologists** work together to reduce or control aquatic wildlife's exposure to pollutants?

To find more information on these careers, head to: *www.projectwild.org/aquatic*.

In Step with STEM

- Explore how pH can be tested using qualitative and quantitative measurements and observations, using litmus tests and a pH probe.

- Use cabbage to create a pH indicator solution and test various water sources, such as a local pond or tap water at the school. Visit *www.projectwild.org/aquatic* for more information.

Lakes and streams become acidic when the water and its surrounding soil cannot buffer acidic precipitation enough to neutralize it.

As lakes and streams become more acidic, the numbers and types of fish and other aquatic animals may decrease. Generally, the young of most species are more sensitive to acidic precipitation than adults.

2. Collect the paper towels, and discard them in a self-sealing plastic bag. Inform students that you wanted them to experience the discomfort of a kind of "pollution" in their environment.

3. When the seedlings are just established, have students begin to water the plants with the corresponding vinegar solution: 0 percent, 1 percent, 5 percent, 10 percent, 25 percent, and 50 percent. Place the corresponding amount of vinegar in a graduated cylinder and fill the remainder with distilled water. For example, a 5 percent solution would be made by pouring 5-ml of vinegar into a 100-ml graduated cylinder and then adding 95-ml of water. Have students hypothesize which concentrations the plants will not tolerate. The plants should be watered regularly, and all plant trays should receive the same amount of liquid. If possible, use a spray bottle to spray several trays with the corresponding vinegar solution. What are the outcomes?

OPTIONAL: Students should determine the pH for each solution each time they water, and they should record this number. Does the pH stay the same? How does it vary over time? Why? Explain that pH balance occurs in situations in which buffer systems "hold" the pH so it will resist change.

4. Each time the plants are watered, the number of living plants and their heights should be recorded as a measurement of their growth. Average the heights of all the seedlings in the tray. Qualitative observations should also be made on their appearance. Student should design and create the data sheets to record the data.

5. After two weeks (or whenever a difference in the plants becomes obvious), graph the average heights for each tray over that period. Allow students to create the graph if possible. Students can do one graph for each type of solution, or they can put all findings on one graph using a key to identify the symbols for each type of solution.

6. Why were each of the trays watered the same amount? Why did they all have the same kind and amount of soil? What else was the same for each tray? What might have happened if some of these conditions were different for some trays? What are the advantages of using grass when growth rates are measured? Why were so many plants used? Why were the heights averaged? How does using a large number of plants affect the reliability of the findings?

Extensions

1. Collect water samples from several sites in the community and test the pH. Research local sources to discover if the pH level has changed in local aquatic habitats in recent years. Sources for this

What's in the Air?

type of information might be water quality control offices, state regulating agencies, or state wildlife agencies.

2. Investigate the reported effects of acidic precipitation in the industrial northeast region of the United States. Compare your findings with those of the reported effects in the Rocky Mountain region.

3. Develop a hypothetical master plan for dealing with acidic precipitation. Is it feasible? Why or why not?

4. Research the ways acidic precipitation could be reduced, how much it could cost to reduce it, and how much it could cost not to reduce its effects.

5. Research the effects of buffering acidic lakes and streams with high pH materials such as lime.

Evaluation

1. What is acidic precipitation? What are some of the causes of acidic precipitation? What are some of the effects of acidic precipitation? Write at least three paragraphs to respond.

2. Predict what might happen to each of the following as a result of acidic precipitation: plants, fish, soil, outdoor artwork, buildings, aquatic insects, aquatic birds and mammals, aquatic habitats, and humans.

... all organisms within an ecosystem are interdependent, and the loss of acidic-sensitive plants and animals will in time affect all the organisms in the ecosystem.

What's in the Water?

Get to the point (or nonpoint!) of water pollution.

Objectives

Students will (1) identify major sources of aquatic pollution, and (2) make inferences about the potential effects of a variety of aquatic pollutants on wildlife and wildlife habitat.

Background

Waterways such as rivers, lakes, and estuaries are important to humans and wildlife alike. Waterways are used for drinking water, transportation, recreation, and habitat for many wildlife species. However, many of our nation's rivers, lakes, and estuaries are not fishable, swimmable, or potable because of pollution (Source: American Rivers). Pollutants enter waterways from either point or nonpoint sources. Point sources are clearly defined, localized inputs such as pipes, industrial plants, sewer systems, and oil spills. Federal and state governments monitor and regulate pollution from point sources. Unfortunately, nonpoint sources are harder to detect and control; therefore they are the major source of water quality problems.

Nonpoint sources are indistinct inputs that do not have a clearly defined source, for instance runoff of petroleum products from roadways or pesticides from farmlands. Nonpoint source pollution occurs when rainfall, snowmelt, or irrigation runs over land or through the ground, picks up pollutants, and deposits them into surface water or introduces them into groundwater. Agriculture, forestry, grazing, septic systems, recreational boating, urban runoff, construction, physical change to stream channels, and habitat degradation are all sources of nonpoint source pollution. Runoff from urban areas is a leading source of water quality impairments to the United States' estuaries.

The most common nonpoint source pollutants are sediment and nutrients. These pollutants enter waterways from agricultural land, animal-feeding operations, construction sites, and other areas of disturbance. Other common pollutants are pesticides, herbicides, pathogens, oil, toxic chemicals, and heavy metals. A growing concern is also the potential toxic effects of chemical

Grade Level: Middle School

Content Areas:
Science, Mathematics, Environmental Education

Method:
Students analyze the pollutants found in a hypothetical river. They graph the quantities of pollutants and recommend actions that could be taken to improve the habitat.

Materials: Nine different colors of construction paper (two sheets each); writing or graph paper; tape or glue; paper punch; *Pollutant Information Sheets* (one for each student); ¼-tsp measure (for paper punch tokens); 1-Tbsp measure (for ½-inch square tokens)

Activity Time: one 30- to 45-minute session or longer

People Power: small groups of three students each

Setting: indoors

Conceptual Framework Topic Reference:
HIIIB1, HIIIB4, HIIIB5

Terms to Know: pollution, chemical, thermal, organic, ecological, point and nonpoint source pollution, groundwater, toxic wastes, sediment

Appendix:
Agencies and Organizations

compounds from medications that enter the water supply through wastewater. Unsafe drinking water, fish kills, destroyed habitat, beach closures, and many other severe environmental and human health problems result from these water pollutants (Source: EPA Office of Water).

Pollution can be categorized into the following types:

- **chemical pollution**: the introduction of toxic substances into an ecosystem (e.g., acidic precipitation, contamination of water supplies by pesticides, improper disposal of medications)

- **thermal pollution**: varying temperatures above or below the normal condition (e.g., water heated by a power plant turbine)

- **organic pollution**: oversupplying an ecosystem with nutrients (i.e., fertilizer inflow)

- **ecological pollution**: stresses ordinarily created by natural processes, such as

  1. Adding a substance that is not naturally occurring in the ecosystem (e.g., extreme tides force saltwater into habitat ordinarily protected from saltwater)

  2. Increasing the amount or intensity of a naturally occurring substance (e.g., abnormal increase in sediments in runoff water produces silt)

  3. Altering the level or concentration of biological or physical components of an ecosystem (changing the amount of something that is already there) (e.g., introduction of aquatic plants via bird droppings, etc.)

In the definitions above, chemical pollution through the introduction of toxic substances is clearly caused by humans. Organic pollution in lakes and rivers typically results when chemical fertilizers used in agriculture enhance living organisms. Thermal pollution is predominately caused by humans through nuclear power plants, fuel-based electrical power production, and many industries. Some hydroelectric dams also produce unnaturally cooled water with bottom discharge of water.

Surprisingly, these three forms of pollution—chemical, thermal, and organic—can take place without human intervention. When this happens, it is most often ecological pollution. Natural ecological pollution may be beneficial, be harmful, or have no effect on wildlife and wildlife habitat. Examples include acidic precipitation resulting from volcanic eruptions, runoff from landslides and avalanches sometimes killing plant and animal life, hot springs and geysers heating water above normal temperatures in lakes and streams, and shifts in oceanic currents affecting water temperature and weather patterns.

Nonpoint sources of pollution are indistinct inputs that do not have a clearly defined source, for instance runoff of petroleum products from roadways or pesticides from farmlands.

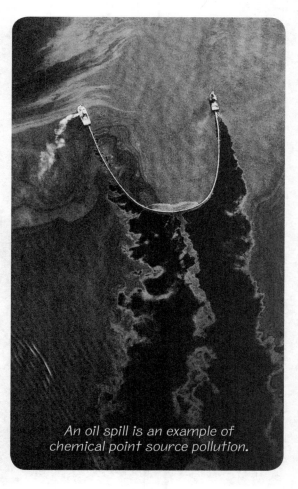

An oil spill is an example of chemical point source pollution.

Runoff from urban pollution usually finds its way into surface and groundwater supplies.

The most common nonpoint source pollutants are sediment and nutrients. These pollutants enter waterways from agricultural land, animal-feeding operations, construction sites, and other areas of disturbance.

State and federal governments have made advances to protect water quality by regulating, monitoring, and enforcing clean water programs. Examples of federal government water pollution control are the 1987 Clean Water Act Amendments to the 1977 Clean Water Act and the 1990 Coastal Zone Act Reauthorization Amendments. More recent updates to legislation include: the Beaches Environmental Assessment and Coastal Health (BEACH) Act of 2000; the 2000 amendments to the Marine Protection, Research, and Sanctuaries Act of 1972; and the 1996 amendments to the Safe Drinking Water Act of 1974. Public and private businesses are using more pollution prevention and pollution reduction initiatives to control water pollution. More citizens are also practicing water conservation and participating in more community area cleanups (Source: EPA Office of Water).

Procedure

Before the activity, make 100 tokens of each of the nine colors of construction paper for a total of 900 tokens. The construction paper may be folded in quarters to speed up the process of cutting or punching. For younger students, tokens can be made by cutting construction paper into ½-inch squares. For older students, simply use a hole-punch to make the tokens from construction paper. Put all tokens in a container. Stir them so the colors are thoroughly mixed. Make one copy for each student of the *Pollutant Information Sheet* on page 211.

1. List the four major categories of pollution (chemical, thermal, organic, and ecological) on the chalkboard and discuss each. Refer to the background for a description of each.
NOTE: Humans primarily cause the first three types of pollution, although there are cases in which natural processes can cause them. Ecological pollution is typically natural, although there are cases in which humans cause it.

Runoff from livestock introduces nitrates and disease-causing pathogens into waterways.

What's in the Water?

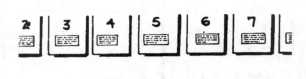

2. Pass out the *Pollutant Information Sheets*. Review each kind of pollution with students. Discuss how some pollutants can fit into more than one of the four categories. Assign each of the pollution types a color. Then write a short description of the pollution and glue it to construction paper, making sure it's the assigned color. Post each sheet of colored paper with its corresponding description of the kind of pollution it represents in a row in a convenient place.

3. Once pollution types have been discussed and students understand that each kind of pollution will be represented in this activity by one color of paper, have them divide into research teams of three students. Each team will analyze the pollution content of a hypothetical river. Supply each team with a piece of graph paper. Pass the container of colored paper tokens to each research team to measure out their share (¼ teaspoon of the paper-punched tokens or 1 tablespoon of the ½-inch square tokens).

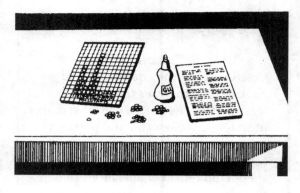

4. The teams first must separate the colored tokens into piles. Then, using the color key, they should identify each type of pollutant. Next, have students count the number of each kind of pollutant they identified and use graph paper to construct a simple bar graph by gluing or taping the tokens onto the paper. Make sure students show the whole array of pollutants, arranging them in the same order as displayed in the color key posted in the classroom. This step makes it easy to compare each team's findings. Remind teams that each has a different river. Their results are not likely to be the same.

5. When students have completed the bar graphs and compared results, tell them that any quantity above two units of each kind of pollutant is considered damaging to wildlife habitat. In their hypothetical rivers, what pollutants would likely cause the most damage to wildlife and wildlife habitat? Give examples, and discuss kinds of damage that could be caused.

OPTIONAL: Invite students to match the pollutants with the four categories of pollution listed at the beginning of the activity. Some seem to fit rather easily; others could fit in more than one category, depending on the source of the pollution. For example, is thermal pollution human or naturally caused (power plant water effluent or thermal hot springs)?

Extensions

1. List five things you can do to reduce the number of pollutants you add to the environment.

2. Conduct a field trip to a local waterway; attempt to identify what, if any, kinds of pollution are affecting it.

State and federal governments have made advances to protect water quality by regulating, monitoring, and enforcing clean water programs.

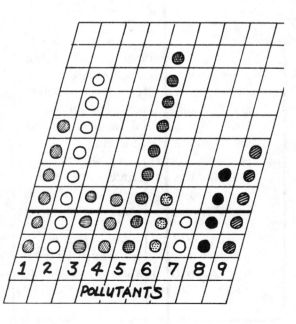

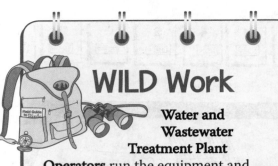

WILD Work

Water and Wastewater Treatment Plant

Operators run the equipment and control the processes that treat wastewater. They often collect samples of water or wastewater and perform routine laboratory tests. Employers seek applicants with at least a high school diploma. Persons interested in this work should take math, science, industrial technology (to learn the care and use of tools), and subjects on industrial development.

Wastewater Treatment Plant Engineers ensure and optimize plant operation, guarantee the quality of purified wastewater, coordinate plant teamwork, and build and develop relationships with customers and partners. Education requirements include a graduate degree with a specialization in wastewater treatment. For more information, see WILD Work at *www.projectwild.org/aquatic*.

In Step with STEM

■ Visit a local waterway or find drainage points around your school site. Attempt to identify evidence of point and nonpoint sources of pollution. Use a GPS to record the locations and use a camera to document photos of the area and sites of pollution. Post findings on a student blog, with discussion of ways to reduce pollution that threatens the waterway.

■ Use online aerial images to locate a nearby waterway and identify land uses that may contribute to nonpoint source pollution.

3. Get information about current national and state laws protecting water quality in the United States. Write a short history of the U.S. Clean Water Act.

4. Is DDT still being used, and where? Find out the current status of this pesticide's use in the United States and other parts of the world.

5. Conduct community service on urban or rural waterways through a class trip to collect and properly dispose of trash. Prior to the clean-up day, contact local press to provide media coverage of the effort.

Evaluation

1. Describe the effects that large quantities of different pollutants might have on an aquatic environment. Consider short-term and long-term effects of hot water, fertilizer, soil (silt), heavy metals, etc.

2. Water is taken from a river, treated, used by people of a community, sent to a city sewage treatment plant, and returned to the river. Is this aquatic pollution? Defend your response.

Additional Resources

The EPA launched a website and mobile application to help users find information on the condition of thousands of lakes, rivers, and streams across the United States from their computers, smartphones, and tablets. Available at *www.epa.gov/mywaterway*, "How's My Waterway" uses GPS technology or a user-entered location to provide information about the quality of local waterbodies.

© *Council for Environmental Education (CEE)*

Pollutant Information Sheet

Sediments

Particles of soils, sand, silt, clay, and minerals wash from land and paved areas into creeks and tributaries. In large unnatural quantities, these natural materials can be considered pollutants. Construction projects often contribute large amounts of sediment. Certain lumbering practices affect sediments in runoff. Sediments may fill stream channels and harbors that later require dredging. Sediments suffocate fish and shellfish populations by covering fish nests and clogging the gills of bottom fish and shellfish.

Petroleum Products

Oil and other petroleum products such as gasoline and kerosene can find their way into water from ships, oil-drilling rigs, oil refineries, automobile service stations, and streets. Oil spills kill aquatic life (fish, birds, shellfish, and vegetation). Birds are unable to fly when oil loads their feathers. Shellfish and small fish are poisoned. If it is washed on the beach, oil requires much labor to clean up. Fuel oil, gasoline, and kerosene may leak into groundwater through damaged underground storage tanks.

Human and Animal Waste

Human waste that is not properly treated at a waste treatment plant and then released into water may contain harmful bacteria and viruses. Typhoid fever, polio, cholera, dysentery, hepatitis, flu, and the common cold are examples of diseases caused by bacteria and viruses in contaminated water. The main source of this problem is sewage entering water. People can come into contact with these microorganisms by drinking polluted water or through swimming, fishing, or eating shellfish living in polluted waters. Often unexpected flooding of barnyards or stock pens can suddenly increase the toxic effects of animal waste in water. Animal waste can also act as a fertilizer and damage the ecosystem by increasing nutrients. Especially in urban areas, pet waste can enter water environments through stormwater systems that carry water directly to bayous, bays, and other waterbodies.

Organic Waste

Domestic sewage treatment plants, food-processing plants, paper mill plants, and leather tanning factories release organic wastes that bacteria consume. If too much waste is released, the bacterial populations increase and use up the oxygen in the water. Fish die if too much oxygen is consumed by decomposing organic matter.

Inorganic Chemicals

Inorganic chemicals and mineral substances, solid matter, and metal salts commonly dissolve in water. They often come from mining and manufacturing industries, oil field operations, agriculture, and natural sources. These chemicals interfere with natural stream purification. They destroy fish and other aquatic life. They also corrode expensive water treatment equipment and increase the cost of boat maintenance.

Detergents and Fertilizers

Many of these substances are toxic to fish and harmful to humans. Some are very poisonous even at low concentrations. The major source of pollution from agriculture comes from surplus fertilizers in runoff. Fertilizers contain nitrogen and phosphorous that can cause large amounts of algae to grow. The large algae blooms cover the water's surface. The algae die after they have used all of the nutrients. Once dead, they sink to the bottom where bacteria feed on them. The bacterial populations increase and use up most of the oxygen in the water. Once the free oxygen is gone, many aquatic animals die.
This process is called "eutrophication."

Heated or Cooled Water

Heat reduces the ability of water to dissolve oxygen. Electric power plants use large quantities of water in their steam turbines. The heated water is often returned to streams, lagoons, or reservoirs. With less oxygen in the water, fish and other aquatic life can be harmed. Water temperatures that are much lower than normal can cause habitat damage. Deep dams often let extra water flow downstream. When the water comes from the bottom of the dam, it is much colder than normal.

Acidic Precipitation

Aquatic animals and plants are adjusted to a rather narrow range of pH levels. When water becomes too acidic because of inorganic chemical pollution or from acidic rain, fish and other organisms die.

Pesticides, Herbicides, and Fungicides

Chemicals that are designed to limit growth of or to kill life forms are a common form of pollution. This pollution results from attempts to limit the negative effects of undesirable species on agricultural crop production. Irrigation, groundwater flow, and natural runoff bring such toxic substances to rivers, streams, lakes, and oceans.

Something's Fishy Here!

Grade Level: Middle School

Content Areas:
Language Arts, Environmental Education

Method:
Students read and discuss a story, inventing their own endings that lead to environmental action in their community.

Materials:
One copy for each student of the story *The Swimming Hole Tragedy*, writing materials

Activity Time:
two or more 30- to 45-minute sessions

People Power:
any

Setting:
indoors/optional outdoor session

Conceptual Framework Topic Reference:
HIIA, HIIIB4, HIIIB5

Terms to Know:
pollution, action, responsibility, siltation

Appendices:
Let's Go Fishing!, Service Learning, Using Local Resources, Agencies and Organizations

How have your favorite local waterways changed?

Objectives

Students will (1) identify potential cause-and-effect relationships involving aquatic-related pollution, (2) generate and evaluate alternative solutions to problems of aquatic pollution, and (3) outline a plan to reduce the consequences of possible aquatic pollution in their communities.

Background

Individual citizens often feel helpless when an issue is presented in their community. Yet successful action to resolve community issues frequently begins with individual action. Students have initiated community projects that improved the safety of neighborhoods, created greenspace, and preserved major habitats for wildlife.

Communities face many issues today. Reducing or eliminating pollution is one example of an area where individuals can make a difference. Significant aesthetic improvement can result from reducing the most common forms of water pollution: litter and siltation. Other forms of pollution are far more elusive and more difficult to detect and eliminate. Many organizations are working to identify and eliminate sources of pollution in groundwater, brooks, streams, lakes, rivers, and oceans.

Pure water cannot be found in nature. Even as water falls from the sky, it picks up carbon dioxide and other gases and becomes more acidic. Water is known as the universal solvent, which means that it can dissolve many kinds of substances. Water can also carry suspended particles such as soil and plant materials to rivers, lakes, streams, and so forth. These particles affect the penetration of light and, in turn, the plants living below the water's surface. Water temperature and the amount of dissolved gases also change and affect the life in it.

Water pollution is usually described in relation to how humans use that particular body of water. For example, because trout are sensitive to many changes in aquatic chemistry, water in a trout stream may be labeled polluted for human use if conditions reach a point at which trout die. However, the water could still support other types of fish and not be considered polluted for that species. In other words, water could be described as polluted for some purposes and not for others.

Adding chemicals to water affects certain organisms, depending on the concentration of the chemical. Some chemicals can be toxic to some organisms even at very low concentrations. Scientists usually measure concentrations of materials by comparing the parts of that substance to the parts of water containing it. When concentrations of materials reach critical levels, certain organisms die.

Aquatic organisms need the oxygen that is dissolved in water. When oxygen levels fall below certain points, those organisms die. The temperature affects the amount of dissolved oxygen that can be present in water. The warmer the water, the less oxygen it can hold. Some animals need more oxygen than others; therefore, warm water can be described as polluted for some kinds of fish and not polluted for others.

Procedure

1. Have each student silently read the story *The Swimming Hole Tragedy* located at the end of this activity.

2. After all students have finished, discuss the story with them. Ask students to think about as many different endings to the story as possible. **OPTIONAL:** Ask each student to write an ending for the story.

3. In small groups, ask students to share their recommendations for how the story could end.

4. Ask each small group to decide on the ending they most prefer. It is fine if students do not agree. Have each group report to the other groups the ending or endings they recommend. List the essential points of each recommended ending on the chalkboard.

5. Discuss various endings with the entire class. Identify cause-and-effect relationships. Look for possible relationships between the story and problems regarding water use and the aquatic habitats that might or do exist in the students' own community.

6. Next, have students generate a list of possible aquatic pollution sources in their community. As an option to help expand the list of topics, at this point you may want to take students on a walk/trip to visit and observe the local waterways and look for signs of any potential aquatic pollution (trash, chemicals, erosion, etc.).

WILD Work

What's the difference between a **Water Quality Specialist**, a **Hydrological Technician**, and an **Environmental Protection Specialist**?

How does a **Public Affairs Specialist** connect people with the wildlife in a neighboring park or wildlife refuge?

What does a **Law Enforcement Officer** do to protect aquatic wildlife?

Start researching the answers to these questions with students by going to *www.projectwild.org/aquatic*.

In Step with STEM

Frog Populations

■ Visit a local waterway with an organization or business that monitors water quality. Write about each procedure used, how data is collected, how data is analyzed, and a summary of the overall water quality at the monitoring site.

■ Use online satellite imagery, aerial photos, and street views to explore different ways land is being used around a local waterbody. How might various land uses either positively or negatively impact water quality? What actions can your community take to influence how land is used in a way to support healthy aquatic ecosystems?

7. Have them form groups that have a common interest in one or more of the concerns, and ask them to develop a plan to find out more about the situation in their community. That is, what will they need to know to address this need? (Will they need to know the history of the selected issue? Will they need maps of the area in question? Where can they get information to identify constituent groups or individuals?)

8. Once they have identified the information needed, they should devise a plan to collect it. (Who in the group collects what data? Where does each person acquire his or her assigned information? When can all students obtain their information?) Have each group report to the class the concern it selected and its plan to research the background information.

NOTE: Coach students to choose problems that they might actually solve. For example, pollution in a nearby brook is far more realistic for them to address than that in an entire river system.

9. Allow each group time to research the aquatic concern it selected.

10. When the research is completed, ask each group to report its findings to the class.

11. After each presentation, have the entire class brainstorm ten things that might be done to address that group's issue. Make sure each presenting group records the suggestions offered by the class. Allow class time for students in each group to discuss the various suggestions among themselves and to form an implementation plan.

12. Facilitate students' action projects by helping them establish timelines and specific assignments to carry out their implementation plans.

Additional Resources

The EPA launched a website and mobile application to help users find information on the condition of thousands of lakes, rivers, and streams across the United States from their computers, smartphones, and tablets. Available at *www.epa.gov/mywaterway*, "How's My Waterway" uses GPS technology or a user-entered location to provide information about the quality of local waterbodies.

Extensions

1. Follow through with class members on the implementation plans they created to address aquatic concerns or needs in the community.

2. Find a way to publicize what the groups have accomplished. Contact broadcast media, the city council, garden clubs, a parent-teacher association, etc.

3. Work to raise interest among other students to address additional important aquatic wildlife and habitat-related issues.

Evaluation

1. Identify potential types of aquatic pollution in the community. Identify the pollution source. Describe some of the issues associated with pollution.

2. Water is taken from a river, treated, used by people of a community, sent to a city sewage treatment plant, and returned to the river. Is this aquatic pollution? Defend your response.

3. Sam Smith and Jill Jones each caught a fishing line on a dead tree in a stream. They couldn't get their line loose, so they cut off about 15 feet of line. Is this aquatic pollution? Defend your response.

The Swimming Hole Tragedy

The swimming hole in the Creston River below Midvale was one of the most popular places, especially during the long, hot summer months. Even as early as May, groups of students would enjoy this special spot.

We had to drive five miles of unpaved road to a place where the river widened out and deepened. There we could take turns jumping off the overhanging branch of a big cottonwood tree into the cool dark waters. Most kids in town had known about this swimming hole since they were young. It was where most of us learned to swim. We went there to catch frogs and fish and to float around on old inner tubes. That place brought back those special memories of childhood that still seemed as fresh as yesterday, even though years had passed.

On hot, lazy, vacation days, Midvale residents would be drawn to the wet oasis to play, relax, and learn some important lessons. It was there that I first learned that dragonfly "dive bombers" really didn't sting or sew up your lips. It's strange how those old stories get started. Sometimes I'm sorry that those myths have to die. They always added excitement and mystery to growing up and playing along the river. It was there that I learned that the best way to find stonefly larvae was to carefully lift a stone from the river bottom and scrape the clinging animals off with a leaf. It was easy to figure out how they got their name.

I reached the point where I knew almost every log that jutted out into the river's current below the surface. That was where those lunker bass were. I knew the locations of the best logs as I knew the back of my hand—at least until the next heavy rain and high water came along. I can still close my eyes and see the sparkle of sunlight on the rippling waters. I can feel and smell the dank moisture down under the big trees by the swimming hole. All of those memories and more made the swimming hole a special place—both in my head and in my heart. You probably know some special places in the outdoors that do the same thing for you.

No one could ever guess that such a paradise would turn our hearts so dark. This place took my sister's hearing away and came close to claiming her life. I was crushed, and I never will forget the feeling. Here's how I think it all happened. One day my sister Jenny, Jeff, and I went down to swim at our favorite spot. The swimming hole gradually had changed over the years. No one had been able to catch any big bass recently. More junk was floating downstream and the water wasn't as deep as it used to be. Fewer insects were hatching, and piles of trash were gathered around fence posts.

On the day we went swimming, the water was especially warm and it had a greenish tinge, but that didn't stop us. In fact, we invented a contest to see who could dive down and bring up the biggest rock from the bottom. We stayed longer than usual that day and made over 50 trips diving from top to bottom. A couple of days later, we all had earaches and had to stay home from school. There was little doubt how our pains came about. We had not told our families that we were going to go to the swimming hole. When my Mom found out, she said that the river had become an open sewer. She said that we had taken our last swim in the river. It was too late for my sister, Jenny. Jenny's ears got worse and, after an intense fever, she lost her hearing forever.

We called the health department and soon after someone came to the swimming hole to take water samples. In fact, they took samples all along a stretch of river that passed by three towns, including Midvale. I was there to watch them take the samples. The person from the health department told me that they suspected one or more of the towns might be dumping raw sewage directly into the river. The sewage treatment plants were all over 40 years old, and the towns had grown by leaps and bounds since then. Human sewage can carry germs that can cause more damage than just earaches, the official told me.

It was a long time before I could again return to the river, but when I did, I noticed that it was harder to find stoneflies and other creatures that lived in the river. I also noticed that the water color had become greener and murkier. It all had happened so slowly that, until our earache incident, I didn't pull all the pieces together. When I did, the conclusion was clear—even if the water in the river wasn't. The Creston River was polluted, and now I had a painful reminder that this was hurting the living things I cared about—including my sister.

It seemed ironic that the river that had taught me so much and had given me so much pleasure had now changed. What should I do about it? Could one person make a difference? I had some important reasons to try.

Water Works

Grade Level: Upper Elementary, Middle School

Content Areas: Social Studies, Environmental Education

Method: Students create a "water web" to illustrate the interdependence among water users and producers.

Materials:
Copy of *Descriptions of Water Users* (pages 220–222), index cards, marking pens, tape or string, one 1-gallon plastic milk jug (labeled "source water"), large ball of string or yarn
OPTIONAL: index cards

Activity Time:
Preparation time: 30 minutes
Activity time: 50 minutes

People Power: any; 10 to 30 students ideal

Setting:
classroom

Conceptual Framework Topic Reference: IDIB, ECA1, AAIIB, HIIIA, RAIC

Terms to Know:
direct water use, indirect water use

Appendices:
Using Local Resources, Agencies and Organizations

What do a loaf of bread, a sheet of paper, and an automobile have in common?

Objectives

Students will (1) distinguish between direct and indirect uses of water, (2) illustrate the interconnectedness of water users in a community, and (3) demonstrate the complexity of resolving water shortages among interdependent community water users.

Background

When students think of using water, they probably consider direct uses: drinking a glass of water, brushing their teeth, or taking showers. They may not realize they are using water when they eat a pear, crumple a piece of paper, or listen to the radio. The complexity of water conservation issues becomes more apparent as students experience the needs of and interconnectedness among water users.

People use water for direct and indirect purposes. Direct purposes include bathing, drinking, and cooking. Indirect uses of water include the large quantities of water needed to grow grains for our bread, to process wood for making our paper, and to produce steel used in the automobiles we drive.

Agriculture, industry, and energy production are society's major water users. Sometimes we are critical of the amount of water a manufacturer requires to create a product; however, we are often the major consumers of that product. To resolve this dilemma, many water users are searching for ways to maintain production but reduce water consumption.

Today, many farmers practice more efficient irrigation methods. Manufacturers use less water by incorporating recycled materials into their products or by recycling water within their factories. For example, producing one ton of recycled paper uses 60,000 gallons (230,000 liters) less water than producing one ton of virgin paper. Individuals who conserve water and energy and use recycled products support the efforts of conscientious manufacturers and farmers, ensuring the availability of water for all water users.

Before the activity, have students list various ways they use water. If students do not include indirect uses of water, ask them if they think they use water when they ride in a car or read a newspaper. Explain that producing both cars and paper requires water. Have students suggest other ways they indirectly use water. Ask students to estimate how much water is required to make each of the items listed in the box below. Do not tell them if their estimates are accurate.

Procedure

1. Instruct each student to select a water user from the *Description of Water Users* or from a class-generated list (for large classrooms, consider dividing the class into "water user" groups). Make nametags to identify water users. (Students may research how their water user depends on this resource.)

2. Have each student read silently the description of his or her water user. Ask "water users" to consider how they depend on products and services supplied by other users. For example, the steel manufacturer uses water to process steel and wash away waste materials. The production of steel requires not only water, but also energy; therefore, the car manufacturer is dependent on the power plant.

3. Clear an area in the room. Place a milk jug labeled "Source Water" on a desk or chair in the middle of the cleared area. Tie the loose end of the ball of yarn to the jug. Explain that the jug represents sources of water and the yarn symbolizes the water user's need for water.

4. Ask students to stand in a circle around the jug of water.

5. Select a student to describe the goods or services his or her water user provides and how this product or service uses water. Run the ball of yarn to the student (who remains holding the yarn) and back through the jug's handle or around the lip of the jug. This indicates that this water user consumed water. This can be repeated for each student.

Indirect uses of water include the large quantities of water needed to grow grains for our bread, to process wood for making our paper, and to produce steel used in the automobiles we drive.

A pair of jeans made from cotton	1,800 gallons (6,840 l)
A loaf of bread	1,000 gallons (3,800 l)
A pound of hamburger	4,000 gallons (15,200 l)
A 12-ounce can of soda	16.5 gallons (62.7 l)
A ton of finished steel used to make a car	32,000 gallons (121,600 l)
40 sheets of paper	100 gallons (380 l)

6. Choose one water user (Student 1) and hand him or her the ball of yarn. Ask other students to raise their hands if they use the goods or services offered by that student.

7. Ask Student 2 (one of the students who raised his or her hand) to describe how he or she uses the products or services of Student 1. Tell Student 1 to pass the ball of yarn to Student 2.

8. Ask if other students use the products manufactured by Student 2. Have Student 2 pass the ball to another student (Student 3). Have all students repeat the process until connections are made among all or most class members.

9. To emphasize the interdependencies among water users, have one student tug gently on the yarn. Ask those who felt the pull to raise their hands. The tug symbolizes reliance on both water and that student's product.

10. At some time during the activity, the water jug may shift or be lifted from the chair or table. Explain that this indicates the supply is being over-extended. Ask students if they think one water user should leave the circle. What will happen if one student lets go?

Water Works
© *Council for Environmental Education (CEE)* and *The Watercourse*

Variation

As an alternative way to make connections among water users, give each student five index cards. Have each student write the name of his or her water user on each of the five cards. Students may decorate the "business card" of their water user with illustrations of goods or services provided. One at a time, or in small groups, have students distribute their cards to other water users on whom they depend for goods or services. Students should end up holding index cards with names of other interdependent water users. Conclude by having students read aloud their cards and describe the connections they have made.

Evaluation

1. Describe your direct and indirect uses of water.

2. Draw a diagram showing how water users rely on the goods and services provided by other water users.

3. Conduct a town meeting where proposed solutions to a community water shortage are being discussed. If community water supplies are over-extended, how would the community decide which user group should reduce water consumption?

Extensions

1. Tell students a bottle of food coloring represents a source of pollution. Place a drop in the jug. Have students explain how water quality affects the quantity of water available to water users.

2. Have students form groups of common water users. How do groups relate to other water user groups? Although a common bond is shared in our need for water, discuss how conflicts can arise among water user groups.

3. Have students contact local manufacturers, asking them how they use water and what conservation measures they practice. Students can create a mural of the water user groups in their community. Include how community members use water, depend upon each other, and, if appropriate, conserve water.

WILD Work

Finance professionals assist companies in managing and reducing costs, which can result in conserving resources such as water and energy. For information on the related careers of **Budget Analyst**, **Statistician**, **Accountant**, and **Wildlife Economist**, head to: *www.projectwild. org/aquatic*.

In Step with STEM

■ Ask students to identify how water is used at school. How can they find out how much water is used for different purposes? Have them design a project to explore water use. For example, using a hose, a sprinkler, and a 5-gallon bucket, how could a measurement be taken of the quantity of water used when watering grass?

■ Compare school water usage to the flow in a local stream. Measure the depth and width of the stream. Place a floating object in the stream such as a bobber, stick, or leaf. Use upstream and downstream markers to calculate the rate of flow. For more information, visit *www. projectwild.org/aquatic*.

■ Research greywater systems with students and discuss how recycled wastewater could be used at school or home.

Description of Water Users

In addition to the descriptions listed below, students may research a specific water user during the week prior to this activity.

 Agriculture: Water is used to produce food and fiber for processing and consumption.

 Sugar cane grower: Uses water to irrigate crops and transport chemicals (pesticides and fertilizers) to crops.

 Cattle rancher: Uses water to grow food and provide drinking water for cattle, and to clean their areas for living and feeding, transporting waste to holding ponds.

 Wheat farmer: Uses water to irrigate crops.

 Dairy farmer: Uses water to grow food and provide drinking water for cows, and to sanitize milking equipment and stalls.

 Mining: Water is used in the extraction process of raw materials (coal, iron, gold, copper, sand, gravel, gas, and oil.

 Miner: Uses water to carry and wash rock material during the mineral removal processes.

 Sand and gravel company: Uses water to wash fine soil and rock material out of sand and gravel formations. Sand and gravel are used in cement and road construction.

 Petroleum company: Uses water in the process of fracturing rock layers to retrieve stored petroleum or natural gas.

 Logging: Water is used to grow and harvest trees.

 Forest manager: Uses water to support tree growth and control fires.

 Logging company: Uses water to float rafts of logs (on rivers and lakes) to collection points.

Description of Water Users

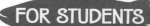

 Transporting/Shipping: Water (rivers, seas, oceans) is used to transport raw materials and finished products to points of distribution (ports).

 Slurry pipeline owner: Uses water to transport crushed coal through pipelines to distant coal-fired power plants.

 Ship's crew: Uses water to haul raw materials (e.g., logs, oil, gas, wheat) and finished products (e.g., automobiles, appliances, processed food) to points of transfer.

 Wildlife: Water provides habitat for countless plant and animal species.

 Mammals: Beavers, muskrats, and otters live in and near waterways.

 Fish: Trout, salmon, and carp live in water and eat organisms that live in water.

 Insects: Aquatic insects are a food source for many other organisms.

 Vegetation: Trees and other plants use water in photosynthesis and to transport nutrients.

 Business/Industry: Water is used in the processing and manufacturing of goods (cars, food, medical supplies, etc.).

 Steel producer: Uses large volumes of water to process iron ore into steel.

 Textile manufacturer: Uses water to wash and process raw materials (e.g., wool, cotton, mohair). Dye is mixed with water to color fabric.

 Soft drink company: Uses water to produce soft drinks and to sanitize equipment.

 Paper mill: Uses water to transport pulp fibers for paper making and to carry away waste.

 Chemical manufacturer: Uses water in the production of pesticides and fertilizers.

Description of Water Users

Recreation: Water is used by people for exercise and enjoyment.

 Cruise ship: People travel to many parts of the world on cruise ships.

 Fishing: People catch fish in rivers, lakes, and oceans.

 Water theme park: Uses water to transport people on exciting and fun rides.

 Scuba diver: People enjoy exploring underwater environments.

 Winter sports: Snow and ice provide fun for skaters, skiers, and sledders.

 Power Generation: Water is used to generate electricity.

 Hydropower plant: Water flowing in rivers is stored behind dams in reservoirs. As water is released by the dam, it turns turbines that generate electricity.

 Nuclear power plant: Uses water in cooling towers to maintain safe operating temperatures.

 Coal-fired power plant: Burning coal produces steam heat that turns turbines, creating electricity.

 Community: Water is used by community members for domestic, maintenance, and recreational purposes.

 Domestic users: Water is used in a multitude of ways in and around the home and lawn.

 Fire department: Uses water to extinguish fires.

 Restaurant owner: Uses water to cook meals, clean the kitchen, wash tables and floor, and water lawns.

 City government: Uses water in fountains and reflecting ponds and for landscaping and maintenance needs.

Alice in Waterland

Follow the journey of water up, down, and around to travel through the hydrologic cycle.

Objectives

Students will (1) trace domestic water to its source prior to human use and to its destination after use, (2) identify potential effects from human water use on terrestrial and aquatic wildlife, and (3) develop and practice responsible water conservation behaviors.

Background

The hydrologic, or water, cycle is a model that traces the cyclical journey of water. This path involves (1) precipitation—such as rain or snow—on a watershed; (2) runoff that flows into streams, groundwater systems, lakes, reservoirs, estuaries, and oceans; (3) evaporation and evapotranspiration, which returns water to the atmosphere; (4) cloud formation; and (5) condensation as water falls again in the form of precipitation on a watershed (see Diagram A). The great storehouses of water—glaciers and icecaps—are also part of this cycle. All forms of life on Earth are dependent upon and affected by this dynamic and continuing process. In between the watershed and the ocean, humans divert water from its natural course to be used in a variety of ways.

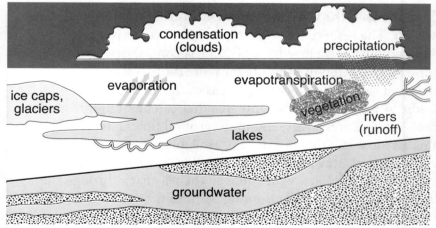

Diagram A

Grade Level: Upper Elementary, Middle School

Content Areas: Science, Environmental Education, Mathematics, Social Studies, Expressive Arts

Method: Students use a simulated field trip, lecture and discussion, and student-gathered data to explore water use and its effects on wildlife habitat.

Materials: One "Water Consumption Chart" (page 226) per student; several long sheets of paper for murals; art materials for the murals (poster paints, vivid pastels, chalks, etc.)

Activity Time: two or three 45-minute sessions

People Power: any

Setting: indoors or outdoors

Conceptual Framework Topic Reference: HIIIA3, HIIIB

Terms to Know: water cycle, hydrologic cycle, conservation, evapotranspiration, transpiration, condensation, evaporation

Appendices: Service Learning, Using Local Resources, Agencies and Organizations

Human consumption of water affects wildlife and wildlife habitat. For example, building a dam may provide water for electricity, but it also modifies wildlife habitat in stream valleys. Wetland modification can remove water from natural nurseries for wildlife. Once water is diverted from its natural path, it may return to the water cycle contaminated or polluted and the effects may be devastating.

Humans have choices on how water is consumed. Water conservation can be adapted to daily life. Water conservation not only eases the stress on natural habitats by lessening the need for dams and other interventions, but also reduces the depletion of groundwater that provides moisture for many riparian and other habitats. Groundwater conservation also benefits human populations that depend upon underground aquifers for municipal water supplies.

Conservation of both groundwater and surface waters protects the continued availability of water for humans, wildlife, and the environment. Paying attention to what is put into water and the water cycle—being careful with pesticides, detergents, fertilizers, motor oils, aerosols, cleaning fluids and powders, and caustic acids, as well as fuels and their byproducts—is another way to conserve water resources.

Procedure

1. Using a simulated field trip, ask students to sit quietly, close their eyes, and imagine themselves shrinking down to a size that would let them travel up through their faucet and into their water pipes. Ask students to picture in their minds what you will describe for them in the following words.

NOTE: Educators may want to adapt the text so it will apply to local settings. Or, if many students have well water as their domestic source, educators can convert the simulated field trip to a school or other organizational setting. Even if this scenario does not apply exactly to the students' situation, it can be used to explore a typical source of water and its routes in the United States and other countries.

Simulated Field Trip: "Picture yourself small enough to climb into the faucet in your kitchen. See yourself with magic powers that allow you to travel through the water from the faucet to its origins. You will be able to pass through all the pipes, valves, and other barriers on the way. The first part of the journey takes you through the pipes in your house to where they connect to your water source. If you live on a farm or ranch, the source would probably be a well or perhaps a spring.

"In the city, the water source for your home would probably be far away. First, you link into a water main. Then, you come to a pumping plant where water pressure is maintained. Past the pumping plant is a place where the water is purified. This structure may be very complex—a place with filters, chemical tanks, and treatment equipment.

"Beyond the purification plant, the water may be in an aqueduct or open channel coming from a reservoir. The reservoir is a huge lake where water is stored. There are often trees and bushes on its edges. Wildlife is common; fish are usually abundant; and people often use the site for recreation. Natural streams usually flow into the reservoir. They drain large areas of the land's surface, which are called "watersheds." A watershed is the land area that catches and transports water through runoff, streams and rivers, and underground flow. The water in a watershed contains all the water that is naturally available for use by all living things in that area. If you want, stay in the watershed. Try to see the plants and animals that live in the area. Or, follow your route all the way back through the reservoir, channels, treatment plant, and pumping plant to the water main and the pipes in your house and out your faucet. Then, open your eyes."

Alice in Waterland

2. After this simulated field trip, discuss the journey of water from its source to the faucet. Identify the components of the journey. Emphasize the places where wildlife habitats are affected—positively, negatively, or with unknown effects—by the intervention of people as they consume water or influence how water is consumed.

3. Repeat the process for a journey down the drain into the wastewater system:

Simulated Field Trip: "Picture yourself small again. This time the journey will be down the drain in your sink. You move along through the used-water system to a treatment site. If you live on a farm, the site will probably be a septic tank. A septic tank is usually a large concrete box. Here microorganisms break down the substances carried in the water. Once the water is partially cleansed, it flows out through drainage fields and back into streams or groundwater. If you live in a city, much more water is being used, and large water treatment plants cleanse the water before it is returned to nature. In the treatment plants are great filters and holding tanks. The water must be held in place for solid substances to settle out by gravity. Air is often pumped through the wastewater to increase the oxygen content so microorganisms can break down the impurities more quickly.

"Eventually, the treated water is released into nature. It again enters the natural habitat for wildlife. There it provides an essential component for sustaining life. If all was done well, animals, plants, and humans will safely reuse the water. It will nourish the crayfish caught by the raccoon. It will provide the pond for the box turtle. It will provide the refreshing drink for someone like you in some downstream city. After you have followed the water out into the environment, open your eyes."

---

4. Discuss the journey of water through the wastewater treatment plant. Identify the journey's components. Emphasize the places where wildlife habitats are affected—positively, negatively, or with unknown effects by the intervention of people as they use water or influence how water is to be used.

5. Divide students into two groups. Instruct one group to research the water cycle. Ask some students to find out details such as how much precipitation falls in their community and what contaminants are likely found in the precipitation. Instruct others to investigate runoff, where it goes, how much seeps into the ground, and how much travels overland. Why is it important for water to seep into the soil? Could this runoff pick up contaminants along its path? Which ones? How can runoff be reduced? Other students might look at evaporation. What conditions could accelerate or inhibit evaporation? How might changes in evaporation rates affect wildlife?

6. Ask the second group to research the waste treatment process. Some students might look up information on "primary treatment," some might research "secondary treatment," and others might find out about "tertiary treatment." Perhaps some students could find out how much water passes through the local treatment plant, which types of treatment it uses, and how much it costs to operate. Ask one team to compare the microorganisms used in treatment plants to break down wastes with those that break down wastes in soil and in septic tanks.

7. Have students in the first group create a mural on a single long sheet of paper, depicting the origins and journey of water through a natural system (i.e., emphasizing the water cycle and watershed processes). Have students portray wildlife and habitat throughout the mural.

In Step with STEM

- Conserving water supplies saves money. Drawing, storing, heating, and disposing of water can have economic costs. Calculate how much money your family would save in water and energy bills if you carried out conservation practices for a year.

- Design a closed-loop water system for a space station.

- Use a computer program, such as a word processing program, to create a flow chart to trace water in your community.

- Continue on to the activity "Where Does Water Run?" in which students calculate the amount of impervious surface on a study site and the amount of runoff from rainwater.

8. Ask students in the second group to create a mural of the journey of water through a human system (i.e., emphasizing plumbing and waste treatment plant processes). Have them portray human effects along the way.

9. Look at the entire mural—natural and human. Identify, list, and discuss places in which the quality of water may be affected by human activities, not just the quantity of available water.

10. Now shift the emphasis to the amount of water that people typically use. Pass out the "Water Consumption Chart" provided below.

11. Ask students to keep track of how much water is used in their homes for five days. Suggest that the sheet be posted on the refrigerator and that each family member help by putting a mark in the section designated after each water use. The miscellaneous section is for special uses not listed. Suggest that the students use empty 1- or 2-liter soda containers to estimate amounts.

12. After the water-use data have been gathered, make a master chart that summarizes the total use for the class for the entire week. Discuss places where water might be conserved. Challenge students to intentionally reduce their water consumption and invite their families to join in. Have them monitor use for another five days and tabulate the results.

Conservation of both groundwater and surface waters protects the continued availability of water for humans, wildlife, and the environment.

Water Consumption Chart (all values are approximate)	
3–5 gallons (12–20 liters)	Flushing a toilet
3 gallons (12 liters)	Brushing your teeth and letting the water run
5 gallons (20 liters) per minute	Shower
8 gallons (30 liters)	Cooking three meals
8 gallons (30 liters)	Cleaning house
10 gallons (40 liters)	Washing dishes (three meals)
20–30 gallons (75–115 liters)	Washing clothes
30–40 gallons (115–150 liters)	Watering a lawn
30–40 gallons (115–150 liters)	Taking a bath
30–40 gallons (115–150 liters)	Washing a car
---------------------------------------	Miscellaneous use

13. Once the results are tabulated, discuss how wildlife, habitat, and humans can benefit from human water-use conservation. Discuss the potential appropriateness and effectiveness of a variety of water conservation behaviors. Examine potential negative and positive effects. Discuss not only ways to reduce and conserve water use, but also ways to protect the quality of the water we use.

Extensions

1. Monitor water use by the school or organization. Identify ways to conserve water use.

2. Take field trips to water purification systems and wastewater treatment plants.

3. Modify the murals to show the effects of water conservation and improved water quality on wildlife habitat.

Evaluation

1. Draw and label a flow chart tracing water in your community from where it originates, to your home, and to where it goes after it leaves your home.

2. Estimate the number of gallons of water you use each day for personal use. What do you do that uses the greatest amount of water in a year?

3. Name three ways you might conserve water. How much water could you conserve using each method for a year? How might wildlife be affected by your water conservation actions? How might plants be affected?

4. Rank the following water uses from those that use the most water to those that use the least in the United States: domestic, industrial, agricultural or irrigation, and recreational (1 = most).

5. What effect, if any, does human water consumption have on animals that live on the land? What effect, if any, does human water use have on animals that live in or around water?

6. Give examples of ways that water quality can be negatively affected by human consumption. Give examples of actions people can take to protect the quality of water.

WILD Work

Water Masters monitor human withdrawal of water in watersheds where supply may be limited.

Water Works Engineers design systems for the transport of water, often in municipal settings, and control the discharge of water from places of storage.

Environmental Consultants evaluate ecosystems to determine environmental impacts from proposed actions and provide reports to businesses, industries, and governments to ensure quality environments.

Administrative Assistants may prepare and disseminate information concerning agency programs and services; maintain records and files; assist in compiling data for charts, databases, and reports; and assist in researching, composing, designing, and editing agency publications. For more information on these occupations, see WILD Work at *www.projectwild.org/aquatic*.

The Glass Menagerie

When it comes to nutrients and aquatic environments, there can be "too much of a good thing."

Objectives

Students will describe the characteristics of oligotrophic and eutrophic aquatic habitats, emphasizing the effects of nutrient loading.

Background

A healthy body of water is a delicate balance of dissolved oxygen, nutrients, temperature, and transparency. The amount of plant and animal life in a pond or lake depends on the balance of these factors.

When the water of a young pond or lake is cold and clear, it supports very little life. Over time, erosion and runoff bring organic material into the lake. The organic material—drainage from surrounding watersheds (runoff), bottom sediments in the lake, and organisms (living and dead)—are broken down by the bacteria and become food for nutrient-loving algae. As the algae multiply, so do the number of fish that feed on the algae. Over time, as the lake fills with the silt from the erosion and runoff and as the water becomes warmer, marsh plants take root and fill the lake basin. Fish populations and other aquatic organisms decline because of the limited dissolved oxygen. When this change happens, a lake or pond supports more plant life than animal life, and its waters are rich in nutrients.

A pond or lake low in nutrients is called "oligotrophic." Low plant production and high transparency (clear water) characterize lakes that are oligotrophic.

The clarity of the water is correlated to the absence of an abundance of plant life. Oligotrophic lakes often have a relatively small surface area and greater depth. They also tend to have sand or gravel bottoms.

Grade Level: High School

Content Areas: Science, Environmental Education

Method: Students observe and describe changes in the physical characteristics of several different experimental aquatic habitats they create.

Materials: Seven 1-quart (1-liter) glass jars; masking tape for labels; 1 gallon (4 liters) of distilled water; tap water; a small bottle of household plant fertilizer; a roll of aluminum foil; 1 gallon (4 liters) of recently gathered pond water (with abundant life forms); microscopes, both stereo (dissecting) and standard; soda straws; identification guides for pond life

Activity Time: four weeks for classroom observations

People Power: any

Setting: outdoors and indoors

Conceptual Framework Topic Reference: HIIIB5

Terms to Know: oligotrophic, eutrophic, nutrient loading, eutrophication

Appendices: Field Ethics, The Ecosystem and Project WILD

In eutrophic systems, the organic materials, or nutrients, can cause modifications to the lake such as algae blooms and small fish kills. While algae produce oxygen during the day through photosynthesis, oxygen producing ceases at night. During the night, the algae continue to use oxygen that fish and other aquatic organisms need to breathe.

A sudden bloom of algae uses up the nutrients rapidly and is often followed by an algae die-off. The algae that have died begin to decompose rapidly. Bacteria promoting the decomposition use up much of the available oxygen in the water.

Eutrophication can be good or bad, depending on degree and perspective. Usually, lakes in the early stages of eutrophication provide excellent recreation and fishing. In later stages, as nutrients build up, lakes can become obstructed with vegetation and covered with algae. This condition typically indicates that a lake or pond has a nutrient overload. Domestic sewage, industrial wastes, and chemical fertilizers are some sources of human-caused nutrient enrichment. These "unnatural" nutrients are frequently introduced into lakes through municipal and industrial discharges. While eutrophication is a natural process, this acceleration by humans of the process is called "nutrient loading," and it has complex effects on people, wildlife, and the environment.

Procedure

NOTE: The following procedure is designed to have students explore the aspects of eutrophication. Further investigation and discussion of the characteristics of oligotrophic and eutrophic lakes in terms of depth, surface size, temperature, and turnover are encouraged.

1. Collect (with students if possible) a gallon of viable pond water. The water must be a source of active organisms, both plant and animal. A microscope may be needed to verify how active the organisms are.

2. Label and prepare the seven jars as follows:

Lake Tahoe is an example of an oligotrophic aquatic environment.

- Jar 1, Control—3 cups (750 ml) distilled water.

- Jar 2, Distilled Water—3 cups (750 ml) distilled water, ½ cup (125 ml) pond water.

- Jar 3, Tap Water—3 cups (750 ml) tap water, ½ cup pond water.

- Jar 4, Pond Water—3 ½ cups (875 ml) pond water.

- Jar 5, Distilled Water with Fertilizer—3 cups (750 ml) distilled water, normal amount of fertilizer (as on instructions), ½ cup (125 ml) pond water.

- Jar 6, Distilled Water with Fertilizer Overload x 10—3 cups (750 ml) distilled water plus 10 times the normal fertilizer, ½ cup (125 ml) pond water.

- Jar 7, Distilled Water with Fertilizer Overload x 20—3 cups (750 ml) distilled water plus 20 times the normal fertilizer, ½ cup (125 ml) pond water.

A healthy body of water is a delicate balance of dissolved oxygen, nutrients, temperature, and transparency. The amount of plant and animal life in a pond or lake depends on the balance of these factors.

Algae blooms in this pond indicate a eutrophic aquatic environment.

NOTE: Be sure to agitate the pond water by shaking each jar for a few moments before introducing it into the other jars. It is best to have equivalent concentrations of life forms in each of the experimental jars. Save the leftover pond water for examination with microscopes.

3. Cap the jars loosely with aluminum foil to prevent excessive evaporation. Place the jars in a cool, visible, and well-lighted place. Avoid placing the jars in direct sunlight. Students will now observe and record what takes place in the jars for a 4-week period. As a pre-assessment, ask students to generate a hypothesis concerning the effects or outcomes in each of the jars. Tell them they will test their hypotheses against the evidence they gather during the 4-week observation period.

4. Have students use microscopes, either standard or stereoscopic, to examine the pond water not used in the experimental jars. Have them record their observations, including drawings or illustrations of the various life forms found in the water. Research the names of the animals in identification guides or other resource books on pond life.

5. Throughout the observation period, record daily entries on a data sheet for each jar. These observations may be completed with or without the use of microscopes, as changes will be visible to the eye without optical assistance. Have students work on a rotation basis for the data recording.

6. Some changes will begin to appear during the second week of the experiment. When life forms begin to be visible, use an eyedropper to remove some organisms carefully for study with a microscope.

7. Observe changes in the jars, and discuss the findings.

8. At the end of the 4-week observation period, discuss the role of nutrients and how they occur in nature. Label the jars with abundant organisms "eutrophic," showing nutrient loading. Label the jars without many organisms "oligotrophic." What is the role and impact of accelerated growth caused by introduced nutrient loads? What are the natural sources of nutrients and human-related sources? Compare the similarities and contrast the differences. How does nutrient loading change the number of life forms in the water? What are the indications of these accelerated changes? What kinds of effects might nutrient loading have on aquatic wildlife? On people? **OPTIONAL:** If possible, end the activity with a visit to the pond where the water was collected. If possible, visit lakes or ponds at various stages of eutrophication.

The Glass Menagerie
© *Council for Environmental Education (CEE)*

Extensions

1. Investigate the role of temperature and dissolved oxygen in pond life.

2. Investigate the role of pollutants in pond life.

3. Find out whether a pond or lake in your community is directly affected, indirectly affected, or both by eutrophication.

Evaluation

1. Code each of the following as a characteristic of eutrophic lakes (E), oligotrophic lakes (O), both kinds of lakes (B), or neither type of lakes (N) by writing one letter beside each statement.

_____ Deep, greater than 60 feet (18 meters)

_____ Have many species of plankton (both zooplankton and phytoplankton), but a low number of each species

_____ High transparency (can see a long way down into the water)

_____ Large number of fish that many people consider desirable

_____ Large amount of decaying organic matter

_____ Little oxygen available

_____ Large amount of algae

_____ Taste and odor problems

_____ Bacteria mostly aerobic (oxygen using)

_____ A result of natural or human-caused erosion

_____ High total productivity

_____ Few plant nutrients (nitrates, phosphates, manure)

_____ Considered an old lake, in terms of succession

_____ High rate of nutrient cycling

2. What could be done to alleviate human-induced eutrophication? For each of the nutrient sources (domestic sewage, industrial waste, chemical fertilizers, and others), write about potential solutions.

WILD Work

A **Curator** is responsible for coordinating the design, construction, restoration, preservation, and maintenance of exhibits, artifacts, and displays; coordinating volunteer programs and conducting instructional, research, and public service activities; and conducting research related to collections, exhibits, or historic sites. Requirements to become a curator typically include a bachelor's degree and experience in a museum or other curatorial work. Curators must be skilled in the operation of computers and applicable software. To find more information on this occupation, visit *www.projectwild.org/aquatic*.

In Step with STEM

■ For the activity, use a spreadsheet to record daily entries electronically. Then graph the data and interpret the general trend.

■ Assign one jar to each group. Measure the dissolved oxygen of each jar using a dissolved oxygen meter twice a day, in the morning and afternoon. (Dissolved oxygen meters can be obtained through a variety of classroom science suppliers or borrowed from a local natural resource office.) Graph measurements and discuss at the end of the experiment.

Fishable Waters

Grade Level: Middle, High School

Content Areas: Science, Social Studies, Environmental Education

Method: Students evaluate how healthy fish populations provide multiple benefits for their community. They use a card game to explore the connection between water quality, habitat, and "fishable and swimmable" waters

Materials: For each student, a copy of the *Sample Fishing Report*; for each group, a copy of *Fishable Waters Game Rules*, *Urban Fish Species & License Cards*, *Fishable Waters Action Cards*, cut apart; 40 "fish" tokens (see *Game Options*); **OPTIONAL:** copies of state fishing regulations (available online), photos of local fish, or field guides **NOTE:** Use different colors of cardstock and laminate cards for easy tracking and repeated use.

Activity Time: one or two 45-minute sessions

People Power: teams of 4–6 students

Setting: outdoors or large indoor area

Conceptual Framework Topic Reference: WPIIA2b2, WPIIA2a2a

Terms to Know: migration, limiting factors, habitat, wetlands, waterbirds, shorebirds, biodiversity, lure, bait, channelization, sedimentation, turbidity, nonpoint source pollution, predator

Appendices: Let's Go Fishing, Using Local Resources, Field Ethics, Sustainable Seafood, Agencies and Organizations

Wouldn't you want your waters full of fish?

Objectives

Students will (1) identify and describe the value of clean water and healthy fish populations in their community; (2) infer that populations and species compositions are not static but ever changing; (3) differentiate between harmful and positive impacts on water quality and fish populations, and know that human activities can accelerate natural processes such as runoff, sedimentation, and nutrient cycles; (4) know that management of aquatic species and their habitats is directly influenced by land-based activities in the surrounding watershed; and (5) learn that legislation, such as the Clean Water Act, is a tool used to manage resources for the benefit of present and future generations.

Background

Most major cities in the U.S. were established along water—rivers, bays, or large lakes. People settled along waterways for a variety of reasons: water-based transportation was easier and faster than traveling overland; water was easily accessible for drinking and other household uses, as well as for agriculture and livestock; and fish and wildlife found in or near water supplemented the diet and livelihoods of early communities.

The waters that supported such bounty also provided an easy way to get rid of waste. By the mid-1800s sewage in rivers caused waterborne diseases to reach epidemic proportions. By the 1960s many of our nation's waterways were so contaminated they were closed to swimming. Signs were posted along the Potomac River in Washington, D.C., warning the public not to inhale the air. Ohio's Cuyahoga River was so polluted with chemical wastes that it caught fire. The rivers, lakes, and bays that once sustained communities and provided welcome recreational opportunities had become places to avoid; our nation's fisheries were in trouble.

The Cuyahoga River fire sparked a movement toward regulating industrial pollution and resulted in the passage of the Clean Water Act of 1972. The Act called for a reduction in the direct discharge of pollutants into waterways and to achieve "fishable and swimmable" waters. The Act primarily addressed "point source pollution," pollution that can be traced to a definite point where it enters the environment, such as a factory or sewage discharge pipe.

With point source pollution regulated, water quality in many urban waterways improved dramatically. Today, there are nearly twice as many waterways that meet standards for fishing and swimming as there were before the passage of the Clean Water Act. Yet, approximately 44 percent of U.S. waterways that have been assessed are still too polluted for these activities. Where is all this pollution coming from? Urban sprawl and increasing populations require more energy, overload old sewage treatment facilities, and result in more paved and impervious surfaces. Storm water and snowmelt runoff from a variety of urban, suburban, and rural sources—from city streets, homes, construction sites, lawns, parking lots, and farms— is a form of general "people pollution" that results from activities people do every day. Because you can't necessarily point to any one source, we call this nonpoint source pollution or runoff pollution.

The major problem associated with runoff is the soil, nutrients, and pollutants it often carries. Soil erosion from agriculture and urban development causes fine silt to wash into waterways, where it may settle to the bottom, smothering fish eggs and covering up rocks that provide habitat for small aquatic organisms. When silt doesn't settle, the water will look muddy or turbid. Turbidity blocks light from reaching oxygen-producing aquatic plants, and fine silt particles may clog the gills of aquatic species.

Assessment of U.S. Waterbodies

Waterbody Type	Total Size	Amount Assessed*	% of Total	Assessed Good	Assessed Threatened	Assessed Impaired
Rivers (miles)	3,533,205	971,207	27%	449,960	6,369	514,878
Lakes (acres)	41,666,049	18,944,731	45%	5,868,017	38,681	13,038,033
Estuaries (sq. miles)	87,791	32,668	37%	11,076	17	21,575
Coastal Shoreline (miles)	56,618	9,010	15%	1,746	0	7,263
Wetlands (acres)	107,700,000	1,317,011	1%	208,944	805	1,107,261

Assessed River Miles

46% Good · 53% Impaired

Assessed Lake Acres
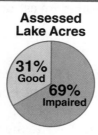
31% Good · 69% Impaired

Assessed Estuary Square Miles
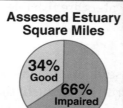
34% Good · 66% Impaired

Assessed Coastal Shoreline Miles
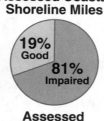
19% Good · 81% Impaired

Assessed Wetland Acres

16% Good · 84% Impaired

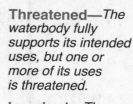
Good—The waterbody fully supports its intended uses.

Threatened—The waterbody fully supports its intended uses, but one or more of its uses is threatened.

Impaired—The waterbody is partially or fully unable to support one of more of its uses.

NOTE: For all waterway types, the percentage of area that has been assessed as threatened is <1%.

The data above are obtained from the Water Quality Assessment and Total Maximum Daily Loads Information prepared by the EPA under Section 305(b) and 303(d) of the Clean Water Act. This database is available at *www.epa.gov/waters/ir/*. Data on most states were collected in 2010, while others were collected from 2004 to 2008.
Visit *www.epa.gov/waters/* to access WATERS, U.S. EPA's Watershed Assessment, Tracking & Environmental ResultS, an interactive tool that connects water quality data from several databases and displays information by generating maps and reports.

Agricultural runoff, containing manure and crop fertilizer, is considered the main source of harmful nutrients (nitrogen and phosphorus) in our waters. Urban pet wastes and fertilizers from lawns and golf courses also contribute significantly. These excess nutrients fuel rapid growth of algae. Like turbidity, floating algal mats block sunlight needed by submerged aquatic vegetation. When algae and grasses die, the decomposition process consumes oxygen from the water, causing "dead zones" where few fish or other aquatic species can survive.

What can be done to address such a large and ambiguous challenge? Communities can "adopt" and clean up local waterways; citizens can vote for change, making tough decisions that balance local economics with sound resource management; and people can educate each other about nonpoint source pollution and how to take preventative action.

Specific actions individuals can take to reduce runoff include planting buffer zones of trees and vegetation between homes and businesses and storm drains or bodies of water; replacing impermeable hardscape (concrete, asphalt, etc.) with gravel, vegetation, or other permeable materials; and installing ponds, wetlands, or rainwater catchment systems to collect excess water. To reduce the amount of pollution collected by runoff, individual citizens can limit fertilizer and pesticide use (especially before it rains), pick up trash and pet waste, and properly dispose of household and other chemical wastes.

Across America many citizens, and even entire cities, have taken action to improve waterways. River front and waterfront revitalization projects have improved communities' water quality, as well as recreational access to these remarkable water resources. The recreation and tourism industry is the second largest employer in the United States, and a significant portion of recreational spending comes from water-related activities, such as swimming, boating, sport fishing, and hunting. Ensuring that local waters are fishable is a sound investment for any community.

The Clean Water Act of 1972 called for a reduction in the direct discharge of pollutants into waterways and to achieve "fishable and swimmable" waters.

Procedure

1. Ask students to name species of fish found in local waterways and write the name of the species on the board. (Hint: Teachers can contact their State Department of Fish and Wildlife to learn about types of local fish species.) Write the word "FISH" in the center of the board and draw several lines with arrows radiating outward from the word (similar to spokes on a wheel; see Diagram A on the following page). Ask student volunteers to describe the values of fish for the local community, and write or draw a different value at the end of each spoke. Encourage students to consider how certain species might be of cultural, religious, economic, or recreational importance in their community.

Fishable Waters
© Council for Environmental Education (CEE)

2. Next, draw a set of spokes with arrows pointing toward the "FISH" hub. Have volunteers indicate factors necessary for fish survival. Encourage students to describe specific water quality factors (e.g., pH, temperature, turbidity, concentrations of oxygen, nitrates, phosphorus, etc.).

3. Facilitate a discussion about the importance of good water quality for fish in your community. Describe the Clean Water Act of 1972, legislation that set a goal for "fishable and swimmable waters" (see "Background" information). Ask students the following question: If waters are suitable for fishing and swimming, what other benefits—for wildlife and people— might be implied? Fish can be thought of as indicators of a healthy aquatic ecosystem that includes the food web necessary for survival and reproduction of other fish and aquatic species.

Diagram A

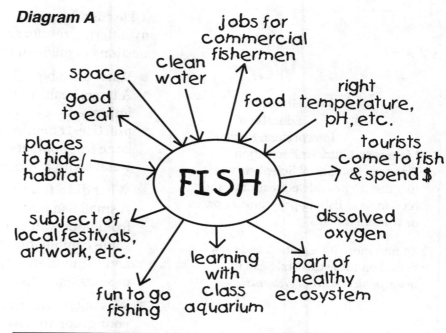

4. Divide the class into small groups of four to six students. Distribute copies of the *Sample Fishing Report* and instruct students to read independently or in groups.

5. Facilitate a class discussion about the reading. Make sure students understand the connections between water quality, fish populations, and different natural and human impacts affecting both.

6. Explain that groups will play a card game to simulate the different ways human activity can impact water quality and fish populations in urban waterways. The challenge is to have the best "fishable waters" possible— indicated by lots of "fish" added to the waterway or by "fish" caught and distributed among players.

NOTE: Make sure students understand that results of actions on *Fishable Waters Action Cards* are presented solely from the perspective of impacts on water quality, fish habitat, or fish populations. The cards are not intended to imply generalized judgment of any of the actions featured. For instance, hydropower dams generate power and store water for municipal and agricultural needs and also often adversely affect fish populations. Determining the pros and cons of building a dam in any particular area and determining whose water needs are most important are, of course, open for debate and beyond the scope of this simulation. This point can be made prior to or immediately following the simulation.

7. Distribute a copy of *Fishable Waters Game Rules* to each group. Review and discuss the rules aloud.

8. Distribute a set of *Fishable Waters Action Cards*, 40 tokens ("fish"), and other game materials to each group. See *Game Options* for possible variations. Allow groups to start the simulation and play until at least one student from each group gets to "go fishing." Circulate among your students to make certain the game runs smoothly. You may pretend to be a fisheries biologist "stocking" waterways with fish. If you do stock fish, be certain to include the impact of stocking when discussing the results of the simulation.

9. After 10 or 15 minutes (or after all cards have been read), stop the simulation. Ask groups to report the number of fish in their urban waterway, the number of fish in their lost fish pile, the number of fish "caught" and stored in their ice chests, and the number of people in their group who had the opportunity and chose to go fishing. Compile class data on the board.

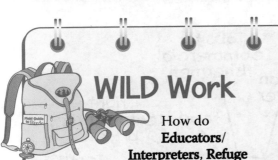

In Step with STEM

■ Inspect the schoolyard for potential sources of pollution that may be carried into local waterways by rainwater. Implement strategies to reduce sources of pollution. Use a GPS to record the locations and a camera to document photos of the pollution on the site, both before and after implementing pollution reduction efforts. Share your results with others to encourage stewardship of water resources.

■ Research in groups how various water treatment facilities operate. Introduce and compare methods of treatment such as sediment and sand filtration and research pollutants that might not get filtered out using these methods. Discuss how the facilities might impact local ecosystems. What are the pros and cons of different methods? Take into consideration the size of the community and the source the water is pulled from.

10. Discuss the results of the simulation, including reasons for any differing results among groups. You may use the following questions to guide the discussion:

■ What did a big pile of playing tokens represent?
A large, healthy (and diverse) fish population resulting from improved water quality and habitat, sustainable harvesting practices, effective stocking, or some combination thereof—a large fish population indicates "fishable and swimmable" waters with a variety of community benefits.

■ What did a few tokens represent?
A small fish population (likely lacking in diversity) resulting from poor water quality, habitat destruction, overfishing, or some combination thereof—indicating the need for habitat and community improvement projects and/or development of sustainable fishing practices.

■ Was obtaining "fishable waters" hard? How long did it take your group to have a "fishable" waterway?

■ What happened as the game progressed and the deck got smaller?
More cards in the deck were fish and license cards, resulting in more opportunities to go fishing. Increased fishing without continued action projects or positive influences on fish populations causes fish populations to decline.

■ Which activities were more effective at improving water quality than others (more tokens added)?

■ Which activities were more detrimental to healthy water and fish populations (more tokens removed)?

■ How does this simulation represent the real world of water quality and fish populations?
Water quality and fish populations are not static; they change over time because of both natural and human influences.

■ How does this activity differ from the real world?
Resource managers and communities make and implement plans for managing water quality and fish populations, whereas actions in the simulation were more random; reproduction and other natural events would occur, causing fish populations to fluctuate differently.

■ How do fishing regulations influence the availability of fish?
Regulations serve to distribute and/or limit fishing opportunities for the purpose of maintaining viable and/ or sustainable fish populations. **NOTE:** Some habitats have changed so drastically that sustaining populations by natural reproduction alone is not possible. In other cases, the demand for fish is higher than the number of fish that is naturally sustainable. In both instances resource agencies may raise and stock fish to maintain populations.

Extensions

1. Students may conduct research on a recreationally or economically important local fish species. Are populations stable and sustainable? Have populations or biodiversity changed over time? If so, why? What management strategies (regulations, stocking, habitat improvement projects, etc.) are used to ensure viable populations? Invite a fisheries biologist to visit your classroom and speak about managing local fish populations in an effort to attain or maintain "fishable waters."

2. Challenge students to identify and report on local water quality or fish population issues. After hearing student reports, encourage members of the class to decide how they would like to take action. Sample projects include: raising fish in the classroom; organizing a river clean up; monitoring water quality or fish populations; and designing projects on runoff/erosion control (building and installing rain barrels, planting rain gardens and trees, etc.).

3. Plan a fishing trip. Most states have resources for urban fishing, including: tackle loaner programs; free "how-to" fishing clinics; lists and maps of places to fish; free fishing days; and print materials, such as fish posters or identification cards.

4. Have students quiz each other using their state's fishing regulations booklet, available online or through the local natural resources office.

5. Conduct your own fishing simulation using casting training tools called "Backyard Bass" (sold by Ironwood Pacific Outdoors). Children and adults learn to operate reels and cast a special weight that "hooks" (using a non-hooking device) a plastic fish. You may also make your own fish using felt and Velcro.

6. Work with your school's physical education teacher to apply for a grant to acquire fishing rods so that students can practice the life skill of casting. Contact the National Fishing in Schools Program to learn about their fishing curriculum (see page 318 for more information).

Evaluation

1. Draw a new "fish wheel," highlighting areas of possible concern regarding fishable waters in your community.

2. List or describe a variety of reasons why fish are important to your community.

3. Identify and describe five issues that have negative impacts on water quality or fish populations.

4. Describe ways to address issues that have negative impacts on water quality or fish populations.

5. Relate how human activities are connected to water quality and how water quality is connected to fish populations.

Discover an Urban Fishing Program Near You

To learn about urban fishing programs in your area, visit *www.takemefishing.org*. Click on the "Fishing" tab and then the "Places to Fish" tab on the following page. Then click on your state. Though information varies, this webpage will yield information such as: highlights of fishing programs in different cities; recommended fishing sites organized by region; information about fishing clinics and free fishing days; links to state fishing license requirements and other fishing regulations; and contacts for tackle loaner programs.

Game Options

1. Use pennies as tokens to represent the economic value of "fishable and swimmable" waters in your community.

2. Use fish-shaped crackers or other snacks to represent an important product of "fishable and swimmable waters," food for wildlife and humans. If you use snack food as tokens, ask students to refrain from eating their "catch" until the end of the game and class discussion. This enables students to tally and compare their catches at the end of the simulation.

3. Enhance the sense of "fishing" by making fishing rods using a pencil, string (approximately one foot in length), flat thumb tack, and small magnet. Use metal paper clips to represent fish. You might use both large and small paper clips, stipulating that large paper clips represent keeper-size fish and that small paper clips represent fish sized below the legal limit. Players should put back (or release) any small paper clips they "catch."

4. At times during the simulation a student may answer a question on a *Fishable Waters Action Card* correctly, but still be required to subtract a "fish" from his or her urban waterway because of the detrimental effect an action has on fish populations. If you feel your students will object to this, you might consider an alternative tracking and reward system to recognize students for providing correct answers to questions.

Directions for making a fishing rod:

A. Tie a small knot in one end of a string. Insert a thumbtack into the knot, and then push the tack into the eraser end of a pencil.

B. Cut a piece of magnetic tape about an inch in length. Don't take the paper backing off the tape—the adhesive is very sticky.

C. Cut two small "v" shaped notches on either side of the piece of magnetic tape.

D. Tie the string onto the tape, securing it in the notch. Make sure the knot is on the paper side of the magnet so that the magnet can work effectively to "catch" paper clips.

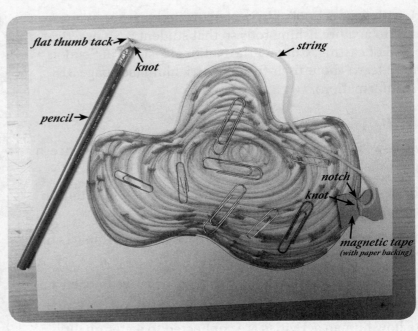

flat thumb tack →
knot
string
pencil →
notch
knot
magnetic tape
(with paper backing)

Sample Fishing Report

What's the Catch In the D.C. Metro Area?
A Fishing Report for April 2012

Cool spring water temperatures in the Potomac River and nearby tributaries mean fishing is "hot." Cold waters hold more dissolved oxygen than warm waters—meaning fish are breathing easily. In the Potomac, Largemouth Bass are hitting lures, including soft plastic jigs and vertically jigged spoons, with frenzy! D.C. and Maryland regulations limit a daily take of five fish measuring at least 12 inches (15 inches after June 15th), and conservation officers will ticket anglers over their limit!

The mouth of Little Hunting Creek (VA) is usually a great spot for catching bass, but runoff from a nearby construction project is washing soil into the river causing high turbidity (muddy water) even after light rains. To compensate for the turbidity, anglers are using dark lures. Later in the season, bass anglers know they can catch fish in the grass beds (submerged aquatic vegetation) near the Woodrow Wilson Bridge.

Yellow Perch have spawned out, but a few are still being caught in Piscataway Creek (MD). Anglers reported strong Bluegill action at Cameron Run (VA) when casting small jigs toward the grass edges, shoreline vegetation or under overhanging trees. This riparian zone provides shade that cools the water. Roots prevent bank erosion and are perfect structure for hiding or resting perch.

TROUT IN WASHINGTON? Paint Branch Creek (MD) is a unique urban cold-water fishery with wild brown trout. Nonpoint source pollution from urban runoff continues to threaten these pollution-intolerant fish. Fisheries biologists and local conservation groups have educated people living along the creek about the need to reduce fertilizer use, especially before a rain. Nutrients in fertilizers, manure, leaky septic tanks, and pet wastes cause

explosive algal blooms. Eventually, this algae rots, causing a stinking mess that consumes dissolved oxygen—suffocating fish and other aquatic critters. To find trout, focus on riffles—the swift, bubbly areas that help oxygenate water.

The Anacostia Park (D.C.) is always good for Channel Catfish. Serious anglers fish right from the shore, using surf rods to get their lines into the river channel. A weighted line with cut bait works best. These fish are fun to catch, but D.C. has published a fish consumption advisory against eating catfish, as they may harbor harmful toxins.

This past spring biologists reported record numbers of spawning American Shad just below Chain Bridge off Fletcher's Boathouse (D.C.). The return of this historic fish is due in part to the hundreds of students raising fish in the classroom and the fishway or ladder at the Little Falls Dam that helps spawning fish navigate the 12-foot dam upstream to their preferred habitat.

Other local improvement plans include a shoreline revitalization project along the Anacostia River. Once completed, people will be able to enjoy fishing piers, boardwalks, and parks—the perfect spot to grill up your catch. In the meantime, we encourage anglers to join a river cleanup organized by the Earth Conservation Corps—Riverkeepers. To date, Riverkeepers have hauled out 536 tons of trash and 8,103 tires.

Homegrown Heroes:

Since 1989, the Anacostia Watershed Society—along with thousands of volunteers—has aimed to make D.C.'s Anacostia River more "fishable and swimmable." Their projects include:

- ✓ Watershed Stewards Academy
- ✓ River Report Card
- ✓ Water Quality Monitoring
- ✓ Invasive Plant Management
- ✓ RiverSmart Schools
- ✓ River Cleanups
- ✓ Trash Trap
- ✓ Shad/Herring Awareness and Restoration Effort (SHARE)

GOOD OLD DAYS? - Old timers might remember when fishing our nation's rivers wasn't this good. Back in the 1950s, the Potomac ran foul with factory discharge and poorly treated sewage (point source pollution). The Clean Water Act in 1972 regulated this pollution, and now 60% of U.S. waterways are "fishable and swimmable"—twice the number of fishable waters as before the Act. Today, the Potomac is considered one of the nation's premier bass fisheries, and anglers can watch nesting Bald Eagles while they fish—an indication that water quality has improved. Biodiversity in a waterway is not just about lots of different fish species—but includes all other animals and plants living in or near the waterway.

Source: Foundation for Ohio River Education, *fore.orsanco.org*.

Fishable Waters Game Rules

Discover how human activities impact fish populations. Take turns drawing cards, answering questions, taking action, and going fishing. The group with the most "fishable" waterway at the end of the game wins!

Setting Up the Game:

1. Place 10 tokens (15 for groups with 5 or 6 players) in the center of your group. The tokens represent "fish" in your urban waterway. Place the deck of cards face down to serve as your Draw Pile.

2. Place remaining tokens in a Stock Tank. You will add these fish to your urban waterway, as directed on cards.

Your group's goals are:

- To improve your fishable waters—indicated by increasing the fish population (# of tokens) in your waterway; and

- To have each individual in your group collect three (3) fish cards and one (1) fishing license card in order to "go fishing."

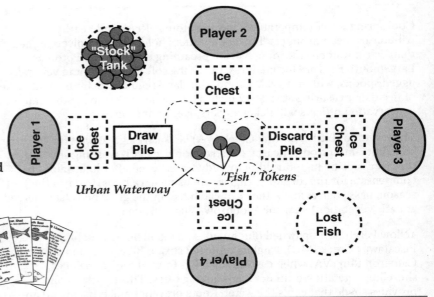

Playing the Game:

1. Decide who will go first. Begin the game by drawing a card from the Draw Pile.

2. If the card has a ⭐, read it aloud and ask the player to your left to answer the question. Instruct the player to add or subtract fish from your urban waterway, as directed on the card. Subtracted tokens represent fish lost because of negative impacts on water quality and habitat. Make a separate pile of "Lost Fish" for later comparison. Place the used question card face up in a Discard Pile.

3. If the card has a ⬤, read it aloud and do what it says.

4. If you draw a fish or license card, read it aloud and keep it.

5. Play moves clockwise (to player's left). Take turns drawing cards, answering questions, and collecting **fish** and **license** cards.

6. When you collect 3 **fish** cards and 1 **license** card, you may "go fishing." Fishing regulations limit your "catch" to 5 fish. If using large and small tokens, only large fish may be kept; release small fish back into the waterway.

Before going fishing, decide whether waters are "fishable."

- What if there aren't enough fish in the waterway to take your limit of five?

- Should you take fewer than five?

- Should you take any?

- What if you practice "catch and release" where you return all fish "caught" back into the waterway?

Decide whether to take what's available or wait to go fishing until the waters get more "fishable."

7. If you do go fishing, shuffle your **fish** and **license** cards back into the Draw Pile. Keep all fish in your "Ice Chest" for later comparison.

8. If you draw an extra **fish** (you have more than 3) or **license** card (you have more than 1), shuffle it back into the Draw Pile and draw a new card.

9. If you draw a **Wild Card!**, you may go fishing right away. Keep any **fish** or **license** cards you have accumulated, but shuffle the **Wild Card!** back into the Draw Pile.

10. When your teacher calls time to end the game, count and record the number of fish in your Urban Waterway, Lost Fish pile, and Ice Chests. Also record how many people went fishing.

RULES AT A GLANCE

- You may go fishing only when you have 3 fish cards AND 1 fishing license (fish cards can be any species)—OR when you draw a Wild Card! After fishing, return your collected cards to the Draw Pile and reshuffle.

- When fishing you must follow regulations (possession limit of 5 fish), but you may take fewer if you choose.

- Players must immediately shuffle extra fish and license cards into the Draw Pile so that others can collect them.

Urban Fish Species & License Cards

Yellow Perch

Bait/Lures: Perch are delicious eating and easy to catch, especially during spawning season. Fish near structures using minnows, grass shrimp, or worms. Jigs, small plugs that imitate small fish (minnows) or cray fish, are good lures. Need colder water than many other fish.

jig

Channel Catfish

Bait/Lures: Catfish are active mainly at night, during twilight hours, and during or right after a rain. These are bottom feeders, so fish them deep with a sinker. Cut bait, like herring or chicken liver, work great, but worms, stinkbait, and cheese are good too.

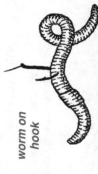

worm on hook

Bluegill

Bait/Lures: Fish for bluegill near "structure" (brush piles, weeds, docks), using worms you dig from your yard or small jigs and spinners. Using a sinker, fish about a foot from the bottom and attach a bobber so you can see when they hit.

bobbers

Brown Trout

Bait/Lures: Trout are smart predators, so you need to think like a trout. Is it winter? Then don't fish with grasshoppers. Your best bet is lures that mimic local baitfish: small crankbaits (crawfish and minnows), spinners, and flies (not real flies, ones made with feathers and fur).

trout fly

Largemouth Bass

Bait/Lures: Largemouth are predators that lurk in weedy, quiet waters and feed mainly on other fish. Minnows are great bait, but live or plastic worms work, too. Bass are often caught on spinner baits and crankbaits.

spinner baits

Fishing License

Most states require an annual fishing license (check your local regulations for specific age requirements).

Did you know that license sales help fund fish research, restoration and stocking programs, access sites (parks, piers, docks, etc.), and education programs? By buying a license, you're not only obeying the law but also helping fish and habitat as well.

Fishing license sales help fish. **(Add 1 "fish")**

American Shad

Bait/Lures: American shad live in the ocean but reproduce (spawn) in freshwater. The best time to fish for them is during their spawning run when they congregate near dams or fishways. Fish for shad with flutter spoons, shad darts, or small Clouser flies.

flutter spoon

Fishing License

Most states require an annual fishing license (check your local regulations for specific age requirements).

Did you know that license sales help fund fish research, restoration and stocking programs, access sites (parks, piers, docks, etc.), and education programs? By buying a license, you're not only obeying the law but also helping fish and habitat as well.

Fishing license sales help fish. **(Add 1 "fish")**

Fishable Waters Action Cards

Diversity Is the Spice of Life

Your class finds high biodiversity in your local waterway.

True or False: This likely indicates a very healthy habitat with a healthy fish populations.

True: Having lots of different species of plants and animals is called "biodiversity." Biodiversity results in a complex and interdependent food web of different predators and prey, producers, consumers, and decomposers. High biodiversity often indicates healthy habitat.

High biodiversity often means healthy fish populations.

(Add 2 "fish")

Fishable Waters Are Good Business

How much does fishing contribute to your state's economy?

Florida $14 billion
California $9 billion
Texas $8 billion
Minnesota $5 billion
N. Carolina $4 billion
Wisconsin $4 billion
Michigan $4 billion
New York $4 billion
Ohio $3 billion

_____
(your state)   (contribution to economy)

A booming fishing industry may mean more $ spent on stewardship of fish and fish habitat. This helps fish.

(Add 1 "fish")

Tough Decisions

As money taken out of a bank, water is withdrawn from waterways for a variety of human uses: agriculture, hydroelectric power, manufacturing, public drinking water, etc. During drought or in drier times, communities are faced with tough decisions: do they continue to "spend" water resources to provide for increasing human needs, or do they restrict additional development so that fish and habitat have adequate water? If put to a vote, which would you choose: **restrictions** or **more development?**

Restrictions can help fish.
(Add 3 "fish")

More development can harm fish.
(Subtract 3 "fish")

Fish Ladders

Imagine trying to exit the freeway but having all the off ramps blocked. You'd be trapped. That's what happens to fish when they encounter a dam.

True or False: Fish ladders can help fish get around a dam.

True: Special structures called fish ladders or fishways can be built to help fish get around a dam. These structures are important for fish that need to get farther upstream to reproduce or spawn.

Fish ladders help fish.

(Add 2 "fish")

Shoreline Revitalization

Urban shorelines were once ideal sites for factories—oftentimes because factory waste could be released directly into the water (point source pollution). Today, many of these areas are being turned into shoreline parks, boardwalks, and community centers, providing access to fishing and other recreation.

Your city is considering a shoreline revitalization project, though taxes would be raised to pay for it. You head to the voting booth to decide on a referendum to support the project. Do you vote **yes** or **no?**

Yes: Revitalization can help fish.
(Add 3 "fish")

No: The status quo is maintained
(Don't do anything)

Adopt a Stream

True or False: Your class can help state biologists manage fish.

True: School classes and other groups can adopt a stream and collect data to share with state biologists. Your class might test for pH, dissolved oxygen, turbidity, and other water quality factors. You might also search for certain aquatic critters; the presence of "biological indicators" is evidence of the health of the stream. Sharing data about streams with state biologists helps them manage fish.

Collecting data and sharing it with state biologists help fish.

(Add 2 "fish")

Where's the River?

In many urban areas it can be hard to find any rivers. Many urban rivers have been converted into concrete channels or metal culverts. Channelization prevents natural processes like the growth of aquatic vegetation and the formation of pools and riffles; in other words, fish habitat. During times of high water, culverts can also:

a. increase erosion
b. increase flooding
c. increase turbidity of water
d. all of the above

Answer: d. all of the above

Channelization can harm fish.
(Subtract 2 "fish")

Wild Card!

Your state's natural resource agency offers FREE FISHING DAYS. The agency, along with partners, host fishing clinics to teach you how to fish and may have a tackle loaner program to help you get acquainted with the equipment you'll need.

Check your state fishing regulation booklet or the agency's website to find out when these days are scheduled.

Go Fishing!

(Subtract 2 "fish")

Fishable Waters Action Cards

Fish In the Classroom

Native fish in your area are in trouble—they aren't reproducing at a rate that maintains a sustainable population.

Your class wants to help by hatching eggs and raising fish in the classroom and then releasing them back into your local waterway. Who might you work with to achieve this goal?

a. environmental education center
b. state fish and game offices
c. local fishing clubs
d. all of the above

Answer: d. all of the above

Raising and releasing fish helps maintain fish populations.

(Add 3 "fish")

Litter: Trash or Treasure?

True or False: Litter may look ugly, but it poses no harm to fish and other aquatic wildlife.

False: Many types of litter can cause great harm to aquatic wildlife. Litter may be mistaken for food and ingested, such as when sea turtles eat floating plastic bags, thinking that they are jellyfish. Wildlife can also become ensnared in plastic rings used to package beverages or in discarded fishing line.

Litter harms fish.

(Subtract 2 "fish")

Storm Drain Stenciling

True or False: It is easier and more cost effective to prevent pollution from getting in our water than to restore water quality, habitat, and fish populations later.

True: Pollution prevention, including public education and storm drain stenciling, can help reduce the often enormous costs of restoring waterways after they have been polluted. You can help by educating your community about the harm in using sewers as dumps by stenciling:

"all drains lead to __name your waterway here__"

Pollution prevention helps fish.

(Add 1 "fish")

Stream Cleanups

We can't prevent all pollution from entering our water—but we can take action.

Your group decides to organize a local cleanup event to help get the trash out. You invite the local media so that your community can learn how they can help maintain "fishable and swimmable waters," too.

Stream cleanups can help fish.

(Add 1 "fish")

Riparian Buffer Zones

How can trees, shoreline vegetation, and wetlands help fish and improve water quality?

a. Trees and shoreline vegetation trap runoff before it gets to our waterways.
b. Wetlands absorb and filter out pollutants and protect young fish.
c. Trees shade waterways, keeping them cooler.
d. all of the above

Answer: d. all of the above

Riparian buffer zones help fish.

(Add 3 "fish")

Fishing Regulations

You know someone who keeps all the fish they catch—no matter how large or small the fish are. *What if everyone did this?*

How can you learn about current fishing regulations?

a. Read your state's current fishing regulations booklet.
b. Ask your fishing buddy.
c. Ask your uncle (he hasn't gone fishing in 5 years).
d. none of the above

Answer: a. Read your state's current fishing regulations booklet.

Following fishing regulations helps fish.

(Add 1 "fish")

Algal Blooms

You discover algae growing out of control in your favorite fishing hole. It is beginning to rot and stink. You see a dead fish floating on the surface of the water and remember that the rotting process (called decomposition) uses up oxygen. This means there is less dissolved oxygen for aquatic animals, such as fish. What is the likely cause of this algal bloom?

a. too much sunlight
b. excess nutrients, including nitrogen and phosphorous
c. emptying aquarium water into the fishing hole
d. none of the above

Answer: b. excess nutrients

Algal blooms harm fish.

(Subtract 3 "fish")

In Hot Water

Thermal pollution, adding warm water to a waterway, reduces dissolved oxygen, changes habitat, and can stress fish if the temperature rises too much. Which of the following cause thermal pollution?

a. direct discharge of warm water from factories and power plants
b. runoff from hot city streets and pavement
c. a summer heat wave
d. both a. and b.

Answer: d. both a. and b.

Thermal pollution harms fish.

(Subtract 2 "fish")

Fishable Waters Action Cards

Fish Consumption Advisories

True or False: All fish are good for you to eat.

False: Some fish may contain high levels of mercury and other toxins, which make them unsafe to eat. Each state publishes "fish consumption advisories." Check your regulations to know which fish are listed as unsafe to eat.

Fish under consumption advisories are living in polluted waters.

(Subtract 1 "fish")

Keep or Release?

Many anglers choose to practice "catch and release." After reeling in a fish, they carefully unhook their catch and gently return it to the waterway. When practiced properly, catch and release does not harm fish. There are no limits on catch and release fishing.

Go fishing and practice catch and release!

Catch and release helps fish.

(Add 2 "fish")

Clean Water Act

The Clean Water Act of 1972 did much to regulate point source pollution—pollution that can be traced to a definite point where it enters the environment. An example of point source pollution is:

a. chemicals leaking from a factory's discharge pipe
b. runoff from fields
c. sewage from a discharge pipe
d. both a. and c.

Answer: d. both a. and c. Both chemicals and sewage from discharge pipes can be traced to their sources. Regulating this type of pollution has led to a dramatic improvement in water quality in many waterways.

The Clean Water Act helps fish.

(Add 3 "fish")

Conservation Officer

True or False: Conservation officers, officials responsible for enforcing fish and game laws, can't ticket people.

False: Conservation officers are like police officers, but their main duty is to protect our natural resources. They ticket people who don't follow regulations and can arrest poachers—people who don't follow fishing or hunting regulations.

Enforcing fishing regulations helps fish.

(Add 1 "fish")

Aquatic Vegetation

True or False: Submerged aquatic vegetation, like grasses, is messy and should be cleaned out of rivers and lakes.

False: Fish need a place to hide from predators and to rest. If you've ever gone fishing, you know that many species of fish hang out near grasses and other aquatic plants. This structure is "home sweet home" to fish.

Submerged aquatic vegetation helps fish.

(Add 2 "fish")

Water Conservation

Water conservation increases the availability of water for all life forms, but sometimes there just isn't enough to go around.

During times of drought, should your city restrict certain water uses, like watering lawns, washing cars, and filling swimming pools?

Yes or **No**?

Yes: Conserving water, especially during drought, helps fish.

(Add 3 "fish")

No: Using water for nonessential purposes, especially during drought, harms fish.

(Subtract 3 "fish")

Construction and Water Quality

Which of the following would help your construction company win a *"Water Steward of the Year Award?"*

a. Leaving as much native vegetation and trees on site as possible
b. Installing silt fencing or wattles to prevent erosion and reseeding after construction
c. Installing raingardens and catchment basins that take up excess storm water
d. all of the above

Answer: d. all of the above

Environmentally responsible construction helps fish.

(Add 2 "fish")

Permeable or Impermeable Materials

You are a member of the city planning commission. A vote has come up to decide whether new parking lots should be made of permeable or impermeable materials. Permeable materials allow some rain to seep into the ground whereas impermeable materials do not absorb water and can cause runoff. You know that controlling runoff helps reduce erosion, but permeable materials can be very costly. Which way will you vote?

permeable or **impermeable**?

Impermeable materials: Increasing runoff can harm fish.

(Subtract 2 "fish")

Permeable materials: Controlling runoff can help fish.

(Add 2 "fish")

Nonpoint Source Pollution

Which is an example of nonpoint source pollution?

a. oil leaking from a docked ship
b. chemicals seeping from a landfill
c. motor oil washing from driveways, streets, and parking lots
d. sewage overflow from a sewage treatment plant

....

Answer: c. When we can't point to the source of pollution in waterways—which may come from many different streets, lawns, construction sites, parking lots, and farms—we call it nonpoint source pollution. Most water pollution today comes from nonpoint sources.

Nonpoint source pollution harms fish.

(Subtract 2 "fish")

Impermeable Surfaces

An example of an impermeable surface is:

a. a wetland
b. a dirt road
c. a concrete parking lot
d. none of the above

....

Answer: c. concrete parking lot. Many urban and suburban areas are concrete: streets, sidewalks, parking lots, and buildings. These impermeable surfaces don't allow rain or snowmelt to seep into the ground. During heavy rains, city storm drains are often flooded by runoff that has picked up chemical pollution and street trash, too.

Impermeable surfaces on land can harm fish.

(Subtract 2 "fish")

Off-season fishing

It's a week before bass season opens. Your buddy hooks a trophy-sized Largemouth Bass. This is:

a. illegal
b. called poaching
c. a great opportunity for his uncle, a taxidermist
d. both a. and b.

....

Answer: d. both a. and b. Poaching means fishing or hunting out of season, taking more than the legal limit, and fishing or hunting without a license. Seasons and limits are set by resource managers to prevent overfishing. License sales help pay for management and track the number of anglers.

Poaching harms fish.

(Subtract 1 "fish")

Hydropower Dams

True or False: A dam provides extra water, which is good for the native fish that lived in the river before it was blocked by the dam.

....

False: Large dams generate power and store water for municipal and agricultural needs. But most fish and other native species prefer their natural river environment—not a warm, still reservoir. Some dams drain rivers virtually dry, allowing only a trickle to pass below—not good for fish or other aquatic species.

Dams can harm fish.

(Subtract 1 "fish")

Turbidity

Turbidity means:

a. cloudy or muddy water
b. still or slow moving water
c. cranking a fishing reel slowly

....

Answer: a. Another word for muddy water is "turbidity." Storms can stir up sediments from the bottom of waterways, and heavy runoff erodes banks and washes soil into streams and rivers. Some fish have a hard time feeding in turbid, muddy water, and sediments can smother fish eggs as well as reduce resting and hiding places.

Turbid water can harm fish.

(Subtract 2 "fish")

Attack of the Aliens

True or False: It's okay to dump or release your live bait when you're done fishing.

....

False: If bait is not native to your waterway, it is called an "alien species." Unfortunately, some aliens can become invasive, meaning they out-compete native species for food and habitat. They can take over and disrupt the natural ecological balance.

Alien species can harm fish.

(Subtract 1 "fish")

Go Green!

Your neighbor removed trees and shrubs from her yard that were blocking her river view.

True or False: She can be fined and forced to replant.

....

True: In many areas setback laws require that business and residents maintain a "buffer zone" of trees and other plants along waterways. This vegetation filters pollutants and stabilizes banks, preventing erosion.

A single tree can keep more than 4,000 gallons of water out of the sewer each year. Just imagine what a whole shoreline of trees can do!

Setback laws help fish.

(Add 2 "fish")

Nutrient-rich Wastes

Excess nutrients in waterways can cause algal blooms, which in turn may cause "dead zones" and "fish kills" by depleting dissolved oxygen. How can we prevent excess nutrients from entering our waterways?

a. Maintain or upgrade wastewater treatment plants.
b. Limit fertilizer use on lawns, golf courses and farms.
c. Scoop pet and livestock droppings.
d. all of the above

....

Answer: d. all of the above

Keeping excess nutrients out of waterways helps fish.

(Add 2 "fish")

Turtle Hurdles

Grade Level: Upper Elementary, Middle School

Content Areas:
Science, Social Studies, Environmental Education

Method:
Students role-play as turtles, or the limiting factors affecting turtles, through a highly active life cycle journey.

Materials:
40 to 60 feet of rope or string, two jump ropes or hula hoops, one paper or plastic bag per student, identity cards for each predator or limiting factor (can be drawn by students), wooden clothes pins, poker chips, dried beans

Activity Time:
one 45-minute session

People Power:
20 or more students

Setting:
outdoors or large indoor area

Conceptual Framework Topic Reference:
ITIB1, ITIIA1

Terms to Know: life cycle, endangered species, threatened species, prey, predator, limiting factors, hatchling

Appendix:
Climate Change

Survival against all odds.

Objectives

Students will (1) describe the life cycle of sea turtles, (2) identify specific mortality factors related to sea turtles, (3) make inferences about the effects of limiting factors on sea turtle populations, and (4) make recommendations to minimize the factors that might lead to the extinction of sea turtles.

Background

Sea turtles are survivors from the great age of the dinosaurs and inhabit nearly all the oceans of the world. The best-known sea turtles are in the family Cheloniidae, which contains the Green Turtle, Loggerhead Turtle, Hawksbill Turtle, and Ridley Turtle. The huge Leatherback Turtle, the largest living turtle, is placed in Dermochelyidae, a separate family. Sea turtles live mostly in warm waters and have limbs modified into flippers. Female sea turtles crawl above the tide line to bury their eggs. Sea turtles leave the water only during these nesting periods. It is during this time that the turtles and their offspring are the most vulnerable to predation by humans and other wildlife.

As with most reptiles, turtles lay eggs. The eggs look somewhat like wet, pliable Ping-Pong balls. Using their rear flippers, female sea turtles dig deep holes on sandy beaches where they lay and bury their eggs. Mature female sea turtles may deposit several hundred eggs in one season. Once the eggs are buried, the females return to the sea or seek additional nesting sites.

The eggs incubate for nearly two months. If the eggs survive predation by raccoons, crabs, foxes, dogs, and humans, then the sea turtles hatch, dig their way upward through the sand, and promptly head toward the sea. Predatory crabs, raccoons, and dogs, with gulls and other birds joining in, typically accompany the hatchlings' journey across the beach. Once hatched, only about one to five percent of turtles survive the first year. In the sea, turtles must mature for nearly a decade before returning to nesting sites as a natural part of their life cycle.

Turtle Hurdles
© *Council for Environmental Education (CEE)*

Biologists are uncertain how long sea turtles reproduce and live. Diagram A illustrates the life cycle of a sea turtle.

The predominant motive for human predation of sea turtles is the consumption of or profit from products that are outlawed in many countries. Jewelry, leather, oil, and food are the primary uses. Turtle eggs are seen by some as a boost to longevity and vigor; tens of thousands of eggs are illegally harvested for vanity sales. Evidence suggests that a serious human threat to turtles is the poaching of their eggs from nesting sites.

There are other human-caused factors. Dune buggies may break the eggs buried in the sand. More damaging, given the scope of the impact, is commercial and private construction (condominiums, private homes, hotels, etc.) on coastal sites. This construction may create a barricade that prevents turtles from reaching their traditional nesting sites and that eliminates many nest sites. Entanglement in discarded fishing gear and plastic waste cast into the oceans is a serious hazard, killing many sea turtles each year. Many turtles also fall accidental victim to the nets of large fishing trawlers. Once caught in the nets, they drown. Efforts are being made to popularize special trawling devices that will prevent turtles from getting trapped in the nets. Turtle Excluder Devices (TEDs) on fishing and shrimping boats allow turtles to escape nets to avoid drowning. With some exceptions, commerical fishing vessels are required by federal regulation to be equipped with TEDs. Furthermore, many turtles mistake discarded, floating plastic bags for jellyfish, a favorite food of sea turtles. When eaten by the turtle, its digestive tract becomes blocked with the plastic and it dies.

Six of the seven known sea turtle species are officially designated as either endangered or threatened. The Leatherback, Olive Ridley, Kemp's Ridley, Hawksbill, and Green are all listed as endangered species by the U.S. Fish and Wildlife Service. The Loggerhead, although not listed as endangered, is listed as threatened and under review by the U.S. Fish and Wildlife Service. A threatened species is one that is likely to become endangered if it is not protected, while endangered means that a species is in immediate danger of becoming extinct and needs protection to survive.

Diagram A

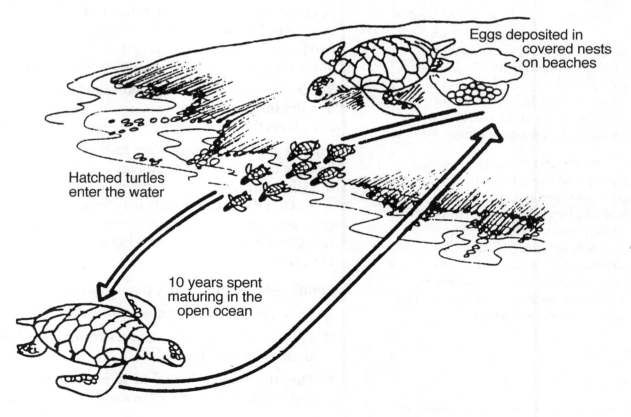

Eggs deposited in covered nests on beaches

Hatched turtles enter the water

10 years spent maturing in the open ocean

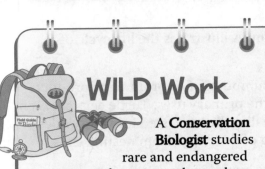

WILD Work

In Step with STEM

■ Visit a local waterway with an organization or business that monitors water quality. Write about each procedure used, how data is collected, how data is analyzed, and a summary of the overall water quality at the monitoring site.

■ Use online satellite imagery, aerial photos, and street views to explore different ways land is being used around a local waterbody. How might various land uses either positively or negatively impact water quality? What actions can your community take to influence how land is used in a way to support healthy aquatic ecosystems?

Procedure

1. Set up the activity areas as shown in Diagram B on the next page. Give each student a paper or plastic bag.

2. Divide the class into two groups.

Group 1—Turtles

Each student counts out 50 beans to place in his or her bag. Beans represent turtles. Each bag of beans represents the turtles that hatch from a single nest.

Group 2—Limiting Factors

Divide this group into two smaller groups, on-land and in-sea.

On-land: Predators (e.g., raccoons, dogs, crabs, foxes, and gulls) and limiting factors from human activities (e.g., dune buggies, human egg collectors, shoreline development)

In-sea: Predators (e.g., sharks, killer whales) and limiting factors from human activities (e.g., entanglement in fishing gear, eating plastic litter, illegal killings by humans)

Give each student a sign that indicates what kind of limiting factor he or she represents. Attach these identity signs to students' clothing with clothes pins.

3. Walk the class through the activity and explain these rules:

A. Turtles must hatch, cross the beach, and spend ten years in the open ocean. The turtles running between the year zones simulate the time in the ocean. They pick up one poker chip at a year zone and then run to the other year zone to pick up another poker chip. Each chip represents two years of successful ocean survival. After collecting five poker chips, turtles return to the nesting area to reproduce.

B. Turtles try to avoid limiting factors and predators. If tagged by a limiting factor, a turtle stops, counts out ten beans, and places those ten beans in the limiting factor's bag.

C. The ocean's sea grass areas are turtle safety zones where limiting factors cannot tag them. The teacher may set a time limit for how long a turtle may rest in a sea grass zone. **OPTIONAL:** Students may only hide within the sea grass areas during the first four years of the game. This rule simulates the turtles growing too big to hide in the sea grass.

D. Limiting factors must obey the following rules:

■ They cannot tag the same turtle twice in a row.

■ They cannot tag turtles that are counting out beans to another limiting factor.

■ They must stay at least four steps away from any turtle that is transferring beans to another limiting factor.

Turtle Hurdles

E. Any turtle that loses all 50 beans is dead. It must go to the beach and become a condominium. If the condominiums (sitting side by side) eventually block access to the nesting beach, the remaining turtles die without reproducing and starting the next cycle.

F. The activity ends when all turtles are either dead or have returned to the nest area.

4. Review the rules two times to make sure students understand their roles and the procedures. Students then become endangered sea turtles or limiting factors and conduct the activity.

5. After completing the activity, encourage students to discuss the results. It is likely that some students will be disturbed by the high mortality of the turtles and will benefit from the realization that there are groups actively trying to diminish human contributions to such high mortality. However, it is also important to emphasize that natural limiting factors are built into the scheme of things. If all sea turtle eggs survived, there might well be an overabundance of these creatures. Many animals produce more young than will survive, serving as food for other species. This is part of nature's dynamic balance. Ask students to briefly describe the life cycle of sea turtles.

Sea turtles are survivors from the great age of the dinosaurs and inhabit nearly all oceans of the world. The best-known sea turtles are in the family Cheloniidae, which contains the Green Turtle, Loggerhead Turtle, Hawksbill Turtle, and Ridley Turtle.

Diagram B

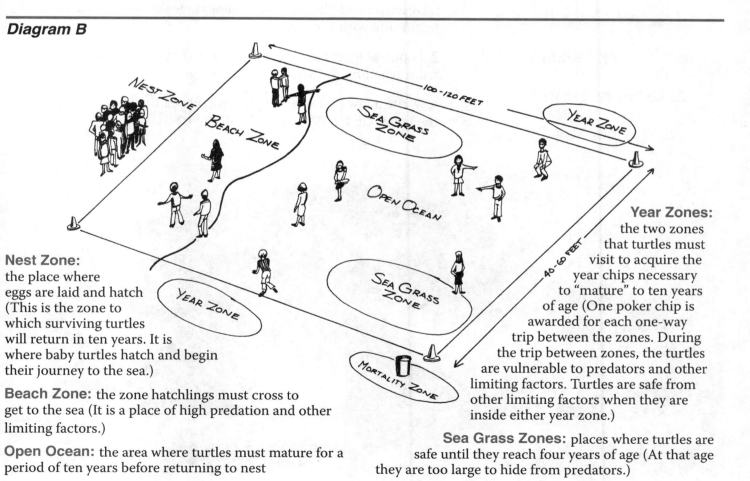

Nest Zone: the place where eggs are laid and hatch (This is the zone to which surviving turtles will return in ten years. It is where baby turtles hatch and begin their journey to the sea.)

Beach Zone: the zone hatchlings must cross to get to the sea (It is a place of high predation and other limiting factors.)

Open Ocean: the area where turtles must mature for a period of ten years before returning to nest

Year Zones: the two zones that turtles must visit to acquire the year chips necessary to "mature" to ten years of age (One poker chip is awarded for each one-way trip between the zones. During the trip between zones, the turtles are vulnerable to predators and other limiting factors. Turtles are safe from other limiting factors when they are inside either year zone.)

Sea Grass Zones: places where turtles are safe until they reach four years of age (At that age they are too large to hide from predators.)

Six of the seven known sea turtle species are officially designated either as endangered or threatened. The Leatherback, Olive Ridley, Kemp's Ridley, Hawksbill, and Green are all listed as endangered species by the U.S. Fish and Wildlife Service. The Loggerhead, although not listed as endangered, is listed as threatened and under review . . .

6. Summarize the importance of the high numbers of turtles that result from reproduction. Ask students to identify and discuss the factors that limit turtles' survival. Because sea turtles are threatened with extinction, the limiting factors affecting their survival seem to be out of balance. What specific recommendations would students suggest to increase the successful reproduction and survival of sea turtles?

Extensions

1. Change the ratio of predators and hazards to turtles (1/3 predators or hazards to 2/3 sea turtles), and replay the simulation. Describe and discuss the differences.

2. Set up a sea turtle information center.

3. Where possible, visit sea turtle restoration sites, and determine what actions may be taken to enhance the stability of sea turtle populations.

4. Replay the activity with all human factors removed from influence.

Evaluation

1. Describe and illustrate the major stages of sea turtles' life cycle, beginning with the egg.

2. Name at least four limiting factors that prevent sea turtles from reaching the adult breeding stage.

3. Write a law that would help protect sea turtles. What would the law include? Who would enforce it?

KEMP'S RIDLEY SEA TURTLE

Turtle Hurdles

Aquatic Roots

Would you recognize outsiders in your local aquatic environments?

Objectives

Students will (1) trace the origins of various species of local aquatic animals, aquatic plants, or both; (2) categorize them into native and exotic species; and (3) evaluate the appropriateness of introducing new species.

Background

A non-native or exotic species is a species that does not naturally occur in a specific location. While species have always dispersed from one place to another, natural land barriers have prevented their large-scale movement. Over time, human modification has changed those barriers. For example, organisms, seeds, and animals can be transported in ships, in ballast water, on clothing, and on boats as people move from one place to another.

Zebra mussels, native to the Black, Caspian, and Azov Seas, and lampreys, native to the Atlantic Ocean, have made their way into the Great Lakes through modern canals and shipping lanes. Female zebra mussels are capable of laying over one million eggs each year. This population explosion is clogging the water systems of power plants and water treatment facilities and is reducing the populations of native mussels. Lamprey eels, common to the ocean waters from Florida to Newfoundland, swim inland into freshwaters to spawn. Lampreys are parasitic on many native fish species, including paddlefish, Lake Trout, and whitefish, causing a reduction in their populations.

Intentional introduction of plants and animals can become unmanageable to state and federal governments. Purple Loosestrife was brought into the United States from Europe in the 1800s for use as a garden perennial and ornamental wildflower. With no natural predators present, the ability to reproduce rapidly, and the capability to benefit from land disturbances, Purple Loosestrife has modified wetlands, marshes, pastures, and riparian meadows. The result is the

Grade Level: Lower Elementary, Upper Elementary

Content Areas: Science, Social Studies, Environmental Education

Method: Students use reference materials to research various local aquatic plants or animals to identify whether these organisms are native or exotic to the area and to investigate their effects on people, other animals, and the environment.

Materials: A world map, yarn, paper, reference materials, and a list of local non-native plants and animals

Activity Time: two or three 45-minute sessions with additional time for student research and preparation of reports

People Power: several small groups or individual students

Setting: indoors

Conceptual Framework Topic Reference: ITIIA2, ITIIA2b

Terms to Know: exotic, native, introduced species, benefits, liabilities, tradeoffs, regulations, invasive, extirpated

Appendices: Using Local Resources, Agencies and Organizations

A non-native or exotic species is a species that does not naturally occur in a specific location. While species have always dispersed from one place to another, natural land barriers have prevented their large-scale movement. Over time, human modification has changed those barriers.

GYPSY MOTH CATERPILLAR

degradation of habitat where native plants grow, fish spawn, and wildlife live and breed. Another example of an introduced non-native species is the Gypsy Moth, a large European moth. French naturalist Leopold Trouvelot, who hoped to begin operating a New England silk industry, first introduced the Gypsy Moth to the United States in Medford, Massachusetts around 1868. During this time, the moths escaped and their larvae (which feed on leaves) became a serious economic menace by destroying fruit orchards. The Gypsy Moth has since spread to other parts of the United States where the caterpillars devour the foliage of numerous trees, especially oaks and birches.

Why do these invaders have such success? While not all non-native species succeed, those that do are aided by their ability to out-compete native plants and animals for resources and by the lack of natural predators.

NOTE: Local wildlife agencies, garden clubs, nature societies, and wildlife organizations may be able to assist in developing a list of invasive species. Look for information in reference materials under exotic species, introduced species, and species introduction.

Procedure

1. Provide students with a list of local non-native species. Ask them to predict which of the plants and animals are "native" and which are introduced, or "non-native." Establish clear working definitions of "native" and "non-native." A native species occurs naturally in an area. Any plant or animal not naturally occurring in the local ecosystem is non-native.

2. If students' predictions are not entirely accurate, identify for students the non-native species on the provided list.

3. Next, ask each student or small group of students to research one species known to be introduced as a non-native to the area or state. Ideally a variety of introduced species will be studied, including aquatic species. If feasible, students should attempt to make firsthand observations of the species they are researching at locations near their home, school, or neighborhood. Each student or group should prepare a written and oral report. Include in the research information describing the origins of the plant or animal and its effects in the area. Some introductions may seem to have both positive and negative effects. Has the introduction created more benefits or liabilities for the ecosystem? The students could create a two-column list of benefits and liabilities. In addition to simply listing these, they could assess the importance of each item in the columns. Benefits and liabilities—positive and negative effects—may not have equal value. Some effects will be unknown, so students might also generate a list of unknown effects or questions.

Aquatic Roots

4. Ask each student or group to report to the class. Following the reports, encourage discussion and debate. Ask students to identify and discuss potential benefits and liabilities involved. Then ask students to evaluate the appropriateness of each of the introductions, identifying and describing their criteria for judgment. They might also consider the potential effects of an introduction of a species that is common somewhere else but not yet in their area.

5. Using a world map, have students connect their location with the original location of the non-native species researched. Stretch a strand of yarn from the students' location to the site of origin of each organism, and place a tag on the yarn with the name of the plant or animal.

6. Preventing "accidental" introductions is also important. Develop a list of ways these introductions can occur and ways to help ensure that they don't happen. Discuss the importance of laws and regulations that prevent, control, or allow introductions of species.

Extensions

1. Investigate and compare local, state, and federal laws pertaining to introducing exotics into aquatic environments.

2. Investigate how humans have reintroduced some wildlife species into their original habitat where the species had previously become extirpated. Have students distinguish some differences and similarities between reintroductions and non-native species.

Evaluation

1. Identify three native aquatic plants and animals in your area. Identify three exotic aquatic plants and animals in your area.

2. Give four reasons that an aquatic plant or animal might be introduced in an area. Are these reasons appropriate? Why or why not?

3. A local organization has proposed that a new fish be introduced into a state's rivers or lakes. List at least five questions that could be asked about the fish and its impact on the state's watercourses before the proposal is approved or rejected.

WILD Work

What's the difference between a **Horticulturist**, a **Plant Pathologist**, and a **Plant Physiologist**? How does an **Investigative Reporter** conduct research? What does a **Fish and Wildlife Technician** have to do with invasive plant species?

Start researching the answers to these questions with students by going to *www.projectwild.org/aquatic*.

In Step with STEM

- Go online to research local aquatic plants and animals. Determine which are native or non-native.

- Visit a local aquatic area and have students draw and identify aquatic plants. Have students distinguish whether the plant is native or non-native and/or invasive. Observe and record species in the local aquatic habitat through photographs. Students should record time, date, and location of their observations and photo/illustration records. They can later try to identify species observed using field guides.

- Choose one aquatic invasive species to research how this organism was transferred to a non-native home. As a group, discuss methods to remove, control, or prevent this species from continuing to disperse to new habitats.

Where Have All the Salmon Gone?

Grade Level: Middle, High School

Content Areas: Science, Mathematics, Social Studies, Environmental Education

Method:
Students graph and interpret actual fish population data in relation to historical events.

Materials:
Graph paper, one copy per student of the *California Chinook Salmon Population Data*, *Historical Events Data Sheet*, and *A Transformed Watershed* map

Activity Time:
one or two 40- to 60-minute sessions

People Power: any

Setting: indoors

Conceptual Framework Topic Reference:
ITIA, ITIB2, ITIVA

Terms to Know:
population, inventory, trend, anadromous, fluctuation

Appendices:
Inventory Methods, Service Learning, Using Local Resources, Field Ethics, Agencies and Organizations, Climate Change

---

Solve the case of the missing California Chinook!

Objectives

Students will (1) interpret and make inferences about fluctuations in fish populations from actual data, and (2) analyze the effects of human use and habitat changes on a fish population.

Background

Researching a wildlife population over a period of time, rather than a single study, is useful in detecting trends in that population. Fluctuations in populations are often influenced by multiple factors, and it can be difficult to identify and measure the effect of a single factor. Thus, scientists often work collaboratively to understand how each factor works together in sustaining or hindering a population over time.

For most species, only a sample of the population can be obtained, and inferences about the total population must be made from this sample. Errors or inconsistencies in gathering the data over time may influence its accuracy. Despite this and the influence of unknown factors, regularly conducted counts or inventories of a population result in greater accuracy of information from which informed decisions can be made.

This activity uses actual data on Chinook Salmon from rivers and streams in California's Central Valley, where this species is closely monitored by the state fish and wildlife agency in cooperation with scientists and citizens. Population counts from 1954 to 2011 are provided for students to analyze and correlate to historical events that occurred in or near Chinook Salmon habitat.

Chinook Salmon are anadromous, meaning they migrate from freshwater to the ocean and back to freshwater to spawn. After hatching from eggs in gravel beds of a freshwater river, a juvenile Chinook begins its migratory journey to the ocean, where it will spend two to five years growing to maturity before returning to its freshwater birthplace.

Chinook are one of seven species of Pacific salmon but are the largest, often weighing over 50 pounds. They are a source of food for people and predators in the waterways they travel, and they recycle vital nutrients back to the environment when they die after spawning.

Scientists track Chinook populations by estimating the number of Chinook that return to their spawning grounds each year. The fish are counted as they move from the ocean and reenter freshwater streams. The amount of time between the birth and return of a Chinook varies from two to five years. Interpreting possible influences on population changes must take into account the time delay between when a Chinook hatches and when it returns to the river to spawn. For example, a historical event that negatively impacted salmon in 1999 may not be reflected in lower population counts until 2002 due to the lifecycle of the species.

Procedure:

1. Provide students with the *California Chinook Salmon Population Data*. Instruct students to graph the estimated return numbers from Historic to 2011. Tip: Educators may want to graph the data first themselves using digital presentation software for students to check their work and use during discussions.

2. What inferences can students draw from the data provided? Does the graph show any long-term trends? Are there periods in which the numbers of returns change rapidly in a short time? What inferences about population abundance and rebounds can be made from the graph?

3. Provide students with the *Historical Events Data Sheet*. Have them review this information in relation to what their graph shows. Integrate the two pieces by making notes on the graph at the points where significant historical events might have affected the population. What new inferences can be made? What factors may be affecting the number of returns or the population levels? A new event or factor may take some time to have an effect on a population or to be detected. Do the student graphs seem to show any of this delayed effect in relation to a possible historical event? Are there different interpretations that individual students make from the same information? If faced with making a management decision on the basis of one interpretation, how would students decide which interpretation to use?

4. Examine the historic event that took place in 2005–2006. Why might a food chain collapse from a change in nutrient availability? How might this affect species populations besides Chinook Salmon? Ask students to research this event and describe efforts in California to increase salmon populations in the following years.

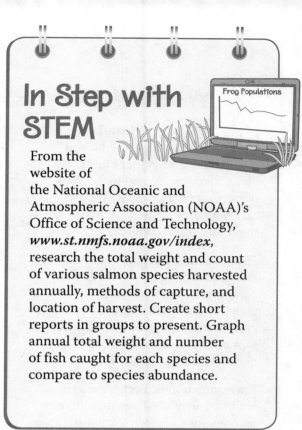

In Step with STEM

From the website of the National Oceanic and Atmospheric Association (NOAA)'s Office of Science and Technology, *www.st.nmfs.noaa.gov/index*, research the total weight and count of various salmon species harvested annually, methods of capture, and location of harvest. Create short reports in groups to present. Graph annual total weight and number of fish caught for each species and compare to species abundance.

Salmon migrating in Clear Creek, California

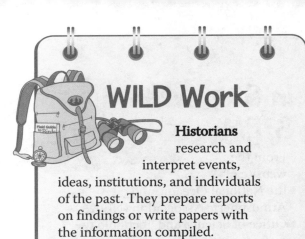

WILD Work

Historians research and interpret events, ideas, institutions, and individuals of the past. They prepare reports on findings or write papers with the information compiled.

Fisheries Biologists measure and interpret data in rivers, streams, oceans, and hatcheries on a daily basis to identify trends in population, reproduction, etc. These trends help guide management decisions for fish species.

Environmental Project Managers are involved with the comprehensive planning of a project. Responsibilities include writing and editing environmental reports, data collection, performing field surveys, and marketing. For links to more information on these occupations, visit *www.projectwild.org/aquatic*

Salmon hatcheries operated by fisheries professionals help sustain Chinook populations.

5. Have each student develop a hypothesis and write a short scientific summary explaining the data, analysis, and interpretations. Then have students present their papers to the class and defend their hypotheses.

Extensions

1. Have students contact their state fish and wildlife agency. Invite a fisheries biologist to review the class's data and make an analysis. Does it differ significantly from the students'?

2. Contact the state fish and wildlife agency or a nearby university with an associated wildlife and fisheries department to arrange for students to participate in fish counts. Encourage students to contact fish hatcheries for possible participation in stocking projects.

Evaluation

Study the graph below to answer these questions:

- Which fish population appears to be the most stable?
- Fish #3 appears to be a prey species for which fish?
- What do you think is the primary diet of Fish #1? Fish #2? Fish #3? Why?
- What natural or human events may have accounted for the decrease in Fish #2's size between years 2 and 4 and between years 16 and 18?
- What effect did the introduction of Fish #4 appear to have on the other fish species?
- What actions might the state fish agency have taken to maintain the populations of Fish #2?
- What natural and human events may have caused all fish species to die in year 20?

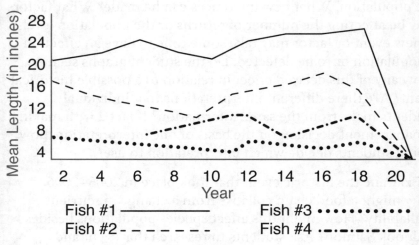

Activity adapted with permission from the California Department of Fish and Game.

Where Have All the Salmon Gone?
© Council for Environmental Education (CEE)

California Chinook Salmon Population Data

Historical Background:

By 1852, sediment from California gold mines had nearly destroyed Chinook Salmon spawning grounds and resting pools on the Sacramento, Yuba, Mokelumne, Feather, and American Rivers. In 1878 public concern over the decline in fish species, especially salmon, led to the creation of the State Board of Fish Commissioners. The board established salmon hatcheries as a means to stabilize fish populations. The focus of commercial fishing in California was placed on ocean fisheries by 1920. Construction of the California network of dams began in 1923 with the O'Shaughnessy Dam built on the Toulumne River, followed by Shasta Dam in 1945 (historic salmon spawning grounds were eliminated). In 1951 the Friant Dam eliminated the spring-run salmon in the San Joaquin River. From 1940 to 1960 all Central Valley rivers of any size (except the Cosumnes River) were dammed in the foothills. See the attached map.

Estimates of Returning Central Valley Fall-run Chinook Salmon
Historical Through 2011

Year	Number of Salmon	Year	Number of Salmon
Historic	1,000,000	1984	280,000
1954	500,000	1987	300,000
1957	120,000	1990	100,000
1960	480,000	1993	225,000
1963	290,000	1996	350,000
1966	200,000	1999	400,000
1969	305,000	2002	880,000
1972	175,000	2005	450,000
1975	200,000	2008	66,000
1978	190,000	2011	122,000
1981	280,000		

Source: California Department of Fish and Wildlife

The dams of the Central Valley present a major challenge for sustaining Chinook populations. They prevent Chinook from swimming to higher elevation streams where colder water temperatures provide the necessary conditions for spawning. Between 1942 and 1980, a total of eight hatcheries were established to help mitigate the impact to salmon populations in California's Central Valley caused by water development projects. These hatcheries release more than 40 million juvenile salmon annually. California, from 1950 to the present, has been the national leader in agricultural production; farming and ranching use 30% of the state's land, and most crops require irrigation and use 85% of the state's developed water. The California Central Valley grows approximately one third of U.S. food.

Visit *www.projectwild.org/aquatic* for links to additional information on the San Francisco Bay-Delta Watershed, as well as an electronic color version of the map titled *California's Central Valley: A Transformed Watershed* included in this activity.

O'Shaughnessy Dam

1957	The California Water Plan creates a framework for making water decisions.
1960	Log jams and sediments from lumber harvesting clogged most salmon habitat.
1965	Draining and filling San Francisco tidal land halted, 77% of wetlands destroyed.
1968	US established Wild and Scenic Rivers Act; 1,900 miles of California rivers (about 7%) are under wild and scenic protection.
1970	National Environmental Policy Act established the Endangered Species Act.
1972	The Federal Clean Water Act improves quality of municipal and industrial effluent, urban and agricultural runoff remain a major pollutants source.
1975	28% of state population lives in San Francisco Bay and the Central Valley watershed.
1976	Magnuson Fishery Conservation and Management Act gave federal authority over ocean fishing 3 to 200 miles from shore and created the Pacific Fishing Management Council (PFMC).
1976–77	California drought years (1977 the driest on record).
1979–80	Woody riparian habitat along Sacramento River decreased to 2% of historic levels and valley riparian vegetation less than 10% of historical level.
1987–92	California drought years.
1992	Central Valley Project Improvement Act gave 800,000 acre-feet of water for environmental use and ecosystem restoration for Sacramento and San Joaquin rivers. U.S. Fish and Wildlife Service began the Anadromous Fish Restoration Program (AFRP).
1994	Delta Accord signed to protect listed fish species, including Chinook Salmon, steelhead, and Delta Smelt.
1998	20% of state population lives in the 9-county San Francisco Bay Area, 17% reside in remaining 28 counties of the Central Valley watershed.
2005–06	NOAA documented a collapse of the marine food chain structure resulting largely from a weak and delayed upwelling of cold and nutrient rich water that typically greets and sustains the juvenile salmon when they reach the ocean.
2006	Bay Delta Conservation Plan provided for conservation of Delta fisheries while supplying water to 25 million Californians.
2007–08	California drought years.
2008	Inland and Ocean Salmon Fishing Season closed for commercial and recreational fishing.
2010	Commercial and recreational fishing resumes.

Historic Event References:
From the Sierra to the Sea: The Ecological History of the San Francisco Bay-Delta Watershed by The Bay Institute, July 1998
California's Rivers: A Public Trust Report, prepared for the California State Lands Commission 1994
California Department of Fish and Game publication: Pacific Salmon: King of California Fish, 2009
Outdoor California Magazine Special Issue: Salmon Crisis, July-August 2009

California's Central Valley: A Transformed Watershed

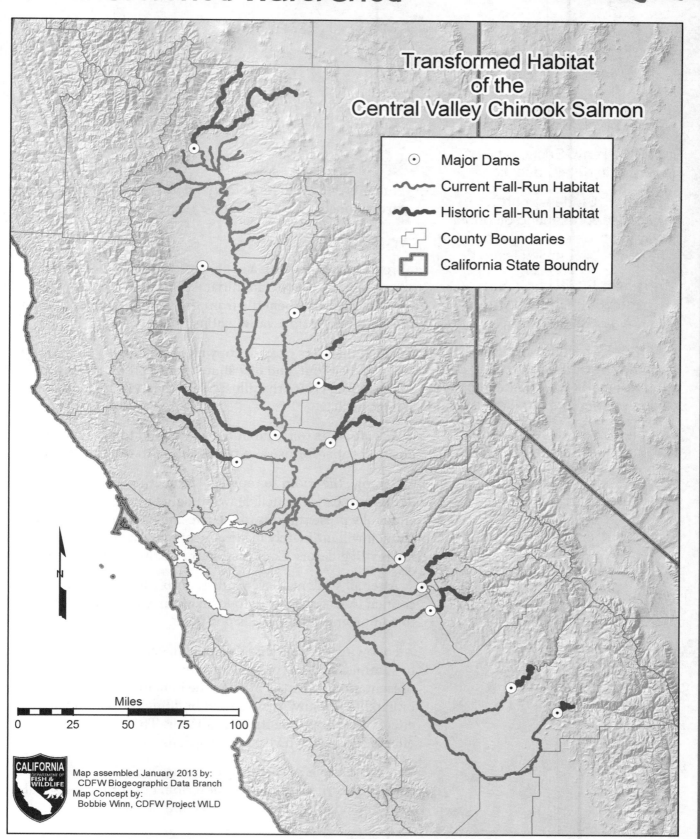

Transformed Habitat
of the
Central Valley Chinook Salmon

Legend:
- ⊙ Major Dams
- Current Fall-Run Habitat
- Historic Fall-Run Habitat
- County Boundaries
- California State Boundry

Miles
0   25   50   75   100

Map assembled January 2013 by:
CDFW Biogeographic Data Branch
Map Concept by:
Bobbie Winn, CDFW Project WILD

To Dam or Not to Dam

Grade Level: Middle School

Content Areas: Social Studies, Environmental Education

Method: Students portray individuals representing differing perspectives and concerns related to a complex issue.

Materials: *Situation Summary* (page 262); *Role-Playing Cards* (page 263)

Activity Time: two or three 45-minute sessions, depending on whether time is used to develop position papers and write essays.

People Power: developed for 30 students, can be modified for smaller or larger groups

Setting: indoors

Conceptual Framework Topic Reference: ITIA, ITIVA, ITVA, ITVA1

Terms to Know: dam, consensus, costs, benefits, tradeoffs

Appendices: Using Local Resources, Agencies and Organizations

---

Who will be convinced in a dam-building debate?

Objective

Students will evaluate potential positive and negative effects from constructing a dam on a river.

Procedure

1. Provide students with a copy of the *Situation Summary* found on page 262. Generate an initial discussion with them about the possible costs and benefits from the construction of this dam, considering it from a variety of perspectives.

NOTE: Educators need to copy the *Role-Playing Cards* on page 263, cut them out, and distribute them to the students. Create any additional roles that illustrate a variety of major perspectives and interests.

2. Ask students to research their roles and to develop a short position paper for use as a presentation to the city council.

3. Arrange the room to represent a meeting room for the Rocksburg City Council. Have students role-play their positions and make presentations to the five-member council. This council will ultimately make a recommendation to the Federal Energy Regulatory Commission on a siting permit for the dam.

4. After all students have made their presentations, ask the city council to work together to form a consensus plan that attempts to compromise the various positions.

5. Following the council's decision, have a brief class discussion to summarize the pros and cons that emerged from students' presentations. Identify and list the benefits, if any, and the costs or liabilities, if any, as a result of building the dam. Include effects on people, plants, and animals. The pros, cons, and effects can be listed visually on a chalkboard.

6. After the role-play and class discussion, ask each student to write a brief essay describing his or her personal recommendation on whether to build this dam.

Variation

Describe a hypothetical community debating the removal of a dam. Have students role-play representatives of the various interest groups, research the issues, present findings, and attempt to determine a consensus plan.

Extensions

1. Change roles and conduct the council meeting again. Note any differences in the results, as well as in the perceptions of the process and experience.

2. Inquire at a local regulatory agency to see if there are any proposals to create new dams or any other proposals that will affect wildlife habitat in your region. If so, investigate the benefits and challenges of one or more of these proposals.

3. If possible, visit a dam in your area. Can you make any observations about its positive or negative effects on wildlife or people?

Evaluation

1. If a dam were constructed on a river, what would be the benefits to wildlife?

2. If a dam were constructed on a river, what would be the challenges to wildlife?

WILD Work

How do **Architects**, **Civil Engineers**, **Maintenance Mechanics**, and **Electricians** work together to build and maintain an efficient dam?

To find more information on these careers, head to: *www.projectwild.org/aquatic*.

In Step with STEM

■ Design and build a dam using craft sticks, small rocks, sand, and other common materials. For more details, see resources at *www.projectwild.org/aquatic*.

■ To better understand the technical aspects of building a dam, continue on to the Aquatic WILD activity, "Dam Design."

Irrigation is one of the main uses of water withdrawn from a dam reservoir.

Situation: The town of Rocksburg, population 900, is located along the scenic Jones River, approximately 60 miles from the closest city. The city's mayor and city council have proposed that a dam be constructed two miles upriver from Rocksburg. In the environmental impact statement drafted by city engineers and others the following information was identified:

- The dam would meet the area's electrical power demand for ten or more years.

- The dam would provide some water for irrigation and would help with flood control.

- The dam would be of rock-fill construction, and it would be 75 feet high and 300 feet across. Seven miles of river would be turned into a lake.

- The dam construction would take five years to complete and would employ more than 2,000 workers. After the dam was finished, approximately 150 employees would be needed to operate the facility.

Wildlife would be affected in the following ways:

- 20 percent loss to deer herd due to lost forage

- 20 percent loss to small mammals living in the river valley due to loss of habitat

- 20 percent loss to the area's songbird population due to lost riverbank nesting sites

- blockage of fish migration due to the creation of the lake and dam

- increase of the area's wintering bald eagle population

- reduction and possible elimination of fish species adapted to cooler or flowing water, including trout, minnows, and darters

- increase in warmer, nonflowing water habitat suitable for bass, bluegill, and carp

- growth in the economy resulting from the new tourist industry

The citizens of Rocksburg are concerned about the challenges and benefits resulting from the increased visitation to their town during and after the construction of the dam. As mentioned, they project the addition of 2,000 employees, plus their families, during construction for five years and those 150 permanent employees plus their families who would stay after the dam was finished. They are concerned about effects on schools, sewage disposal, roads, home sites, property values, and the rural atmosphere, as well as police, fire, and hospital emergency capacities. They see potential benefits from the development, such as new recreation opportunities for the people of Rocksburg and the city that is only about an hour away (water skiing, sailboarding, motorboating, swimming, fishing, camping, picnicking, and other lake-related sports).

Other impacts could include these:

- flooding of Native American archeological sites;

- cultural changes for local Native American community that has fished the river for generations;

- water for irrigation at a lower cost;

- potentially less expensive power when compared to other forms of power production (e.g., nuclear, coal, oil, fossil fuels);

- potential increase in total power bills that may be necessary to pay for construction of the dam; and

- loss of 7 miles of prime whitewater, resulting in lost whitewater rafting and kayaking businesses.

Role-Playing Cards

Representative of Farmer's Coalition: the coalition is interested in the dam's potential for protecting crops from floods, as well as in its ability to provide water for irrigation.

Lobbyist for Power Company: the municipal electrical power company is interested in developing the dam.

Bird Club President: the local bird club has organized eagle-watching trips to the river every winter for the past 15 years.

Sporting Goods Store Owner: a local sporting goods storeowner and avid fisherperson who is concerned with the loss of migration routes for the fish on the river.

Local Species Activist: the president of the "Save Our Native Plants and Wild Animals" organization.

Archaeology Expert: an archeology professor from the local university who has done extensive research on the archeological sites of Native American fishing camps along the river.

Director of Municipal Water Agency: the agency is responsible for providing quality drinking water for the city. It believes in the dam's potential for providing a reservoir of high-quality water for the long, hot summers.

Homeowner Association Representative: a representative of all homeowners in the river valley below the dam who would like to see more flood control.

Sheriff: the local Rocksburg sheriff concerned about maintaining police protection, peace, health, and safety with only a one-person staff as the sole legal authority in the region.

Lumber Company Owner: the owner of a lumber company whose land would be inundated by the reservoir.

Fly-fishing Enthusiast: a long-time resident who champions the purity of fly-fishing and insists on pristine habitat, noting the necessity of whitewater riffles.

Owner of Water Recreation Company: the company uses the river for commercial rafting. Concerned about loss of the "best 7 miles of the river," the owner argues that the lake would submerge the best rapids.

Vetern Water Skier: an avid water skier who sees the new lake as a real boon to skiing interests.

Avid Kayaker: kayaker concerned with loss of the whitewater stretch for canoeing and kayaking.

Senior Citizen Advocate: a local representative of the Sociable Seniors, a group of retired people who are concerned about any rise in power bills.

Angler: an older fisherperson who enjoys throwing the boat on the top of the car and putting in at the closest float spot—especially lakes!

President of Moose Conservation Organization: the president of "More Moose Now," who believes that the lake will provide more moose habitat.

Scientist: a respected biologist who is prepared to testify about potential effects on wildlife from the building of the dam.

Sales Representative: a salesperson for motor boats, water skis, and other recreational equipment.

Forest Manager: a trained forester who has worked in the area woods for more than 50 years.

Local Tribal Authority Leader: a tribal leader who is concerned about the loss of native heritage from flooding the region for the dam.

Entrepreneur: a local businessperson who is concerned about the long-range business potential of the area.

Land Developer: a wealthy land developer who has architects working on designs for lakeside condominiums and resort homes.

Aquatic Times

Grade Level: Upper Elementary, Middle School, High School

Content Areas: Language Arts, Environmental Education

Method: Students investigate, write, and produce a newspaper that features aquatic information and issues.

Materials:
Online or library resources; current nature magazines (Ranger Rick, National Geographic, etc.); writing and art materials
OPTIONAL: Cameras/film, audio recorders, computers, video equipment (Educators may want to invite a local newspaper editor or writer to come to the class to discuss the mechanics of newspaper production.)

Activity Time:
several sessions or longer

People Power: small groups or individual activity as part of a class project

Setting: indoors

Conceptual Framework Topic Reference:
ITIA, ITIB

Terms to Know:
issue, aquatic, editorial, satire

Appendix:
Using Local Resources

What local stories have yet to be uncovered?

Objectives

Students will (1) identify a diversity of issues related to aquatic organisms and habitats, (2) develop their own opinions concerning some issues involving aquatic life and habitats, and (3) communicate their findings in writing.

Background

The production of a newspaper requires an array of skills that include design capabilities, writing, composition, research, and decision making. This activity provides an opportunity for students to experience newspaper production while researching aquatic resource information and issues.

Procedure

1. Using an actual newspaper as a model, discuss the various parts of a newspaper. Help students recognize that in addition to news articles, other departments exist in most newspapers. Comics, sports, editorials, employment opportunities, political cartoons, food and nutrition, entertainment, business, advertisements, weather, obituaries, and many other sections are featured in a newspaper. Ask each student or team of students to choose one section of the newspaper to develop and write.

2. The theme of this newspaper is aquatic animals and plants, aquatic habitats, or aquatic-related issues. Encourage students to visit, research, and photograph local water-related resources in your community, such as wetlands, streams, fountains, detention ponds, water towers, etc. Ask students to gather information and ideas for their chosen section. Show students how to properly acknowledge and credit any sources they use.

NOTE: If using the optional materials listed in the sidebar, familiarize students with any resources they can use, such as the audio recorders, websites, software, cameras, and so forth.

3. The articles in the newspaper could tie aquatic life or habitats to columns such as world news, local news, sports, human interest, food, cartoons, and entertainment. For example,

- "Oil Spill Threatens Gulf Coast"
- "Too Many Wells Deplete Local Aquifer"
- "Sustainable Seafood Recipes"
- An interview with three grandparents about historic, local aquatic resources
- "Fishing Action Heats Up at Local Lake!" (sports)

4. Once students have compiled their research and begin writing their articles, encourage them to share their work. In this way, interests can merge and different talents can be called upon. Keep students on track, making sure their writing is accurate even though they may have chosen humor or satire as their approach.

5. When most of the articles have been written, assign a small group of students to begin the production phase of the paper. The artwork can be photographs or drawings that illustrate a particular point in the article. Computer graphics can also be used to highlight specific articles. Most word processing programs include a newspaper template.

6. Once the newspaper is complete, copies can be made for the class or for distribution at school or throughout the community.

7. Summarize the activity with a discussion of each article or feature, emphasizing what students learned about aquatic life and habitat from this activity.

Extensions

1. Have an aquatic poster contest.

2. Establish a current events corner about aquatic wildlife.

3. Visit a local newspaper and offer student articles for submission to the newspaper.

Evaluation

1. Identify three issues involving aquatic animals, aquatic plants, or aquatic habitats.

2. Explain why it is important to accurately report environmental information to others.

3. What are the characteristics of a good environmental reporter?

WILD Work

How do **Marketing Directors, Copy Editors, Business Managers, Journalists**, and **IT Administrators** work together to produce a newspaper?

To find more information on these careers, head to: *www.projectwild.org/aquatic.*

In Step with STEM

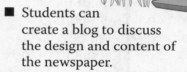

- Students can create a blog to discuss the design and content of the newspaper.

- Convert the newspaper to a video news broadcast.

- Locate a conservation group that focuses on your local watershed, groundwater issues, or protection of a local body of water. Interview them to learn about issues facing your community. Use audio-visual tools to record the interview. Use graphic design software to layout the paper electronically.

- Publish aquatic news online by producing electronic posters, bulletins, magazines, or multimedia presentations. For links to free or low-cost web resources, see *www.projectwild.org/aquatic.*

Silt: A Dirty Word

Silt and sand may spoil your stream with sedimentation!

Objectives

Students will (1) describe how sand, silt, or both affect water flow; and (2) identify human activities that add sand, silt, or both to surface water.

Background

Sedimentation is excess amounts of silt and other particles entering streams and rivers from the surrounding watershed. Sediments enter water in two main forms: (1) surface erosion sends small amounts of particles into the water, and (2) mass erosion (e.g., landslides) dumps huge amounts of dirt into water. Causes of surface erosion vary. They can include anglers walking trails to favorite fishing spots or cattle trampling and consuming streamside vegetation that holds soil in place. Logging, mining, and road construction can also contribute to surface erosion. Mass erosion, such as mudslides or earth slumps, occurs more frequently on hillsides altered by human activity, such as clear-cut logging, road construction, or home building.

Regardless of its source, sedimentation may affect aquatic wildlife by reducing nutrients, diminishing sunlight to plants, and altering stream energy and velocity. One important effect of sedimentation is diminished flow to organisms residing in bottom substrates. The flow of clean water is important in most aquatic environments because flowing water often carries dissolved oxygen that aquatic animals need for respiration. Depletion of oxygen in bodies of water affects organisms even at early stages of development. For instance, some fish lay their eggs in gravel that receives a flow of clean water, either from a stream or river or from spring water percolating up from the lake bottom. As the water flows over the eggs, it delivers dissolved oxygen to them. If the eggs do not receive enough oxygen, they die. Silt and sand act like concrete to block water movement and thus diminish the amount of oxygen reaching the developing eggs. Once the erosion-causing activity is stopped,

---

Grade Level: Upper Elementary

Content Areas: Science, Environmental Education

Method: Students create a model to simulate changes to a stream and its water flow when silt, sand, or both are added to the system.

Materials: For each group of four students: a clear plastic 1-gallon container such as a storage box; enough pea-sized gravel to cover the bottom of the container; enough water to fill the container to one inch from the top; 1 cup coarse sand; 1 cup silt (silica powder from the edge of a stream); three straws per person **OPTIONAL:** brightly colored beads (pea-sized or larger); plastic tablecloth; paper towels

Activity Time: one hour

People Power: small groups of four

Setting: indoors or outdoors, must have source of water

Conceptual Framework Topic Reference: WMIIB2

Terms to Know: silt, habitat, spawning, erosion, sedimentation

Appendix: The Ecosystem and Project WILD

streams may cleanse themselves. (Depending on the extent of the problem, self-cleansing can take from 1 to 50 years.)

The major purpose of this activity is to show that aquatic wildlife and its habitat can be influenced by land-based activities in the surrounding watershed. Students experience what happens to a stream and its flow of water when sand, silt, or both are added to the water.

Procedure

1. Before class, set up a demonstration—a container with gravel covered by water—so that students can see how to proceed. Post a large sheet of paper on the wall for groups to record their results. (See the "Sample Observations Chart" below.)

2. Place students into groups of three or four. Ask each group to gather the supplies and set up its demonstration. Ask students why oxygen is important to aquatic animals. Explain the three parts of the procedure (Steps 3, 4, and 5 below), and ask students to predict what will happen as each sediment type is added to the water.

3. Each person in the group should simultaneously blow bubbles into the water with a straw. Make sure the straw is at or near the bottom of the container so that the end is pushed into the

Regardless of its source, sedimentation may affect aquatic wildlife by reducing nutrients, diminishing sunlight to plants, and altering stream energy and velocity. One important effect of sedimentation is diminished water flow to organisms residing in bottom substrates.

Sample Observations Chart				
Each group of students selects one difficulty level for each water type by placing a check in the appropriate box in its column. They may record additional observations in the boxes as well.				
Difficulty Levels	Group 1	Group 2	Group 3	Group 4
Clean Water				
Easy to blow				
Less easy to blow				
Hard to blow				
Sand in Water				
Easy to blow				
Less easy to blow				
Hard to blow				
Silt in Water				
Easy to blow				
Less easy to blow				
Hard to blow				

WILD Work

Geoscientists are engaged in geologic data gathering and research that provide information for managing the nation's land, energy, and mineral resources. They conduct laboratory and field work at many different locations, determine the distribution of mineral resources, study the processes of mineral deposits, and conduct surveys to characterize the influence of Earth's natural systems and the impact of human activities on the global environment. Geoscientists typically have earned a Bachelor's degree in geology or a related earth science field. To find more information on this occupation, visit *www. projectwild.org/aquatic*.

In Step with STEM

Tape a small word or picture to the side of the container near the bottom. Blow bubbles into the water. Observe from the other side of the container and count the number of seconds it takes to clearly see the picture or read the word. Discuss how this procedure enables one to take a measurement of turbidity in a way that can be easily replicated and used to compare turbidity at different times, at different locations, or under different circumstances.

layer of gravel. Have the group discuss the ease or difficulty in blowing the bubbles and record its observations on the sheet on the wall. Remind students that the blowing of bubbles is meant to demonstrate how things move through water in different situations.

4. Instruct groups to add 1 cup of sand to the water and then blow bubbles again. Be sure that the straw is pushed through the sand so that it reaches the gravel. Have each group discuss the difficulty level and record its observations on the master sheet on the wall.

5. Now instruct groups to add 1 cup of silt to the water, allow it to settle, push the straw end into the layer of gravel, and blow bubbles again. Have each group discuss the difficulty level and record its observations on the master sheet on the wall.

6. Conduct a class discussion about the demonstration and results, and describe what these results might mean to aquatic organisms and their need for clean water. How do sand and silt get into the water in nature? Which of these sources are human and which are natural? What can happen to fish and other aquatic organisms if too much sediment gets into aquatic systems?

Extensions

1. Add brightly colored beads to the container to represent fish eggs.

2. Research and discuss ways to minimize the addition of sand or silt into natural aquatic systems.

3. Show students pictures of a secchi disk and turbidity tube. Ask students how they might design a procedure with these instruments that can be replicated and used to compare turbidity under different circumstances. For more information about using secchi disks and turbidity tubes, go to *www. projectwild.org/aquatic*.

Evaluation

1. Write on a chart or blackboard all the observations and ideas generated by the students; engage them in a discussion about the meaning of these results.

2. Ask each group to create two illustrations: (1) a healthy stream that could support a variety of aquatic life and (2) a human activity that causes siltation in that stream.

*Activity adapted from from *WILD About Salmon*, Idaho Department of Fish and Game, 1999.

Silt: A Dirty Word

Dam Design

Put on your thinking cap and design a salmon-friendly dam!

Objective

Students will (1) identify problems experienced by salmon in migration; (2) evaluate the social, political, economic, and ethical consequences of an environmental concern; (3) identify mitigation projects that have worked and those that have not; and (4) identify and propose strategies and technologies to address an environmental concern.

Background

In the northwest region of the United States, salmon populations have declined. One of the reasons for this decline is that dams block salmon migration routes. Biologists and engineers have tried a number of ways to help salmon move through and around the dams. For a time, these methods seemed to work. Unfortunately, salmon numbers continue to decline—a sign that the salmon populations are not stable and something new must be tried.

Some agencies and organizations have proposed removing some of the dams. Even if this occurs, many dams will need to remain if both the needs of people and wildlife are to be considered. New ideas are needed to help the salmon around these dams. Who is better to begin this work than tomorrow's biologists and engineers?

The purpose of this activity is to demonstrate the complexity of many wildlife management decisions that must consider political, social, economic, and biological concerns. Wildlife management applies scientific knowledge and technical skills to protect or conserve wildlife and its habitat.

Grade Level:
Middle, High School

Content Areas:
Science, Social Studies, Language Arts, Environmental Education

Method:
Students will design and draw a dam appropriate for salmon survival.

Materials:
For each group of students, paper and drafting equipment

Activity Time:
semester project

People Power:
small groups

Setting:
primarily indoors

Conceptual Framework Topic Reference: WMIB, WMIIB2, WMIIC, WMIIC2

Terms to Know:
migration, reservoir

Appendices: Using Local Resources, Agencies and Organizations

The purpose of this activity is to demonstrate the complexity of many wildlife management decisions that must consider political, social, economic, and biological concerns.

Procedure

1. Write the following topics on a board, large sheet of paper, or digital presentation slide:

- Salmon migration—downstream and upstream
- Location of dams in a river system such as the Columbia or Snake River systems (see Diagram A)
- Designs of current dams, including turbines
- Purpose of dams in the system
- Problems that dams create for migrating salmon
- Modifications to help the fish (their efficacy, cost, and benefits)
- Roles that salmon play in the watershed

2. Divide students into small teams of three or four. Instruct teams to decide who will research which topic. To cover all topics, teams may need to choose more than one topic. Encourage students to visit a dam site if possible and record firsthand observations of environmental conditions and human activity in the vicinity that are affected by the dam.

Diagram A*

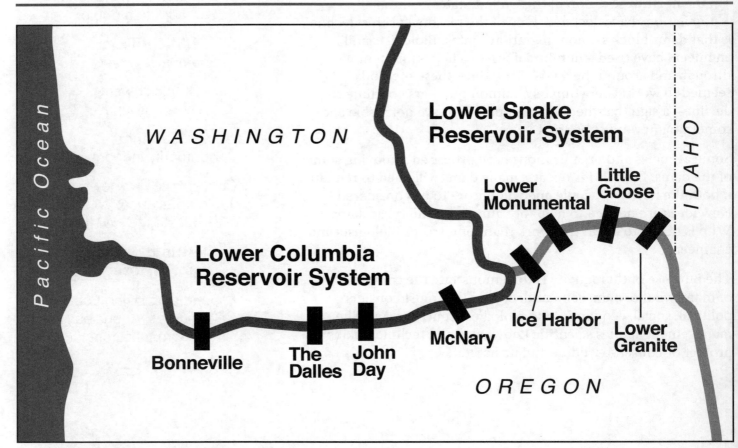

* Adapted from *WILD About Salmon*, Idaho Department of Fish and Game, 1999.

Dam Design
© *Council for Environmental Education (CEE)*

3. Allow sufficient time for groups to conduct their research, compile a bibliography, and present their information.

4. Reassign students into new small groups so that each group contains an "expert" on each topic above. The group then synthesizes and organizes the information into a documented paper on the problem of declining salmon as it relates to dam construction and design. Students analyze and evaluate the costs, benefits, and consequences for various options.

5. Instruct the new teams to design a dam that will produce electricity efficiently or store irrigation water and that will provide safe passage for salmon. The teams may draw or construct the model.

6. Have each team present its design to the class, noting important features that address the needs of humans as well as wildlife.

Extension

Arrange for a field outing that allows students to observe how fish and wildlife management agencies address migration barriers that dams create for fish species.

Evaluation

1. Each presentation needs to include a diagram or model of the dam and its migration features.

2. Encourage students to question the design and conclusions of each group, and remind them that constructive criticism demonstrates understanding of the problems.

Construction began on the Bonneville Dam in 1934, and by 1937 the dam was in operation.

WILD Work

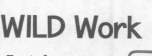

For information on the related careers of **Civil Engineer, Hydraulic Engineer, General Engineer, Fisheries Biologist,** and **Land Surveyor,** head to: *www.projectwild.org/aquatic.*

Explore this information with students, or have students do a guided exploration on their own.

In Step with STEM

- For links to lesson plans on constructing a model dam in the classroom or schoolyard visit *www.projectwild.org/aquatic.* At a small stream in a local area, recreate the dam using rocks and other natural materials. Discuss the impact of the dam on the waterbody over time.

- Explore innovations in the design of dams by researching the Deschute River Dam. Visit *www.projectwild. org/aquatic* for more information.

Wildlife management applies scientific knowledge and skills to protect or conserve wildlife and its habitat.

Gone Fishing!

Field Investigation

Grade Level:
Middle, High School

Content Areas: Science, Physical Education, Environmental Education, Language Arts

Method: After making simple fishing rigs and practicing casting, students conduct a field investigation focused on fish and fish habitat.

Materials: This activity requires special materials. Please see page 273 for a full list.

Activity Time: two or three 45-minute sessions, plus an off-site fishing field experience

People Power: any size group; support from experienced adult anglers, one adult per 4–5 students recommended (community volunteers or fishing resource professionals)

Setting: indoors and outdoors, field investigation in fishable waters

Conceptual Framework Topic Reference: HNI, HNII, CAII, BDII, ECII, AAI, WMI, WMIII. Concepts will vary depending on students' research questions.

Terms to Know: controlled variable, manipulated variable, responding variable, angling, spin casting, catch-and-release, fishing ethics, clinch knot, creel survey, adaptations, sport fishing

Appendices: Let's Go Fishing! Inventory Methods, Using Local Resources, Field Ethics, Agencies and Organizations

What can you learn about local fish species and habitat by fishing?

Objectives

Students will (1) develop and write questions and detailed procedures for investigating fish species and habitat through angling; (2) collect, organize, and analyze data to draw conclusions; (3) explain necessary preparations and safety considerations for a fishing trip; and (4) demonstrate proficiency in assembling and casting a fishing rig.

NOTE: This activity is best conducted with the assistance of an experienced angler or angler education staff from your state wildlife or natural resources department. In addition to ensuring permits and regulations are addressed for the group, they can provide instruction on fish natural history and biology to introduce students to their local aquatic wildlife. In preparation for the fishing component, these professionals can impart the necessary fishing skills with students including equipment introduction, casting, baiting, knot tying, catch and release protocol, and more. Many of these organizations can provide fishing equipment for loan during your investigation. Visit *www.projectwild.org/aquatic* for a listing of organizations.

Study Site

Consult with angler education staff employed by your state wildlife or natural resources department to plan the natural history and fishing skills portions of this activity. These professionals will be able to provide suggested sites close to your school or facility, such as locations along rivers, shorelines, or urban fishing ponds. Additionally, these professionals will be able to connect you with fishing outreach programs that offer equipment loans. For comparative or correlative investigations, consider the option of fishing and data collection at multiple locations within one body of water as well as from different bodies of water (see "Aquatic WILD Field Investigations" [page xiv] for more information on correlative, comparative, and descriptive field investigations).

Background

Fishing is an ancient practice with archeological evidence dating back 40,000 years. Hunter-gatherers fished for food. Recreational fishing for sport or leisure dates back to the 16th century. People fish not just for food but to experience natural beauty and solitude. Some enjoy the challenge of catching fish or perhaps just being out on the water. Many people benefit from the camaraderie of others with related hobbies such as fly-tying, rod making, entomology, taxidermy, and photography. Fishing with a rod, reel, fishing line, and bait, also known as "angling," is a popular outdoor activity for many people that adds fun to camping, canoeing, boating, and travel. Fishing also provides opportunities to investigate local fish populations and habitats at sites in urban and rural settings.

Fisheries management ensures the wise use of fish resources so that future generations also have fish and healthy fish habitat. Regulations are an essential part of fisheries management and serve to restrict the locations, seasons, and equipment for catching fish, as well as the species, quantities, and sizes of fish caught. Funding that allows state wildlife agencies and natural resources departments to manage fish populations is generated largely through the sale of fishing licenses. Fishing regulations, age requirements for licenses, and other information about fishing are published annually by state wildlife and natural resources agencies.

Introducing the Field Investigation

1. Discuss with students their knowledge and experiences with fishing. Why do people go fishing? Has anyone in the group been fishing before or know anyone that fishes? What do they know about fish and fishing?

2. Explain that one benefit of fishing is an opportunity to learn more about local fish species and habitats. Ask students what they would like to learn about fish and where they live. Record questions on a board or flipchart. Students' "big picture" questions might include:

- What is needed to provide fish habitat or a good fishing spot?

- What makes a healthy aquatic environment for fish and other species?

- How can our community sustain healthy aquatic environments?

These big picture questions are a good starting place to narrow down to a researchable question(s) (see "Forming the Question").

3. Discuss plans to visit a local site to conduct an investigation through fishing.

Materials

- ☑ *Planning Your Fishing Trip* (page 277)
- ☑ *What's My Question?* (page 388)
- ☑ *Conclusions and Next Steps* (page 389)
- ☑ notebooks for data collection

Fishing equipment:

- ☑ rods and reels, cane type fishing poles, or hand line or casting rigs that students make
- ☑ hooks, bobbers, appropriate lures, flies, or bait
- ☑ long-nose pliers to help remove hooks from fish
- ☑ bucket or tub
- ☑ linen/cotton/nylon gloves
- ☑ fish field guide
- ☑ ruler, first-aid kit, tape
- ☑ fish stringer and/or ice and cooler to keep fish you are planning to eat or dissect
- ☑ a balance or spring scale for weighing fish
- ☑ life jackets (PFDs) if needed
- ☑ sport fishing regulations for the area.

NOTE: If needed, secure fishing licenses for students before the field investigation.

Forming the Question

Discuss students' questions. Can they be answered through information gathered by fishing? Are there other data collection methods in addition to catching fish that might also help answer questions? Help students articulate and decide what researchable question(s) will be investigated. Students can record their big picture questions and their more focused researchable question(s) on the *What's My Question?* page. Choosing a single investigative question for the whole class will allow educators to more easily assist students as they collect data. The increased amount of data relating to a single question should also help improve reliability and accuracy when drawing conclusions.

See "Questions to Investigate" in the sidebar on the next page for possible research questions.

Conducting the Investigation

1. After revisiting your investigative question, identify the variables in your research. For comparative and correlative questions, help students identify which condition will be changed (manipulated variable) and which condition will be measured (responding variable).

2. Discuss and plan with students what type of data should be collected and how data will be collected. What types of information and observations will be needed to answer the research question? How will you go about collecting data? Why is it important for all students to take measurements the same way? Similarly, why is it important to take measurements the same way when collecting data at different times or locations?

3. Explain that when we determine a way to control how we take measurements, collect samples, or make observations in order to ensure we are doing it the same way each time, this is known as a controlled variable. As an example, if we are investigating at which location in a pond we are more likely to catch fish, we might use the same type of bait at each location for one of our controlled variables. This way, we know that if greater numbers of fish are caught in one location rather than another, the difference is not explained by the type of bait used.

4. Have students write a plan for conducting the investigation, including: 1) a prediction or hypothesis about what they will find or how their question will be answered; 2) materials they will need to conduct the investigation; 3) the manipulated variable, the responding variable, and at least one controlled variable; and 4) each step they will take, with enough detail so others could conduct the same experiment.

5. Have students plan to enter data directly into a science notebook or create a data collection form. See "Aquatic WILD Field Investigations" (page xiv) for criteria on creating student data forms.

NOTE: Data collection involving identification of species (such as fish) or nonliving components found at the study site may be difficult without prior

Gone Fishing!
© *Council for Environmental Education (CEE)*

experience. In such cases, encourage students to make and label illustrations and take photographs that they can later refer to when using field guides back in the classroom. Provide multiple copies of fish field guides to assist in on-site identification.

6. Review the *Planning Your Fishing Trip* page with students and make necessary preparations. Assemble your supplies and review safety measures and fishing ethics. Discuss expectations and what to wear. Practice casting as needed.

7. Go fish! After arrival at the study site, students can record a description of the site conditions. In pairs or small groups, students record observations about the fish caught or other relevant variables at the site.

8. For improved accuracy, take multiple measurements over time and/or location if possible. Students may also need to repeat individual measurements.

Organizing and Analyzing the Data

1. Either back in the classroom or at the study site when fishing is completed, use a whiteboard, flipchart, or projector to record and display a summary of the cumulative results.

2. What calculations will help answer the research question? How can the data be best displayed graphically? Are any patterns found in the data?

3. For comparative and correlative investigations, describe how sampling, measurements, and observations were kept consistent for the two or more locations, times, or organisms (your controlled variables) and how they were random and representative of the site.

Drawing Conclusions

1. Using the *Conclusions and Next Steps* page, students write a clear statement explaining the answer to the research question.

2. Ask students to describe any problems they may have experienced when collecting data. Were there any factors that might have impacted the research (time of day, weather, etc.)?

3. Were the procedures developed by students logical and sufficiently detailed to provide data needed to answer the research question? If not, how could the procedures be modified?

4. What other data would help answer the research question?

Questions to Investigate

Student questions that help **describe** could include…

- What fish species are at the study site?
- How many fish might we catch in this particular waterbody?
- What is the food preference of the fish identified as possible to catch?
- What are the physical characteristics of the fish species caught?
- What is the ratio of fish species we will catch?
- What sizes of fish will we catch?

Questions that help **compare** could include…

- How do physical characteristics such as shape, color, weight, and length compare between species?
- Will one area of the fishing site have greater angler success than another?
- Will one type of bait/lure show greater catching success than another?
- Will more fish be caught in the morning or at the end of the day?

Questions that help **correlate** could include…

- Is there a relationship between type of lure or bait used and number of fish or species of fish caught?
- Is there a relationship between the hook size or fishing tackle used and the number of fish caught?
- Is there a relationship between the experience level of the angler and the number of fish caught?
- Would we expect to see a relationship between the number of anglers in one particular area ("angling pressure") and the number of fish caught?
- Does time of day affect fish activity? Would we expect more fish be attracted to bait earlier or later in the day?

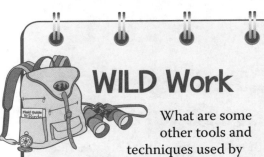

WILD Work

What are some other tools and techniques used by **Aquatic Biologists** to gauge fish populations and assess fish habitat? Follow the links at *www.projectwild. org/aquatic* for information on macroinvertebrate surveys or electro-shocking fish surveys.

The recreational aspect of fishing provides employment throughout the world—professional angling, fishing tours, bait and gear sales, lodging, and more. Research the nearest location to your school where fishing impacts the economy.

In Step with STEM

■ Examine commercially or skillfully made lures or flies. Invite someone experienced in these crafts to demonstrate how they are made. An expert fish fly-maker can help students make their own flies using barbless hooks, wire, feathers or fur (from a craft store), brightly colored threads, and other shiny and colorful items.

■ Observe the action of commercial or homemade lures in a tank of water, and investigate what characteristics make some wiggle, spin, or dive.

■ Students can design their own models of lures with clothespins, modeling clay, aluminum foil, paint, markers, waterproof glue, colored chenille stems, colored yarn, fabric, fur, feathers, etc.

■ Research the technology available for fishing, including depth finders, waterbody mapping systems, and smartphone applications.

Extensions

1. Research the method fisheries managers use to gather data on fish populations, known as a creel survey or angler survey. Conduct a creel survey at a local, popular fishing site.

2. Invite an experienced angler to visit the class and/or accompany students on a fishing trip. The angler could provide assistance and tips, relate personal experiences, and demonstrate fishing tackle.

3. Have students make a journal to record their fishing experiences, with a chart to record date, time of fishing, weather, name and location of the body of water, type of gear and bait used, type of fish caught and their size, whether fish were released or kept, how fish were cooked, and how they tasted. They should leave space to record interesting observations and a description of the experience. Discuss how such information would be useful to the fisheries manager.

4. Catch and study live bait (e.g., aquatic invertebrates, worms, grasshoppers, crickets, minnows).

5. Design a travel brochure with tips and tricks for organizing a good fishing trip.

6. Have students create a map of the study site based on online maps or aerial photographs that indicates their anticipated "good" fishing areas. Students then test these areas and discuss the successes or failures of their hypotheses.

7. Investigate local or global organizations that are dedicated to ensuring healthy fish populations and/or promoting fishing.

Evaluation

1. Have students list other questions they generated during the field investigation that they did not explore. Which of these questions are researchable? How would they find the answers to these questions?

2. Ask students to explain why or why not angling is an accurate or meaningful way to gather information on the overall health of the water and habitat at their study site.

3. What can students do to help maintain or improve habitat for a diversity of fish species at the study site?

4. Have students confirm proficiency in: tying a clinch knot; baiting their own hook; successful casting; and responsible catch and release procedures.

Planning Your Fishing Trip

Getting Ready . . .

- Consult your state wildlife or natural resources department to determine dates and locations where you will be permitted to fish.
- Determine if fishing licenses will need to be acquired.
- Invite parents and other adult volunteers to come along and assist.
- Acquire life jackets (PFDs) as needed.
- Take swimming and water-safety lessons.
- Heed warnings for lightning and windstorms.
- Decide in advance if you will keep or release fish that you catch. If keeping fish, check regulations on what fish species and sizes you are allowed to keep.
- Practice your skills! See the sections on "Knot-tying," "Building a Casting Rig," and "Casting Practice" on the next page.

What to Bring . . .

- Dress for weather, and remember it is often windier and colder near water. Raincoats can double as windbreakers. Wear a sunhat and apply sunscreen to exposed skin.
- Protect your eyes—sunglasses and baseball caps or other hats with brims can protect the eyes from the sun and fish hooks when casting and reeling in.
- Bring a first-aid kit and insect repellent.
- Use barbless hooks or flatten the barb with pliers.
- Fishing gear (see "Basic Fishing Tackle" to the right).
- Don't forget a fish stringer and a cooler with ice if you are planning to bring home fish to eat or dissect.

While Fishing . . .

- Always be careful near water. Beware of steep or slippery banks, strong currents, or piers without protective railings.
- As necessary, wear life jackets (PFDs).
- Handle fish carefully, with wet hands. Take care with sharp teeth, spines, and gill covers.
- When ice fishing, be sure you are on sound blue ice that is at least ten inches thick. Check with state agencies that announce when ice is thick enough for ice fishing.

Fishing Ethics . . .

- Obey fishing and boating laws.
- Support conservation efforts.
- If not keeping fish, practice catch and release.
- Practice safe angling and boating.
- Respect other anglers' rights.
- Share fishing knowledge and skills.
- Protect fish by never releasing live bait into waters.
- Properly recycle and dispose of trash.

Basic Fishing Tackle

Tackle includes poles, reels, and many fishing accessories such as sinkers, hooks, lures, and bobbers. Spincasting tackle is easy for beginning anglers and is the most popular type of fishing equipment in use today. The spincasting reel mounts to the top of the pistol-type handle or grip on the rod. Most rods are 4.5 to 6 feet in length. Spincasting reels work using a push button to release the line to cast out into the water. It is best to set the drag so that line is released when a firm tug is given. There is a drag adjustment in front of the thumb button. These reels also have an anti-reverse lever that prevents turning the handle backward and forces the drag system to slow the line leaving the reel as a fish pulls. Spincasting tackle is best used for smaller fish in freshwater. It is ideal for bluegill, bream, small catfish, bass, and trout.

Fishing line is made of nylon called monofilament. It is used for most casting. Fishing line comes in a variety of sizes or strengths, called pound-test. The pound-test refers to the amount of force it takes to break the line. The larger the line size, the stronger it is. Six-pound test line is more flexible and casts easily. It is advisable to match your fishing line to your rod and reel capacity and to the species of fish you want to catch. Six-pound test line is best suited for most fishing.

Bait can include natural baits such as worms, insects, and minnows. Check the fishing regulations to make sure the bait you select is legal for the water you fish. Live minnows and other live fish are illegal to use in many states. If live bait is used, left over bait fish should never be released into the water.

Prepared baits can be made from bread and cheese. Commercially made baits are available in abundance. A few examples include salmon eggs for trout and floating paste-type bait available in many colors. Canned corn and hot dogs can also be used for bait.

Artificial lures can include jigs, spoons, plugs, and spinners. These are available in a wide variety of sizes, shapes, and colors.

Learn all you can about fish behavior and how to choose the best bait for different situations. Discovering which bait works best for the particular fish and the body of water will help ensure you make a catch!

Planning Your Fishing Trip

Knot-tying

Before your trip, practice tying a fishing line on a barbless hook with a clinch knot. Links to online demonstration videos are available at *www.projectwild.org/aquatic*. When practicing knot-tying, try using a fairly large diameter string and paper clip. Be careful with hooks, and if showing others how to tie knots, be sure to demonstrate safe handling of hooks.

Build a Casting Rig

If a rod and reel is not available or desired, an alternative is to make a tin can casting rig. Make sure the tin has no sharp edges by covering it with tape. Tape one end of a 30-foot piece of fishing line to the can near the closed end. Carefully wrap the line around the can toward the open end, trying not to overlap it. Too many overlaps may spoil the cast. When all the line is wound, tie a casting weight to the end and secure the end with the rubber band.

For each person fishing, you will need: tin can, elastic or rubber band, 3 feet of rope; thick string (30-cm long); paper clips; scissors; 30 feet (or more) of fishing line of about 6-lb test strength); one small (size 6–8) barbless hook or pliers to bend down the barb; adhesive tape; a sinker (e.g., 4- to 6-oz split-shot, non-lead sinker).

If you do not wish to use baited hooks, you could use artificial lures such as spinners or artificial flies on a clear, floating bobber.

Casting Practice

Practice casting and reeling in. To designate a casting area, use chalk on pavement or align ropes on grass to represent a stream or lake shoreline, including the features that might harbor a fish and obstacles to avoid (rocks, logs, fast water, pools, vegetation, etc.). Casting targets could be as simple as cardboard boxes or hula-hoops on a gym floor. Upside-down aluminum pie plates make good targets because they reward good aim with a loud bang.

A Few Fishing Tips

There are many fishing techniques. "Still fishing" is the easiest—just cast line out and simply wait with the hook dangling from a bobber or resting on the bottom. If the hook is not too deep in the water, you can see light-colored bait. Watch for the bait disappearing from sight. This signals that the fish has taken the bait, and that it's time to set the hook by jerking the line.

If fishing with a spinner, move it regularly by jigging it or by casting it out and reeling it in. The advantage of casting is that it can place the bait or lure in locations that are otherwise difficult to reach, and it adds the attraction of movement for the fish. Cast bait gently into the water, not too close to the fish. Try to keep the bait off the bottom and watch and feel for fish nibbling or biting the bait or lure. Retrieve the line slowly between casts.

When a fish takes the bait, set the hook (pull up with one swift motion to ensure the hook has firmly set in the fish), pull it toward the surface, and scoop it up in a net. If this is not possible, lift the fish out of the water and lower it into a bucket of water. Keep any fish you plan to eat on a stringer in the water, or clean them and place in a cooler.

Catch-and-Release

Unless you plan to eat the fish you catch, you will want to release them. Many anglers fish just to be outdoors and enjoy the experience. They release fish so they can be caught again. Careful handling of fish when catching and releasing demonstrates good angling ethics. Fish that are caught out of season or do not meet legal limits also need to be released. Carefully check the area's sport fishing regulations.

The most critical aspect of releasing fish is to do so quickly. A fish may die of exhaustion if dangling on the line for too long. If possible, keep the fish in water so it can breathe. Hold it firmly but gently. Sliding the hook out will be easier if you use barbless hooks. Long-nosed pliers will be useful if the hook is deep in the fish's mouth. If the hook is barbed and cannot be removed without tearing flesh, cut the line and leave it in.

If the fish is still struggling, release it gently into the water. Do not put it directly into a fast current because it may need time to regain strength. If the fish is unconscious, you may be able to revive it. Hold the fish upright in water heading upstream. Move it gently forward in a figure-eight pattern, so that freshwater flows through the gills. Release the fish as soon as it begins to struggle. Be careful—if there is too much motion then water will not pass over the gills properly. You will drown the fish!

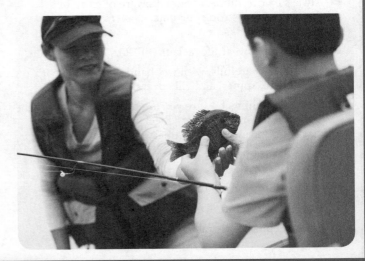

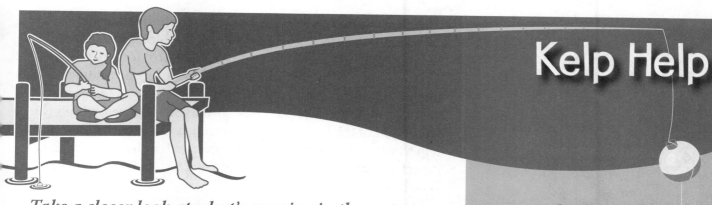

Kelp Help

Take a closer look at what's growing in the water.

Objectives

Students will list and describe different ways that kelp can be beneficial to humans, wildlife, and the environment.

Background

Aquatic plants that are visible at the surface of oceans are called "seaweed." In aquatic habitats, seaweed plays a role central to the rhythm of life in water.

Seaweed are algae. Algae are not restricted to the sea. They live in profusion in lakes, rivers, and streams. Algae are as important to aquatic animals in marine and freshwater environments as grass is to cows, horses, and other grazing animals. Some algae are microscopic. Others, like kelp, are very large. Kelp, a seaweed, is an example of one of thousands of different plant forms found in aquatic habitats.

Kelp is often found in great forests in the sea. Other forms of kelp are smaller and more solitary. Pacific Ocean varieties of kelp often grow to be more than 100 feet long. The plant is held to the bottom by a structure called a "holdfast" (see Diagram A). The holdfast anchors the plant to cobbles, large rocks, or debris in sandy bottoms. It looks like a root but is not. The holdfast cannot absorb nutrients the way true roots do. It serves only to keep the kelp in place during storms and tides. Nutrients are absorbed through most of the kelp's surface area.

The kelp plant grows rapidly in crowded, waving forests, adding as much as one foot of growth per day. The growing tip of a kelp plant is called a "frond" (see Diagram B). As the frond grows upward toward the surface, it forms a long string of leaf-like structures called "blades." Each blade has a float bulb that is attached to the growing main stem or stipe. As the frond grows toward the surface, the kelp plant's stem or stipe becomes the anchor for dozens of these floats and blades. When the frond reaches the surface, the growth rate slows down and soon forms its last blade, called the "terminal blade."

Grade Level: Upper Elementary

Content Areas: Science, Environmental Education

Method: Students research kelp, create a mural, and report their findings to the class.

Materials: Writing materials, references, art materials for a mural

Activity Time: two or three 45-minute sessions

People Power: groups of four to five students

Setting: indoors

Conceptual Framework Topic Reference: RAII

Terms to Know: kelp, algae, seaweed, algin, holdfast, emulsifiers

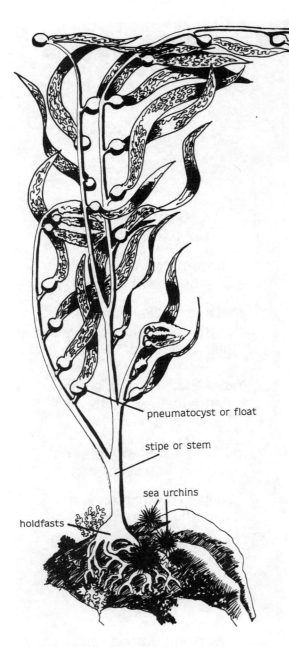

pneumatocyst or float

stipe or stem

sea urchins

holdfasts

Diagram A

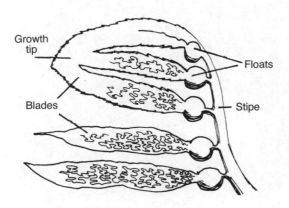

Growth tip

Floats

Blades

Stipe

Diagram B

Some marine biologists suggest that kelp forests provide habitat for as diverse a variety of wildlife as does a tropical rainforest on land. Worms, snails, crustaceans, and mollusks abound in kelp forests. Fish live at all levels within the protection of the kelp forest. Bottom fish thrive at the base of a kelp forest. The dozens of aquatic species that live in kelp beds attract predators. Sharks, seals, and Sea Otters find these forests to be attractive hunting areas.

Kelp is commercially harvested for dozens of products used by people. For example, kelp contains a chemical called "algin." Algin is used as a thickener, stabilizer, and emulsifier. Thickeners increase a substance's density by making the substance less watery. Stabilizers prevent deterioration of foods, and emulsifiers help keep ingredients from separating. Algin from kelp is used in ice cream and a variety of other dairy products, as well as in many kinds of processed foods, beverages, and medicines. Algin is also used in the production of paper, cosmetics, ceramics, paint, and insecticides. Small amounts are used directly as food.

Procedure

1. Divide the class into groups of four or five students. Assign (or have students choose) topics to research such as the following related to kelp:

- algin
- kelp as a habitat for wildlife
- kelp as a food source (kelp recipes)
- emulsifiers
- medicinal uses of kelp
- aquatic weeds of the world (both marine and freshwater)
- the Sargasso Sea
- algae and the oceanic food web
- Sea Otters
- sea urchins

2. Once the research is finished, have each group visually summarize its findings on a large sheet of paper.

3. When all groups are finished, have them place their artwork on a wall and verbally report on their findings. The artwork should be placed so that the edges of the paper overlap, producing a mural related to kelp.

4. Lead a class discussion about kelp, algae, and other freshwater and marine plants, inviting students to react to the information and insights shared by each group.

Extensions

1. Investigate other aquatic plants and their roles in aquatic habitats.

2. Draw an accurate portrayal of a kelp "forest" food web. Keep the animals and plants to their proportionate sizes in the drawings.

3. Visit a beach where kelp can be found. Identify its parts. If a beach is not available, make a small collection of aquatic weeds from a local pond or stream, and identify each.

4. Visit an aquarium that exhibits a kelp habitat.

5. Plan a Kelp Appreciation Day, including a potluck meal where kelp is a part of each dish.

6. Turn part of your classroom into a kelp forest. Use crepe paper, balloons, and construction paper to depict the habitat and its inhabitants.

7. Create an underwater viewer. Visit a local aquatic habitat and determine boundaries of an underwater study site. Identify kelp or other aquatic plants under the surface. Observe the habitat and diagram or sketch the area. Record observations over time and describe any changes to populations or the habitat.

Evaluation

1. What is kelp? Write a paragraph and draw a picture to illustrate your response.

2. Describe two ways that kelp is helpful to each of the following: humans, wildlife, aquatic habitats.

WILD Work

A **Marine Biologist** may be responsible for managing an aquatic/marine species, such as kelp, for a local bay, harbor, or coastal area; writing technical reports and scientific publications on research findings; and participating in collaborative efforts with government officials, business leaders, residents, the fishing industry, and other scientists to improve the health of the bay and coastal areas. Marine biologists typically have earned a graduate degree in marine biology or a related field. They must be able to work outside and have the ability to travel. For more information on this occupation, visit *www.projectwild.org/aquatic*.

In Step with STEM

- Explore the question, "Where in the world are kelp forests?" Go to *www.projectwild.org/aquatic* for a link to a kelp forests distribution map. Discuss and then research why kelp forests occur primarily in temperate and arctic waters rather than tropical regions.

- For links on how to make an underwater viewer for use with an underwater study site, visit *www.projectwild.org/aquatic*.

Dragonfly Pond

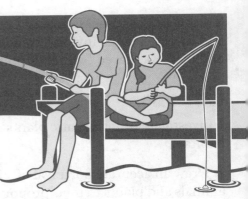

Grade Level: Upper
Elementary, Middle School

Content Areas:
Environmental Education, Social Studies

Method:
Students create an arrangement of human land-use activities around an image of a pond.

Materials:
For each team: scissors; masking tape; paper; two sets of *Land-Use Patterns* (page 287); one *Map of Dragonfly Pond* (page 288); a large piece of paper (18" × 24")

Activity Time:
one to three 45- to 60-minute sessions

People Power:
designed for several small groups; can be modified to be an individual activity

Setting:
indoors

Conceptual Framework Topic Reference:
RAIC2, RAIC3

Terms to Know:
land-use planning, wetlands, tradeoff, lifestyle, smart growth

Appendices: Using Local Resources, Agencies and Organizations

We invite you to a smart growth challenge.

Objective

Students will (1) evaluate the effects of different kinds of land use on wetland habitat, and (2) discuss and evaluate lifestyle changes to minimize damaging effects on wetlands.

Background

Since the earliest times, humans have deliberately planned the arrangement of housing in regular, rectangular patterns and the prominent location of civic and religious buildings along main thoroughfares. These patterns have not only given structure to American cities, but also they have affected wildlife habitat and populations. Sometimes people perceive undeveloped areas of the natural environment as raw material for human use, while others believe that the natural environment is to be preserved without regard for human needs. Still others yearn for a balance between economic growth and a healthy natural environment. "Smart growth" proponents argue that growth can be concentrated in transit-oriented urban centers that build a unique sense of community and avoid urban sprawl.

Growth is at the core of land-use issues. Growth in natural systems has inherent limits that are imposed by a balance of energy among all parts of the system. Energy in natural systems is translated into food, water, shelter, space, and continued survival. The vitality of natural systems is expressed by the ability to be self-regulating. This capacity for self-regulation of all the life and plant forms of an ecosystem is equally important. The microbes in the soil are just as necessary to a habitat as the plants and predators. It is this natural dynamic balance, with all its inherent and essential parts, that much of human land use has tended to disturb. Growth in human activities can often go beyond the natural limits of a setting. Humans have the ability to import energy sources and other resources that allow a system to exceed its natural limits or to remove energy sources that are necessary for a system to stay in balance.

Dragonfly Pond
© *Council for Environmental Education (CEE)*

Wetlands, for example, can be perceived as swamp land that does not have any value. Yet biologists see wetlands as a nursery for hundreds of forms of wildlife. Fish, frogs, toads, migrating birds, snakes, insects, and a remarkable variety of plants all inhabit wetlands. Wetlands are highly vulnerable to development, pollution, and a variety of forms of human interference. On average, about 14,000 acres of valuable wetlands are lost each year in the United States—for example, to draining, dredging, filling, and pollution (Source: U.S. Fish and Wildlife Service, 2004–2009 National Wetlands Inventory).

One of the major challenges now facing our society is how to regulate growth and conserve open spaces. How can we develop necessary practices to restore a more natural dynamic balance in places that have experienced human disturbance?

In this activity, students will struggle with the arrangement of overlapping and conflicting land uses in an effort to conserve a wetland habitat. When students reach some kind of agreement about the local issues, the activity shifts to how what they have done affects other "Dragonfly Ponds." The activity ends with consideration of the idea that the planet is, in fact, a single "Dragonfly Pond."

Procedure

1. Begin by explaining to students that during this activity they will use "Dragonfly Pond" as a microcosm of environmental concerns involved in making land-use planning decisions.

2. Divide the class into teams of three to five, with each group representing one of the interest groups described below. Students will stay in these groups until the end of the activity. Possible interest groups to include:

- Residents—desire to live in the area
- Farmers—want to use the land to raise food and livestock
- Conservationists—want to maintain the land as wildlife habitat
- Business interests—want to use the land for commerce and economic growth
- Gas station owners—want to make a living in servicing and repairing cars
- Parks and recreation department personnel—want people to have a place for recreation
- Highway department personnel—want to maintain access in the area
- Factory representatives—want to protect jobs and commerce

NOTE: Add other interest groups that may be locally important.

Growth in human activities can often go beyond the natural limits of a setting. Humans have the ability to import energy sources and other resources that allow a system to exceed its natural limits or to remove energy sources that are necessary for a system to stay in balance.

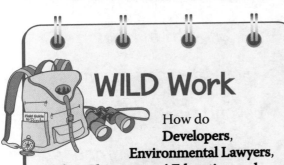

WILD Work

How do **Developers**, **Environmental Lawyers**, **Urban Planners**, and **Education and Outreach Specialists** work together to evaluate how development will affect a wetland and then remove or minimize any damaging effects?

To find more information on these careers, head to: *www. projectwild.org/aquatic.*

In Step with STEM

■ In order to better understand the needs of a particular aquatic environment and explore conceptual models, construct a simple or advanced watershed model. For links to more information on basic and advanced watershed modeling, see *www. projectwild.org/aquatic.*

■ Use satellite imagery, aerial photos, and street views to explore land-use patterns and aquatic habitats in your community as compared to other places. Go to *www.projectwild.org/ aquatic* for online resources.

Growth in natural systems has inherent limits that are imposed by a balance of energy among all parts of the system.

3. Distribute the 18" × 24" pieces of paper that will serve as the base map for each team's pond and its associated land-use activities. Have students cut out the *Land-Use Patterns* and *Map of Dragonfly Pond.* All the land-use patterns must be used. Patterns may be cut to smaller sizes and may touch, but may not overlap. Students may include additional land-use patterns. Suggest to students that they may not want to adhere the land-use patterns to the base map until the team is in agreement.

4. When students are ready to begin the process of making land-use decisions, have them create a list of pros and cons for each land use. Guide the class discussion so that they consider the consequences of each land use. Record these lists on the chalkboard. The following are only a few of the many possible examples:

Farms:

Pro
- 👍 produce food
- 👍 provide some wildlife habitat and open space
- 👍 provide jobs through seasonal employment

Con
- 👎 use pesticides (herbicides, insecticides) that may impact people, wildlife, and the environment
- 👎 may become sources of natural soil erosion
- 👎 sometimes drain wetlands for farmlands

Homes:

Pro
- 👍 provide shelter
- 👍 provide a sense of community
- 👍 contribute to local tax base

Con
- 👎 generate wastes and sewage
- 👎 may strain municipal water supplies
- 👎 contribute to the loss of wildlife habitat

5. Have students work in teams for 30 to 45 minutes.

6. Display each team's base map, and have students report on its work in progress. Encourage discussion of the students' choices, emphasizing that:

- ■ no land use can be excluded, and
- ■ consensus must be built around each decision.

Look for the consequences of students' proposed land-use plans. Be firm about the issues, but fair about this being a very difficult set of choices.

Dragonfly Pond
© *Council for Environmental Education (CEE)*

7. Continue the discussion by asking more teams to share their proposed plans. Again, be firm in discussing the consequences. What would happen if the factory and businesses were to close? Abandoning the farm would have what effects? Do farmlands provide habitat for some wildlife? What happens if wetlands are drained to create farmland?

8. Give students additional time working in their teams to decide on the best possible land-use plan under the circumstances. Being sensitive to their frustrations, display all the final land-use plans. Analyze and discuss the merits of each of the approaches. Point out that although their solutions may not be perfect, they can minimize the damage to Dragonfly Pond.

9. Choose one of the team's base maps and continue Dragonfly Creek downstream. The students may have dumped effluent below Dragonfly Pond and let it flow downstream. Show the route the stream might travel. On the drawing, have the downstream part of Dragonfly Creek become another pond and wetland, and label the new area Laughing Gull Lake. Continue the drawing to Sea Oats Estuary and finally into Whale Gulf. (See Diagram A.) You may also connect several of the teams' maps together, one above another, to indicate the flow downstream.

10. Ask students to brainstorm possible problems that could be faced within each of these aquatic systems as a result of the human activities at Dragonfly Pond. Make inferences and predictions about the potential consequences of such activities. For example, you could emphasize the effluent from the factory. How will it be treated? Where? By whom? Where will it go? With what effects?

11. Ask students to examine all of the land uses in this activity. If they had been considering any of them as inherently bad, have them consider a different question. What could the people who are actually in charge of those various land uses do in their practices to minimize the damage to Dragonfly Pond?

Have the activity end with an emphasis on solutions rather than on problems. Point out, for example, changes that have taken place in the "mining" of industrial effluents through "scrubbers" to extract wastes as profitable resources. (Perhaps students need to make a "scrubbing filter" for the factory.)

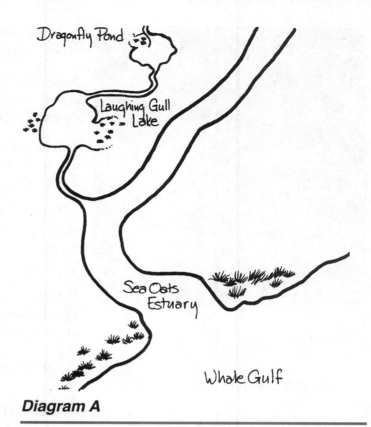

Diagram A

Agricultural practices are changing, reducing the use of potentially harmful pesticides and herbicides. Petroleum wastes are being recycled, and industrial and community awareness regarding uses of harmful chemicals is evolving.

Extensions

1. Do the activity again up to Step 6. After each interest group has presented its plan, form new groups with each one having a representative from each interest group. Have the new groups devise plans that all of the interests can agree on. Discuss how, if at all, this is a realistic experience in working to balance various community interests.

2. Visit a local pond or other body of water in your community. What kind of development exists there? How do you think land use at the site and upstream from the site has affected overall quality of the water?

3. Trace any stream or river system that passes through your community from its source to its entrance into the ocean. List all the sites that you can identify that lower the quality of the waters in their journey, and suggest how to reverse the process.

Wetlands are highly vulnerable to development, pollution, and a variety of forms of human interference.

4. As a current events activity, collect newspaper or web articles concerning local water-related and land-use issues.

5. Learn more about environmental impact statements. Obtain actual copies of statements about wetlands in your area. What concerns are addressed in those documents?

6. Learn about the National Wildlife Refuge System. Are there any wildlife refuges in your area? What animals find refuge in them? Visit a National Wildlife Refuge.

7. Research private organizations that work to protect wetlands, such as The Nature Conservancy and Ducks Unlimited. What do these organizations do, and how do they do it? (See also "Agencies and Organizations" in the appendix.)

8. Research zoning laws and land-use regulations in your area. Would the plan your group proposed for Dragonfly Pond be allowed in your community?

9. How does the Clean Water Act help to protect wetlands?

Evaluation

1. Identify three actions that people can take to reduce or prevent damage to wetlands.

2. Select any action you could personally take to reduce or prevent damage to wetlands. Write a one-page paper about your plan.

Dragonfly Pond
© *Council for Environmental Education (CEE)*

Land-Use Patterns

 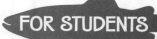

| Grocery | Gas Station | Dry Cleaner | Restaurant |

| Farm Feed Lot | House | House | House |
| | House | House | House | ←Cut

Farm Cornfield

Factory

Park

Fire House

Condominium

HIGHWAY

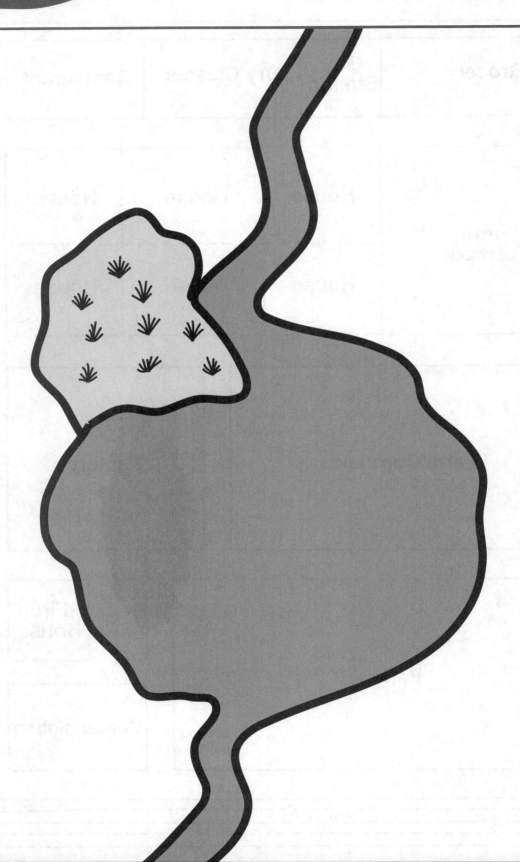

Dragonfly Pond
© Council for Environmental Education (CEE)

Conservation Messaging

Can your advertisement help conserve fish species?

Objectives

Students will (1) research threats to fish and aquatic habitats, (2) explain what can be done to conserve and restore aquatic habitats, and (3) plan and produce a public service announcement (PSA) that helps inform people about actions they can take to conserve fish and their habitats.

Background

Lakes, rivers, and streams provide habitat for countless numbers of fish and myriad other organisms. Reptiles, amphibians, birds, mammals, and aquatic insects are an integral part of healthy aquatic ecosystems. Unfortunately, many people do not realize that these fragile and dynamic systems can be damaged by a wide range of human activities. The introduction of non-native species into an ecosystem may also have far reaching consequences. Any human action that impacts the basic life requirements for fish (including water quality and quantity, food supply, space, or shelter) has the potential to harm many types of aquatic wildlife.

Aquatic ecosystems require protection and conservation, and in some cases restoration efforts, to ensure aquatic life is able to survive. Protection measures include setting aside land as riparian buffers, parks, and wildlife habitat, prohibiting the dumping of trash into aquatic environments, and regulating the use of possible aquatic pollutants like fertilizers. Examples of restoration projects include replanting native plant species, collecting litter from beaches and other aquatic habitats, and rebuilding eroded stream and river banks.

TV and Internet PSA's are vehicles for informing, conveying messages, and influencing people's decisions and activities. A well-designed message encouraging activities that help protect and conserve fish habitats or restore degraded aquatic ecosystems is one way to get people to take action to conserve fish and their habitat.

Grade Level: Middle, High School

Content Areas: Language Arts, Social Studies, Science, Expressive Arts, Environmental Education

Method: Students plan and produce a PSA informing people about actions they can take to conserve fish and aquatic environments.

Materials: Video recorder with microphone; computer with video editing software; audio recorder (optional); copies of *Conservation Messaging Planning Guide* (one for each group of four students, page 292); costumes; art supplies

Activity Time: two or three 40-minute sessions

People Power: any size group divided into 4–6 person teams

Setting: indoors, outdoors

Conceptual Framework Topic Reference: CPIA, CPIB, CPIIB, CPIIC, PLIBI, AAIB, AAIIB, RAIC

Terms to Know: aquatic, habitat, restoration, eutrophication, non-native or exotic, riparian, erosion

Appendices: Service Learning, Using Local Resources, Agencies and Organizations, Climate Change

WILD Work

Photographers, **Videographers**, **Editors**, **Writers**, and **Communications Specialists** help document and publicize wildlife, habitats, ecosystems, and conservation efforts through magazines, websites, TV, and radio. For more information on these occupations, visit *www.projectwild.org/aquatic*.

TV and Internet PSA's are a vehicle for informing, conveying messages, and influencing people's decisions and activities.

Message Box

Issue:

Eutrophication

Problem:

Excess nutrients in waterways are causing harmful algal blooms.

So What?

Algal blooms deplete oxygen which kill fish.

Actions:

Encourage people to use less fertilizer.

Benefits:

It is less expensive to use less fertilizer, and aquatic habitats will be healthier.

Procedure

1. Through a class discussion, have students generate a list of threats to fish and aquatic habitats. Introduce students to common aquatic threats as referenced in the "Background" section.

Encourage students to consider local waterbodies and reflect on personal experiences regarding threats or hazards they have witnessed, including erosion, algal blooms (eutrophication) that remove critical oxygen fish need from the water, litter that may choke wildlife or contaminate water, large fish kills often caused by excessive pollution or eutrophication, etc.

Likewise, fish, frogs, and other aquatic food species are regulated by strict guidelines concerning the size and number of each species that can be kept when fishing and hunting. This is to ensure population numbers are kept at a viable level. Over-harvesting or poaching of fish, frogs, and other aquatic species at certain stages of their life cycles (often determined by their size) can cause an imbalance and threaten the population dynamic of an aquatic system. Have students include possible solutions to these threats on the class list.

2. Divide the class into groups of four and have each group pick a topic from the class list to research. Student research should include exploring local or regional aquatic resource issues. Students will then narrow their focus to a specific issue for which they will design a 60–90 second PSA.

3. Once students have conducted their research, have students identify a target audience they want to hear and/or take action related to the issue. Whom do they want to influence with their message? This will provide the direction for the development of their PSA.

4. Have each group create a message box to outline their message. Each message box should contain five components: 1) the issue, 2) why the issue is a problem for the target audience, 3) why the target audience should care, 4) action(s) they can take to help solve the problem, and 5) how solving the problem benefits the target audience.

Be sure to tell students to limit their message to one main issue in order to make it easier for their audience to understand. Using their message box, discuss and decide upon a strategy to influence their audience through a PSA. An example message box can be found to the left.

5. Distribute a copy of the *Conservation Messaging Planning Guide* to each group and discuss each component. Students then fill out the form as they complete detailed planning of their PSA.

6. Encourage students to include a variety of props, sets, costumes, characters, artwork, photos, graphics, and music to help convey their message. Encourage students to develop a song or slogan to make their message more memorable. Students may find online photos available for use through the U.S. Fish and Wildlife Service or through state wildlife agencies. Be sure to check guidelines or procedures for permission to use photos, audio recordings, or video clips from other sources.

OPTIONAL: In addition to completing the *Conservation Messaging Planning Guide*, students may want to illustrate (storyboard) their PSA's while planning.

7. Have students rehearse their PSA's and then perform them in front of the class. If possible, task students with recording and editing their own PSA's to show to the class.

Extensions

1. Have students identify a local aquatic environment in need of conservation or restoration and design a public awareness campaign around it.

2. Have students design posters that share ideas about how people can care for aquatic ecosystems. Hang these posters in appropriate places in the school and community.

3. Organize a visit to a local TV or radio station where students can discuss their experiences with broadcasting professionals. State wildlife agencies are also involved in TV, Internet, radio, and magazine programming and production. Share ideas for how to promote aquatic conservation in the community.

4. Arrange for students to present their PSA's to different audiences, such as another class or a group of parents.

Evaluation

1. After watching each group's PSA, have students identify (1) the target audience, (2) the main problem or issue, (3) actions that can be taken to help solve the problem, and (4) strategies used to encourage people to take action.

2. Have students critique each other's PSA's. Which PSA's are most apt to be successful and why?

3. List three things that could be done to help conserve aquatic habitats and wildlife.

This activity was adapted with permission from Ontario Ministry of Natural Resources. Copyright 2013, Council for Environmental Education

In Step with STEM

■ Contact your state wildlife agency for information about the location of exotic or invasive aquatic species in your area. Investigate local conservation or park districts, nature centers, and other resources agencies with existing invasive species monitoring programs. Identify ways the class can work with professionals to design a plan to help monitor changes in the distribution of local species over time. Share your data with the state wildlife agency or other organizations involved in monitoring and managing exotic and invasive species.

■ Research existing local or regional radio or video PSA's regarding threats to aquatic habitats. The national and state-specific Sea Grant programs offer a wealth of online audio/video resources.

■ Create computer-generated graphics, images, and audio recordings to enhance videos produced.

■ Take photos, video footage, and audio recordings at local aquatic habitats to incorporate into the PSA's.

■ Visit *www.projectwild.org/aquatic* for links to free digital media production resources for the development, editing, and launching of videos.

Conservation Messaging Planning Guide

Production Title:

Scene No.	Audio (Describe what is heard, including starting and ending times for each sound segment, background sounds or music.)	Camera Shots (Describe what will be seen, including close-ups, zoom-ins, zoom-outs, fade-ins or fade-outs.)	Short Synopsis of Action by Shots	Props & Set	Wardrobe & Character Changes (Indicate who is wearing what costume. If one person is playing the role of more than one character in a scene, indicate when they change costumes.)		
Example Scene #1	*:00-:10 Open boy & girl talking*	*Fade in*	*Two people sitting in chairs talking*	*Chairs, table*	*School clothes*		

Living Research: Aquatic Heroes and Heroines

Who has worked hard to conserve aquatic habitat in your community?

Objectives

Students will describe the importance of the accomplishments of local people who have contributed to conserving aquatic environments.

Background

Students are frequently called upon to write reports about people who are world famous or who have attracted a lot of attention in major media. This attention can give students the impression that active, committed people are very removed from real life. Yet there are people who work tirelessly, year after year, to contribute to the quality of life in local communities. Many volunteer leaders focus on issues involving wildlife and the natural environment. State or local governments employ such leaders. Some are in business and industry. Others work through conservation and wildlife organizations. Many are simply interested and dedicated private citizens, volunteering their time to work on issues of concern.

Efficacy is a word used in political science when talking about whether or not people think they can make a difference. People who believe they can make a difference feel a sense of efficacy.

Some people make a significant difference in local communities. These people feel or see something they care about, and they work to accomplish a goal. Every community has people who contribute to the improvement of wildlife habitat, local planning regulations, conservation of open spaces, and many other quality-of-life issues.

The people who are the objects of this research are not likely to be well known—at least not in major media at national and international levels. Some may be members of local chapters or groups affiliated with national organizations. Others may be involved with purely local groups such as natural history clubs, botanical organizations, bird-watching societies, wildlife organizations, or outdoor recreation groups. Others may choose to have no organizational affiliations whatsoever. Still others may

Grade Level: High School

Content Areas: Social Studies, Language Arts, Environmental Education

Method: Students identify people—through news media, websites, personal contacts, etc.—who have made contributions to conserving aquatic environments; research their contributions, including a personal interview; and then write a biography of one person.

Materials:
Internet access, writing materials, envelopes, postage, telephone
OPTIONAL: audio/video recorder, camera, smartphones, software for processing recordings and images

Activity Time: several sessions of 30- to 60-minutes each

People Power: groups of three or four students each

Setting: indoors and in the community conducting interviews

Conceptual Framework Topic Reference:
RAIC, RAIC1, RAIC2, RAIC3, RAIC4, RAIC5

Terms to Know: efficacy, citizenship

Appendices: Service Learning, Using Local Resources, Agencies and Organizations

Every community has people who contribute to the improvement of wildlife habitat, local planning regulations, conservation of open spaces, and many other quality-of-life issues.

Rachel Carson
Biologist and author of *Silent Spring*, **a ground-breaking book that is credited with launching the environmental movement in America.**

be individuals whose employment entails a day-to-day focus on environmental conservation and protection. Students will have to develop what may be new research strategies and skills in order to undertake this activity. In a sense, they become investigative reporters seeking a local story, using whatever local resources are available—including firsthand interviews and direct contact with people as sources of information. This approach requires sensitivity and skill on the part of students. Educators may find it helpful to refer to the "Using Local Resources" appendix in this guide.

Procedure

1. Introduce the activity by explaining its purposes, with emphasis on the fact that students will be doing some firsthand biographical research on people in their own community.

2. Brainstorm possible sources of information that could be used to find out about people in the community who have contributed to conserving aquatic environments. Examples might include electronic news bulletins, websites from local environmental organizations, public libraries, librarians, school libraries, city hall, government offices, local newspapers and magazines, reporters or editors on the staff of local papers, local television news directors, and the presidents or executive members of local groups or clubs. Students might even place an advertisement in the paper or enlist the aid of a reporter to write a story about their class project.

3. Once a list of names has been compiled, students in teams of three or four draw a name at random from the list. Each group will now become a biographical research team to prepare a biography or living history of the person. In some cases, the person may have been important in the community as a conservationist but is now deceased. In these cases, the team will have to identify relatives, friends, former employers, and other potential sources of information to interview and research.

4. Have each team develop a research plan. It could include the outline of any interviews they may want to conduct, whether with the person directly or with others who know or knew the individual. Discuss each team's plan with the group, and consider suggestions for improvement. After the plans have been discussed and refined, have teams contact the people they want to meet and interview. This contact could be accomplished by sending a letter or e-mail to the interviewee stating the purposes of the research and stating that students will follow the letter with a telephone call.

5. Once teams have confirmed the willingness of the individuals to be interviewed, the teams need to meet with them and conduct the interviews. The basic format for the interview could include any personal history details, but the major questions to be addressed might include:

- How did you become interested in the aquatic environment?
- What prompted you to take action?
- How did you decide on the course of action you took?
- What difficulties did you encounter, and how did you overcome them?
- What do you think your most important contribution has been?
- What is your vision for the future of local aquatic resources?
- What would your advice be to citizens wanting to take positive action to improve the aquatic environment?

NOTE: The list of questions could be modified to include personal interests of students and to reflect particular circumstances.

6. After the interviews and additional research are complete, have each team write a biography of its person. Once completed, ask each team to give a brief oral report. Make copies of the biographies, and send each biography with a letter of thanks to the people who were interviewed and others who assisted. It is recommended that letters of thanks be sent to all who assisted in the process. **OPTIONAL:** Create a visual display or webpage of all the completed biographies, complete with photographs and news clippings. Invite local aquatic heroes and heroines to the school for public recognition of their contributions. The news media could be invited, including local television, radio, and newspaper reporters.

Extensions

1. Form a group in the school to address problems related to the conservation and protection of aquatic resources and habitats. What have you learned from the biographical research that can help the group formulate some action plans?

2. View films or other media presentations to find out about other conservationists.

3. Present a copy of the biographical reports to the school library or the public library to include in its collection. These reports may be important contributions to local history.

Evaluation

1. Identify two people who have helped protect a local aquatic area, and describe what each did. Why are their actions important?

2. What can you do—working alone or with others—to conserve or protect an aquatic habitat in your community?

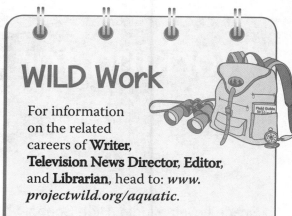

WILD Work

For information on the related careers of **Writer, Television News Director, Editor,** and **Librarian,** head to: *www. projectwild.org/aquatic.*

Explore this information with students, or have students do a guided exploration on their own.

In Step with STEM

- Have students research various engineering careers in aquatic sciences and interview local engineers. Ask to see examples of their work and how math is integrated into projects such as designing dams, mapping wetlands, or constructing a biofiltration pond.

- Volunteer with a citizen science water-monitoring team or with the professionals that were interviewed to get a sneak peek at the workday of a scientist.

Efficacy is a word used in political science when talking about whether or not people think they can make a difference.

Working for Wildlife

Grade Level: Middle, High School

Content Areas: Career Education, Environmental Education, Science, Social Studies

Method: Students conduct a simulated job fair and interviews to learn about jobs in aquatic wildlife conservation, management, and advocacy.

Materials: *Wildlife Career Cards* (page 302), *Job Interview Template* (page 307), *Employer Job Interview Evaluation Form* (page 308), *Job Seeker Interview Evaluation Form* (page 309), job interview sign-up sheets (to be created by educator)

Activity Time: three 45-minute sessions

People Power: ten or more

Setting: indoors

Conceptual Framework Topic Reference: WMIB, WMIC, WMIIA, WMIIIA, WMIIIB, WMIIIC2

Terms to Know: occupation, career, conservation, wildlife management, advocacy, green-collar job

Appendices: Using Local Resources, Agencies and Organizations

---

Take this job and love it!

Objectives

Students will (1) describe the roles and duties of a diverse set of occupations and organizations associated with wildlife conservation and management, (2) describe basic qualifications and requirements for one occupation in the field of wildlife conservation and management, and (3) explain how one's own interest and abilities are compatible with these qualifications and requirements.

Note: This activity supports the American School Counselor Association (ASCA) Standards for Students as indicated below:

C:A1.2: Developing Career Awareness: Students will learn about the variety of traditional and nontraditional occupations.

C:B1.2: Acquiring Career Information: Students will identify personal skills, interests, and abilities and relate them to a current career choice.

C:B2.1: Identify Career Goals: Students will demonstrate awareness of the education and training needed to achieve career goals.

Background

It takes people working in many different jobs to manage organizations that conserve, protect, and advocate for aquatic wildlife and habitat. Some of these jobs, such as fisheries biologist, park ranger, and hatchery manager, are easy to connect to wildlife conservation and management. Other jobs such as accountant, videographer, and electrician may not be as obviously connected to wildlife. However, these jobs play essential roles in protecting land, water, and wildlife.

Aquatic wildlife species spend most or all of their lives in water. Fish, mollusks, whales, otters, alligators, amphibians, waterfowl, seabirds, and wading birds are all examples of aquatic wildlife. This activity focuses on jobs in organizations that conserve and manage aquatic wildlife and freshwater, marine, and wetlands habitats.

Wildlife conservation is the use and regulation of wildlife and their habitats in a way that assumes their continued existence in the future. Wildlife management refers to the application of scientific knowledge and technical skills to the wise use, regulation, and restoration of wildlife and wildlife habitats. Wildlife conservation and management concern all species and often place special emphasis on native, endangered, and vulnerable species and their habitats.

Wildlife advocacy, or wildlife conservation advocacy, refers to efforts by individuals and groups to influence laws, policies, and individual and group behavior and decisions that affect wildlife and their habitat. Wildlife advocacy organizations use a variety of means such as media campaigns, public speaking, lobbying, legal action, and research to promote conservation.

Many kinds of organizations work in wildlife conservation, management, and advocacy, including:

- State and federal natural resource agencies, parks, and fish, game, and wildlife agencies;
- Nonprofit organizations involved in education, land management, or advocacy;
- Corporations that own and manage natural areas;
- Companies that provide habitat restoration services; and
- Fish and mollusk hatcheries.

These wildlife agencies and organizations depend on a variety of employees with a wide array of skills and education to conduct their work. Some jobs with these organizations require

It takes people working in many different jobs to manage organizations that conserve, protect, and advocate for aquatic wildlife and habitat. . . . [Jobs] such as accountant, videographer, and electrician may not be as obviously connected to wildlife. However, these jobs play essential roles in protecting land, water, and wildlife.

A fire management officer monitors the progress of a controlled burn at a National Wildlife Refuge.

A lab technician works with mammalian bacteria.

the following: office skills; physical work such as construction and maintenance; specific training in technology or science; or knowledge of habitat and species conservation. There are "green-collar" jobs which typically require less formal education and more manual labor than other positions in these fields but still allow workers to apply their skills, knowledge, and training in positions that contribute to resource management and conservation.

Types of jobs in aquatic wildlife conservation, management, and advocacy include:

- Science (e.g., marine biologist, fisheries biologist, wildlife biologist, wetlands scientist, water quality specialist, hydrologist, lab technician)

- Construction and maintenance (e.g., engineer, plant manager, carpenter, electrician, maintenance mechanic)

- Administration/office staff (e.g., park superintendent, administrative assistant, purchaser, accountant/budget analyst, clerk/fee collector, human resources manager, attorney, planner)

- Communications, education, and community relations (e.g., outreach specialist, graphic designer, educator, writer, photographer/videographer, webmaster, agriculture extension agent, social media specialist, editor)

- Labor (e.g., truck driver, farmer/farm worker, equipment operator)

- Computer and information analysis (e.g., data analyst, GIS specialist, computer programmer)

- Land acquisition and management (e.g., preserve manager, land surveyor, realty specialist, land manager)

- Wildlife health and care (e.g., veterinarian, hatchery manager, fisheries technician/culturist, captive breeding technician)

- Resource protection (e.g., park ranger, law enforcement officer, law enforcement dispatcher, firefighter, pilot, boat captain, regulatory and compliance professionals)

Students may encounter wildlife conservation, management, and advocacy organizations at a job fair. This activity, in which students learn about potential jobs with these types of organizations, is divided into two parts:

Part A: Wildlife Conservation Job Fair
Part B: Wildlife Job Interviews

Wildlife conservation and management concern all species and often place special emphasis on native, endangered, and vulnerable species and their habitats.

Working for Wildlife
© Council for Environmental Education (CEE)

Preparation

1. Read the procedures and decide in advance how the class will be organized. Depending on class size and grade level, you may wish to have teams of two students represent each of the five wildlife organizations participating in the job fair.

2. Copy the *Job Interview Template* (one for each student) and make a single copy of the *Wildlife Career Cards*. Also copy the *Employer Job Interview Evaluation Form* (one copy per interviewer for each job seeker interviewed) and the *Job Seeker Interview Evaluation Form* (one copy per job seeker).

3. Make one sign-up sheet for each employer organization (five total) for display at the beginning of the job fair, with each job vacancy an organization is trying to fill listed on its sign-up sheet, and with two blank lines under each of the job titles. This will allow two students to sign up to interview for each job. Alternatively, limit the number of blank lines under each job title, depending on the number of job seekers, in order to guarantee that all jobs are selected by at least one job seeker.

Procedures

Part A: Wildlife Conservation Job Fair

Students conduct a job fair focusing on occupations in wildlife conservation, management, and advocacy.

1. Ask students to brainstorm all the people it takes to make their school operate smoothly. Make the point that in addition to teachers, it takes many people working in many different jobs to make a school function well. Some of these jobs may not seem to have anything at all to do with education. The same applies to organizations that work in wildlife conservation, management, and advocacy.

2. Discuss wildlife conservation, management, and advocacy with students. What kinds of organizations might work in this field? What kinds of jobs could be important to help them meet their goals?

3. Introduce the concept of a job fair as a way for employers to meet with prospective employees. Explain that they will conduct a conservation job fair, in which some students will play the role of employers while others will play the role of job seekers. Ask for at least two students to volunteer to represent each of the five organizations that will be offering employment at this simulated job fair (the number of students acting as employer representatives can be adjusted depending on class size). Details about these organizations and the positions they have available are found on the *Wildlife Career Cards* student pages.

WILD Work

Invite representatives of local wildlife conservation and management organizations, or related college programs, to speak to the class about wildlife careers. Alternatively, have students interview professionals in the field about jobs in wildlife conservation, management, and advocacy.

Have students research local high school or college youth internship programs through local park districts, forest preserves, or other city, county, or state government entities.

In addition to the jobs listed on the *Wildlife Career Cards*, information is available on the duties, experience, and training related to other jobs in the field of wildlife conservation and management at *www.projectwild.org/aquatic*.

In Step with STEM

Have students research online two more occupations in the fields of wildlife management, conservation, or advocacy and then write their own *Wildlife Career Cards*. Students should write the job titles, duties, skills, and education or training that are associated with the jobs they selected. Web pages containing job vacancy notices and/or staff listings can help students select and research two jobs.

4. Set up the classroom for the job fair with five tables or stations at which students will gather information about jobs and sign up for job interviews. Give each employer the corresponding *Wildlife Career Cards* and job interview sign-up sheet. Have them arrange these at their stations, leaving plenty of space between the cards so prospective employees can view each card independently.

5. At the beginning of the job fair, ask the representatives of each of the five employers to give the class an overview of their organizations and the jobs available by reading the employer's name and description from the *Wildlife Career Cards*, followed by the job title and brief description of each job. (You may also want to post a complete set of cards in the classroom so students can refer to them during the job fair.)

6. During the job fair, ask job-seeking students to circulate among the stations. Employer representatives will explain their organizations to job seekers and help them identify available jobs that fit their interests and skills. Each job-seeking student should sign up for one job interview and record information from the *Wildlife Career Cards* about the job in a notebook. (Students should be able to describe the duties, skills and experience, and education and training required of the job they are applying for in order to prepare for their interview.). Encourage students to interview for a job they find appealing, even if they believe they are not yet qualified for the position.

Part B: Wildlife Job Interviews

Students conduct simulated job interviews for wildlife conservation and management positions.

1. Give each student a copy of the *Job Interview Template*, and review it as a class. Explain that there are many questions employers and prospective employees may discuss in a real job interview that would be difficult to cover in a simulated interview. These include questions about compensation, details about the organization, and work experience and educational qualifications related to the job. The questions recommended in the *Job Interview Template* help navigate around these types of questions.

2. Discuss with the class what job seekers normally do to prepare for an interview, such as learning about the organization by reviewing its website, reading media releases and news stories, and talking with current or past employees. In addition to studying the *Wildlife Career Cards*, encourage students to individually— or in student groups with others who chose the same interview—research the job online and watch video clips of these professionals at work. This allows higher thinking skills by comparing and contrasting their personal skills to those required by the job, making the interview much more realistic.

A fish hatcheries technician monitors and maintains equipment for raising fish from eggs.

3. Divide the class into five groups, one for each employer. Each employer is represented by two previously designated students. Explain that the five employers will be conducting job interviews, and each prospective employee (the job seekers during the job fair) will interview for one job with one employer. Have job seekers join their prospective employers' group based on their job selection during the fair.

4. Each interviewer should get one *Employer Job Interview Evaluation Form* for each job seeker in his or her group. Interviewees should each receive one *Job Seeker Interview Evaluation Form*.

Working for Wildlife
© *Council for Environmental Education (CEE)*

5. Have employers interview each job seeker in their group. Adjust the time of the interviews to fit your needs, but you may need to limit it to five minutes. If you are tight on time, employers may do "group" interviews with all candidates for a particular job or have multiple interviews occurring simultaneously.

6. During the interview, job candidate(s) and interviewer(s) should move their chairs so they are in close proximity to each other, separating themselves from the rest of the group. The whole group should be able to observe the job interview.

7. Job seekers should answer questions about their skills, interests, and experience based on their personal history. Even though students may not have all of the credentials typically required for these jobs, they can present their education, experience, skills, and interests in the best light during the interviews and indicate how they could further prepare for this job.

8. Likewise, job interviewers will not know all of the details about each job and the hypothetical organizations they represent. These students should draw on information from the *Wildlife Career Cards* and research (optional) to understand the type of organization they are representing before asking interview questions and gauging interviewees' responses.

Evaluation

1. Discuss with students what they learned during the job interviews. What do they think makes a job interview successful? How could they have performed better during the interview, as a job-seeker or as an employer? What might be different between these simulated interviews and a real job interview?

2. Have each interviewer complete the *Employer Job Interview Evaluation Form* for each job seeker he or she interviewed, and have each interviewee complete the *Job Seeker Interview Evaluation Form* for his or her interview. Collect all evaluation forms from employers and prospective employees. Use these to help evaluate student participation in the activity.

3. Have each student describe one new occupation they learned about at the job fair, as well as some of the qualifications required to obtain that position.

Wildlife advocacy organizations use a variety of means such as media campaigns, public speaking, lobbying, legal action, and research to promote conservation.

Extensions

1. Assign each student to participate as both job seeker and employer. Require that students choose different jobs for each role in order to increase their exposure to career opportunities.

2. Have students write "Help Wanted" ads from the employer perspective as well as "Positions Wanted" ads from the perspective of a job seeker for one of the specific job fair opportunities.

---

[1]American School Counselor Association (2004). *ASCA National Standards for Students.* Alexandria, VA: Author.

Federal government agency operating a wildlife refuge

The U.S. Fish and Wildlife Service operates wildlife refuges across the country. These areas include lands and waters that are managed to conserve fish, wildlife, and plants. National Wildlife Refuges also provide wildlife-related recreation and education opportunities such as hunting, fishing, wildlife viewing, photography, and environmental education.

1. Law Enforcement Officer

Description:

Refuge officers enforce wildlife laws and regulations on the wildlife refuge; protect habitat, buildings, and other refuge facilities; and ensure employee and visitor safety.

Duties:

- Participate in patrolling, surveillance, investigations, apprehensions, citations, seizures and arrests, and interactions with federal attorneys and the court system.
- Often work in cooperation with other federal, tribal, state, and local law enforcement agencies.

Skills and experience:

- Knowledge of natural sciences, wildlife management, and criminal justice.
- Good communication skills and computer literacy.
- Valid driver's license and ability to operate a variety of vehicles.
- Ability to pass medical, drug, and physical fitness screening.
- Ability to possess firearms and meet minimum firearms qualification standards.
- Ability to work in an office environment as well as in the field.

Education and training:

- College degree or high school diploma plus one year of specialized work experience. Coursework or major in sociology, psychology, criminal justice, or a related field.
- New Refuge Officers complete 30 weeks of law enforcement training and maintain CPR and First Aid certification.

2. Wildlife Biologist

Description:

Design and conduct wildlife research, management, and monitoring programs for fish and wildlife species and their habitat.

Duties:

- Monitor fish, waterfowl, and other wildlife population levels through aerial and ground surveys.
- Design and run habitat restoration or enhancement projects in wetlands, prairies, and waterways.
- Plan and conduct investigations that determine the impact of development projects on fish or wildlife.
- Design management plans for hunting, fishing, and other uses of wildlife.

Skills and experience:

- Comfort with working outdoors.
- Skills in data collection, including with remote sensing equipment such as avian radar systems.
- Adeptness at analyzing data and using analysis to develop strategies for conservation and management.
- Skill with computers and ability to work both in an office environment and in the field.

Education and training:

- Bachelor's degree in biological sciences, agriculture, natural resource management, chemistry, or another related field.

OR

- A combination of work experience and coursework equivalent to a major in a field related to fish and wildlife biology.
- Some positions require additional work experience or a graduate degree.

Petrochemical corporation

This corporation owns large tracts of coastal wetlands adjacent to many of its manufacturing plants. Much of this land is managed with conservation goals in mind, and some are operated as private wildlife preserves. The preserves and all corporate wetlands provide habitat for waterfowl and wading birds, amphibians, fish, and other aquatic wildlife, as well as birds and land animals such as deer, coyotes, and rodents.

1. Communications and Public Relations Specialist

Description:

Develop and manage a communications program for the corporation's wetlands preserves and wetlands management programs, to include media outreach, public education, website maintenance, and publicity events.

Duties:

- Develop and coordinate an outreach and communications strategy to advance the company's programs, including online communications using the web and social networking tools.
- Promote special events and workshops.
- Generate media coverage for the wetlands preserves and their events.
- Produce a regular newsletter, announcements, and conservation publications.

Skills and experience:

- Writing and editing.
- Event organizing and promotion.
- Social networking and new media tools.
- Organized, detail-oriented.
- Ability to work well in teams and as a supervisor.
- Comfort with communication of all kinds including in-person, written, and telephone.

Education and training:

- Minimum bachelor's degree in communications or an environmental field, with additional work experience in marketing, public relations, and media campaigns.

2. Corporate Land Manager

Description:

Responsible for the overall operation of all corporate lands including the wetlands preserves and other corporate wetlands. Responsibilities include meeting conservation goals by ensuring suitable habitat, providing recreation opportunities for preserve visitors, and working with neighbors and community groups to influence land use and policy decisions that might affect the wetlands and wildlife.

Duties:

- Oversee and generally manage the operations and programs of the wetlands preserves and other corporate lands.
- Work with staff scientists to prepare and implement habitat protection and enhancement projects.
- Meet with neighboring landowners and community groups to promote cooperation.
- Oversee recreational and educational programs on the preserve.

Skills and experience:

- Ability to work and think on both the levels of specific problems and overall goals.
- Enjoyment of supervising, directing, and collaborating with other people.
- Capability to find innovative solutions to problems.
- Clear and concise communications for different audiences.
- Commitment to wildlife conservation.
- Excellent presentation, written communication, and verbal skills.
- Ability to work outdoors, sometimes in wet conditions or bad weather, as well as in an office environment.

Education and training:

- Graduate degree in natural resources, land planning, landscape design, or outdoor recreation management.
- Work experience in conservation project design and management preferred.

State fish hatchery

This fish hatchery breeds native fish to be transplanted into streams and lakes. Fish are hatched here and reared through their early stages of life. Fish raised here are used to help restore native aquatic populations, provide fish for National Wildlife Refuges, and supplement fish stocks in decline.

1. Fisheries Technician/Culturist

Description:

Monitors and maintains the right environment for fish, helping to raise them from eggs and stocking them in lakes and streams.

Duties:

- Assist in propagation, rearing, and stocking of fish.
- Drive and operate heavy equipment to transport fish and maintain facilities.
- Keep accurate records on fish production.
- Educate hatchery visitors about fish biology and fish culture.

Skills and experience:

- Knowledge of aquatic organisms and principles of raising fish.
- Ability to operate and maintain vehicles.
- Ability to collect and record wildlife data.
- Ability to follow instructions and handle stressful situations.
- Physical ability to perform manual labor, including cleaning tanks.

Education and training:

- Entry-level positions require a high school diploma or GED only.
- More advanced positions require two years of experience related to aquaculture or aquatic biology.
- Valid driver's license, and frequently, the ability to obtain a commercial driver's license.

2. Educator/Interpreter

Description:

Teaches hatchery visitors and student groups about the operation of the hatchery, fish conservation, nature, and outdoor recreation.

Duties:

- Develop and deliver educational programs for youth and adults.
- Run hands-on fishing education programs and events.
- Conduct hatchery tours.
- Lead nature hikes, bird tours, and other outdoor education and recreation programs on the lands surrounding the hatchery.

Skills and experience:

- Enjoyment of teaching all ages.
- Comfort with, and willingness to handle, fish, insects, and other aquatic wildlife.
- Physically fit and acquainted with outdoor activities including fishing.
- Ability to write and develop lesson plans and educational materials.

Education and training:

- College degree or equivalent experience, with a major in wildlife management, zoology, fisheries management, botany, or another biological science.
- Course work in natural resource interpretation, environmental education, natural resource communications, or similar subjects.

State park

Like many state parks, this one includes lakes that are popular for fishing, as well as nature trails, a visitor center, a campground, and other visitor facilities. The park is managed by the state government.

1. Park Ranger

Description:

Park rangers are responsible for protecting natural resources, ensuring visitor safety, enforcing laws and park rules, staffing visitor centers, and leading visitor programs at state parks. Many park rangers and their families live within the parks they serve.

Duties:

- Develop and lead interpretive programs for the public and education programs for school groups.
- Greet and provide information to park visitors.
- Collect fees, issue permits, and perform office and clerical duties.
- Maintain campgrounds, picnic areas, and trails.
- Inspect and patrol park grounds and enforce park rules by issuing citations, making arrests, and conducting investigations.
- Participate in search and rescue, emergency response, fire suppression, and traffic patrol.

Skills and experience:

- Adaptability and willingness to perform a wide variety of tasks.
- Ability to maintain comfort and professionalism in positions of authority.
- Ease with working with people of all ages as an educator and source of information.
- Skill in hand and power tool operation and general construction and maintenance techniques.
- Comfort with working in an office environment.

Education and training:

- At least a two-year degree, preferably related to parks management, outdoor recreation, or resource protection.
- During their first few years on the job, new park rangers may go through several months of training to be commissioned as law enforcement officers and to learn skills in emergency medicine, search and rescue, wildfire suppression, interpretation, and environmental education.

2. Budget Analyst

Description:

A budget analyst oversees the use of money to achieve the park's goals and accomplish its programs. Depending on the size of the park, the budget analyst may work for the government agency that oversees state parks, analyzing budgets for several parks or the whole state park system.

Duties:

- Work with other park staff to develop a budget that meets program priorities.
- Maintain the budget as new needs arise and revenues change.
- Monitor spending to make sure it meets the budget.
- Interact with state agencies responsible for finance, parks, and natural resources.
- Prepare budget reports.

Skills and experience:

- Interest in conservation, parks, and recreation.
- Ability to work with, organize, and analyze financial facts and figures.
- Aptitude for seeing relationships between the big picture (program goals) and details (budget allocations and spending).
- Knowledge of spreadsheet and word-processing computer programs.
- Ability to work at a computer for extended periods.

Education and training:

- Bachelor's degree in finance, business administration, accounting, insurance, mathematics, statistics, or a variety of fields related to natural resource management.
- Specific training or work experience in budgeting and analyzing quantitative data.

Nonprofit conservation advocacy group

This organization studies marine and coastal conservation issues in a coastal city, educates the public about the issues, and leads local restoration projects. This group also advocates and lobbies for laws and regulations that better protect marine life, publishes regular reports on the science and policy behind marine conservation, and organizes local support for marine conservation.

1. Marine Biologist

Description:

This job combines hands-on marine research with education, policy development, and advocacy. Occasional travel is involved, mostly in the surrounding region, as is working cooperatively with educators, project managers, policy makers, and other scientists to develop and implement new initiatives and laws that will better protect the wildlife and habitat in the city's harbor and nearby coastal areas.

Duties:

- Manage an aquatic/marine species monitoring program for the local bay, harbor, and coastal areas.

- Participate in collaborative efforts with government officials, business leaders, urban residents and neighborhoods, fishing and other industries, and other scientists to improve the health of the bay and coastal areas.

- Write technical reports and scientific publications on research findings.

- Contribute scientific content to public outreach and education programs.

- Help develop grant proposals to fund the organization's work.

Skills and experience:

- Leadership skills and ability to work in teams.
- Love of the oceans and outdoor work.
- Ability to travel.
- Data collection and analysis skills and computer abilities.
- Excellent writing and public speaking skills.

Education and training:

- Bachelor's or graduate degree in marine biology or a related field.
- Work experience that includes project management.

2. Geographic Information Systems (GIS) Specialist

Description:

The GIS specialist works with Geographic Information Systems, satellite imagery, and other technologies to interpret data and make management and policy recommendations concerning aquatic wildlife and their habitats.

Duties:

- Analyze data and develop maps to support the organization's policy, staff, scientists, and educators.

- Work with scientists and technicians who collected the data to understand and correct errors.

- Manage databases.

- Produce maps for publications and educational programs.

Skills and experience:

- Ability to collect data and work with large databases.

- An eye for design and how to present data clearly in a visual format.

- Knowledge, skill, and experience working with a wide range of GIS, database, word processing, and other software.

- Ability to work at a computer for extended periods.

Education and training:

- Bachelor's degree in marine biology, ecology, wildlife biology, geography, earth science, or a related field.

- Position may require a graduate degree or special training in Geographic Information Systems.

Job Interview Template

At a job interview, employers typically ask many questions about the prospective employee's work history, education and qualifications, and personal characteristics and interests. Job candidates typically ask questions to learn more about the organization, the specific job, coworkers, and the work environment.

Here are some questions that will help you prepare for your wildlife job interviews:

Employer questions

1. Why are you interested in this job?
2. What past work or school experiences would help you do this job? (These might involve jobs, classes, school clubs, sports teams, volunteer work, and other experiences.)
3. What is your greatest strength, and how will it help you do this job well? What challenges might you need to overcome to do this job well?
4. What are your personal interests that apply to this job?
5. What aspects of this job would you enjoy most if you were offered this position?
6. Describe your ability to utilize the types of technology and equipment needed to do this job.
7. What have you done so far that helps prepare you for this job? What else can you do?
8. Can you name a successful project in which you worked independently?
9. Can you refer to a time when you worked on a successful project with a group? Do you believe that you work better independently or as part of a group?

Create two questions below to ask your job candidate:

10.

11.

Job seeker questions

1. Tell me about your organization.
2. How does this organization help conserve wildlife?
3. What skills, experience, and education are you looking for in an ideal candidate for this job?
4. Does this job require a lot of travel?
5. Would I be working a normal work week in this job, or are the hours flexible, unpredictable, or likely to be longer?
6. What are the physical demands of the job?
7. Where would I be doing most of my work?
8. How would I be able to use my particular skills in this job?
9. Can I advance in this job?
10. How would you describe the organization as a place to work?

Create two questions below to ask your potential employer:

11.

12.

Employer Job Interview Evaluation Form

Each interviewer completes this form for each job seeker interviewed.

Your name (Interviewer): _____

Name of Applicant: _____

Organization and Job: _____

Job Interview Criteria	Ranking Circle your response: 1 = Not at all; 5 = Very much so	Notes Add notes to support your rankings.
1. Candidate was prepared for the interview.	1 2 3 4 5	
2. Skills and experience fit the job.	1 2 3 4 5	
3. Education and training fit the job.	1 2 3 4 5	
4. Candidate's attitude and personality fit the job and the organization.	1 2 3 4 5	
5. Candidate was professional in his/her conduct.	1 2 3 4 5	
6. Candidate asked good questions.	1 2 3 4 5	
7. Candidate responded to questions appropriately.	1 2 3 4 5	
8. Candidate explained what he/she could do to further prepare for this job.	1 2 3 4 5	

Critical Thinking Summary

1. For this job, what are critical skills to look for in an employee?

2. How is this job important in the management and conservation of natural resources?

Job Seeker Interview Evaluation Form

Each job seeker completes this form for his or her interview.

Your name (Applicant): _____

Name of Interviewers: _____

Organization and Job: _____

Job Interview Criteria	Ranking Circle your response: 1 = Not at all; 5 = Very much so	Notes Add notes to support your rankings.
1. Interviewers were prepared for the interview.	1 2 3 4 5	
2. Interviewers asked relevant questions.	1 2 3 4 5	
3. Interviewers helped me learn about the organization and the job.	1 2 3 4 5	
4. Interviewers were professional in their conduct.	1 2 3 4 5	
5. Interviewers responded to questions appropriately.	1 2 3 4 5	
6. I would like to work for this type of organization.	1 2 3 4 5	
7. I have identified what I could do to further prepare for this job.	1 2 3 4 5	

Critical Thinking Summary

1. How is this job important in the management and conservation of natural resources?

2. After interviewing for this job, explain why your personal and professional skills match or do not match with the job requirements.

Acknowledgements

Dear Educators:

As we go to press with this new and expanded edition of Aquatic WILD, water issues have been identified as a top environmental issue for decades to come. How can we ensure that decision makers and all water users are prepared to address the complexity of the many water issues that will confront us in the future? Our best avenue is through education. We need to support the building of a water-literate society, and it must be emphasized now with our children wherever they are, in formal and informal settings and at home.

Since 1983, Project WILD has been committed to the important goal of educating children about wildlife and the environment. In 1987, Project WILD Aquatic was developed to address the special connection between water and wildlife and, through the years, it has proven to be a cornerstone program among educators who are dedicated to teaching about aquatic systems and wildlife that depend on them.

Now, a new expanded edition, Aquatic WILD, is available to provide an even better teaching tool that incorporates field investigations, WILD Work career education, and STEM connections, all building upon needs in education and conservation.

To get to this new milestone in Project WILD's 30-year history required tremendous dedication and a lot of skill from a small group of people who are committed to children, the environment, and educators. Our Project Director, Marc LeFebre, planned the initial meeting at the 2011 Project WILD Coordinator's Conference in Michigan to solicit ideas and input from our key partners and program providers, the Project WILD State Coordinators. Input from this meeting provided the building blocks that shaped how the new curriculum and activity guide would be enhanced. From there, Marc led the effort to incorporate needed components into the mainstay guide while preserving what educators have always valued in Project WILD materials. From field test to finish, Marc worked enthusiastically and capably with staff and the Project WILD network to create this next generation of Project WILD. Our hats are off to him as our tireless leader.

Reese-Anna Baker, Production Manager, worked closely alongside Marc and provided invaluable skills in publishing and traffic management. Reese-Anna served as our liaison with typesetters and writers to accomplish all of the detailed work involved in producing a 400 page plus publication. Reese-Anna stepped out of her role as our business administrator to share her publication skills and proved to be a highly valued leader on our team.

We would also like to express our appreciation to Geoffrey Castro, our former Marketing Manager, for his early role in the guide development process including organizing input and photo management. We have also been fortunate to have incredibly dedicated student assistants who have assumed the bulk of research and fact checking associated with the guide. Hayley Hemstreet and Kai Zhang have worked on almost every aspect of the project, and we could not have moved forward in our established timeframe without them.

Jennifer Paschke, veteran CEE associate, deserves a big note of thanks for all of her work typesetting and designing the guide and making all of the words and photos fit in a manner that is "educator friendly." Jen's tedious work spanned the seas from her home base in Australia, but we would have thought she was in our office due to her responsiveness and commitment to our timelines. Additional support with typesetting was provided by the excellent team of Tricia Gernand and Becky Gernand.

Sarah Livesay is much appreciated for being our go-to person on a variety of writing and research needs. From charts to appendices, and research to writing, Sarah pulled out all of the stops to accomplish a variety of writing and organizing projects. Our field test educators and contributing writers also played important roles in helping us to complete the guide, and we convey our thanks to each of them.

Finally, we extend special appreciation and recognition to the powerful network of Project WILD State Coordinators and their sponsoring institutions that work to build capacity for conservation education by teaching others. They epitomize Margaret Mead's words: "Never doubt that a small group of thoughtful, committed citizens can change the world. Indeed it is the only thing that ever has." We thank them for all of their review and input during the guide development process and for the hard work they assume to make our programs available to educators.

To all educators who are committed to teaching young people about wildlife and the environment, we honor what you do each day, and it is because of you that we have such hope and promise that wildlife and natural systems will be there in the future for all to enjoy.

With appreciation,

Josetta Hawthorne
Executive Director, Council for Environmental Education

Council for Environmental Education Board of Directors

Harold Aiken
Bill Futrell
Josetta Hawthorne (ex-officio)
Steve Huffaker
Cynthia Jordy
Barbara Price

Council for Environmental Education Staff

Josetta Hawthorne, Executive Director
Marc LeFebre, Senior Program Manager
Jennifer Paschke, Senior Manager, Publications
Sarah Livesay, Education Program Consultant
Julie Tran, Business Administrator
Casey Bruns, Intern
Raven-Deneice Grant, Intern

Project WILD Program Committee

Tuss Erickson, Chair
Natalie Elkins, Project WILD Coordinator
   Representative
Josetta Hawthorne (ex-officio)
Nancy Heron, At-large Representative
Steve Huffaker, WAFWA Representative
Barbara Price, CEE Board Liaison

Aquatic WILD Fourth Edition (2013) Production Team

Project Director: Marc LeFebre

Production Manager: Reese-Anna Baker

Project Oversight: Josetta Hawthorne

Field Test Coordinator: Marc LeFebre

Field Test Support: Reese-Anna Baker, Emily Maher, Geoffrey Castro

Staff Writers: Marc LeFebre, Sarah Livesay, Reese-Anna Baker

Contributing Writers: Theresa Alberici, Michele Archie, Leslie Comnes, Kiki Corry, Kevin Holladay, Emily Maher, Lindsay Rodgers, Sheri Sikes Soyka, Colleen Welch

Editors: Marc LeFebre, Reese-Anna Baker, Josetta Hawthorne

Copy Editing and Proofreading: Reese-Anna Baker, Josetta Hawthorne, Marc LeFebre

Project Associates and Support Services: Hayley Hemstreet, Kai Zhang, Geoff Castro, Nicholas Fordes, Rachel Tardif, Zahera Tahir, Jennifer Amelang

Typesetting, Graphic Design, Illustration, and Layout: Jennifer Paschke, Tribe Design, Tricia Gernand, Becky Gernand

Expert Reviewers

Brenda Beckley, Barb Gigar, Patricia Otto, Carl Richardson, Jose Rios, Steve Schneider, James Siegel, Cappy Smith, Tracy Thompson, Margaret Tudor, Kyle Wilson, Bobbie Winn

Development and Review Support

Lori Adams, Theresa Alberici, Kimberly Anderson, Lisa Anderson, Tamela Baker, Brenda Beckley, Sandra Bounds, Kiki Corry, Jen Dennison, Kelly Diehl, David Dixon, Natalie Elkins, Anne Elston, Anita Fisher, Rusty Garrison, Warren Gartner, Barb Gigar, Suzie Gilley, Steve Goldman, Rod Gonzalez, Mary Goodyear, Lori Haynes, Nancy Herron, Emily Hogue, Kevin Holladay, Janet Hutchens, Gina Jack, Liz Jackson, Lisa Kane, Hiroshi Kawahara, Tabbi Kinion, Ashlyn Kite-Hartwich, Pat Knighten, Karen Leskie, Karen McClure, Tanya Poole, Lorianne Riggin, Lindsay Rogers, Angel Rohnke, Vilmarie Roman, Susan Sahnow, Cappy Smith, Alison Thompson, Margaret Tudor, Colleen Welch, Megan Wilhite, Kerry Wixted

Field Testers

Diane Bassett, Heidi Brennan, Susan Campbell, Koy Coffer, Rose-Anne Costigan, Christine Danger, Lisa Decker, Debra Glen, Dana Glenn, Susie Hassett, Jason Hoch, Loida Infante, Susan James, Scott Kyles, Linda Laverty, Judith Leshen, Melissa Lewellen, Ashley Miller, Diana Nelson, Libby Overstreet, Maryellen Scuillo, Michel Spence, Suzanne Thebert, Jane Wells, Amy Whitten

If we have inadvertently neglected to acknowledge any individual or organization involved in the 2013 edition of the *Aquatic WILD K–12 Curriculum and Activity Guide*, please accept our sincere apologies. Please contact us about any omissions. We will be pleased to correct this in the next edition.

Third Edition Contributors (2000–2011):

Theresa Alberici, Lisa Anderson, Bill Andrews, Sarah Armstrong, Donna Asbury, Lily Auliff, Steve Bates, Marica Bisnett, Karina Blizzard, Mendy Boyce, Venita Bright, Cindie Brunner, Shannon Caldwell, Laura Carey, Geoffrey Castro, Hugham Chan, Jennifer Coggins, Pam Cullen, Doug Darr, Barbara Devie, Rosemary Drummond, Robin Dublin, Mimi Dunne, Dan DuPre, Roger Ellingson, Connie Elpers, Dale Elshoff, Susan Eschbach, Lisa Evans, Cheryl Fischer, Bill Futrell, John Gahl, Rusty Garrison, Warren Gartner, Tricia Gernand, Barbara Gigar, Suzie Gilley, Mary Goodyear, Anne P. Green, Lindsay Green, Sylvia Gude, Maggie Hachmeister, Shannon Hafner, Carrie Hamby, Hal Hammond, Steve Harding, Xavier Hardy, Casey Harris, Barbara Hart, Josetta Hawthorne, Cheryl Hayes, Nancy Herron, Jake Hohl, Kevin Holladay, Liz Jackson, Dave Jensen, Lisa Jones, Victoria Jordan, Brenda Justice, Valerie Keener, Burnie Kessner, Tabbi Kinion, Margie Klein, Frank Knight, Pat Knighten, Chuck Kowaleski, Jeanine Lackey, Pam Landry, Jeff Laughlin, Marc LeFebre, Sarah Livesay, Kelly Matthews, Lonnie Nelson, O'Conner Group, Laura Olson, Beverly Owens, Page Productions, Bruce Palmer, Amy Parrish, Jennifer Paschke, Barb Pitman, Publications Professionals, LLC, Connie Rasmussen, Sandy Reith, Jennifer Richards, Christina Rolka, Nancy Rolli, Gwyn Rowland Rozzelle, Jeffrey Rucks, Suzy Sanders, Gretchen Sanford, Kelly Schaefer, Rudy Schaefer, Elsie Sellars, Bob Sepanik, Art Shomo, Kate Skowron, Georgia Spencer, Mark Stephens, Charlotte St. Romain, Ted Smith, Roland Stein, Al Stenstrup, Shirley Sypolt, Bryan Thompson, Molly Tkacik, Mack Tobias, Margaret Tudor, John Tyson, Jackie Urband, Laurie Usher, Janet Vail, Diana Vos, Audrey Walker, Sharon Walker, Jay Webb, Jennifer Webb, Colleen Welch, Bobbie Winn, Randy Wiseman, Dr. Barbara Bonsall Wood, Cherie Wyatt, Dell Young

Second Edition Contributors (1992–2000):

Elaine Almeida, Bette Anderson, Dr. Hans Anderson, Louise Ashman, Richard Baumfalk, Susan Beck, Paul Beckwith, Mark Bennett, Carol Beyna, Judy Binger, Sue Bogacz, Evelyn Bologna, Evelyn Boring, Gail Bouslog, Nancy Brown, Becky Brown, Gerry Bryan, Sandra Buck, Nancy Caldwell, Sara Campbell, Sam Carmen, Susan Chambers, Amy Chandler, Cheryl Charles, Rick Chase, Dorothy Chavez, Laurie Christie, Barbara Church, Jane Cleaves, James Colman, Rodger Coombs, Karen Grimes Cooper, Phil Cooper, Randy Cotten, Michael Countess, Kelly Countouris, Ellen Cunningham, Clif Daniels, Jan Davis, Shelly Davis, Judy Dawson, Jerry deBin, Elizabeth DelVerne, Patrick DeSantis, Alvin Diamond, Jo Dodds, Ed Donovan, Susie Duckworth, Barbara Dunbar, Carolyn Dunmore, Miriam Dunne, Linda Eastwood, Mary Beth Eberwein, Jim Edwards, Kathy Farr, Beth Fasnacht, Jack Finger, Carl Finstad, TC Floy, LuAnne Folks, Susan Foote-Martin, Janene Fowler, Terri Franklin, Nancy Franz, J. Frey, Connie Gahl, John Gahl, Warren Gartner, Barbara Gigar, Rick Gilchrist, Susan Gilchrist, Suzie Gilley, Sharon Giza, Jim Goodwin, Alan Gray, Andy Greif, Robert Griffin, Linda Gruberski, Maggie Hachmeister, Corey Hall, Karen Hangrove, Lynn Haralson, Kerry Harkins, Jean Harris, Linda Harris, Bonnie Helzer, Bob Hernbrode, Mel Hickman, Earl Hodil, Carol Holden, Kathie Holden, Jean Holland, Mary Jane Holmes, Bonielee Hooper, Ellie Horwitz, Karen Hostetter, Douglas Housskeeper, Mary Hurst, Susan Ilgner, Elizabeth Javrin, Jodi Jenkins, Laura Jodice, Jan Jose, Twila Kadel, Michael Kamen, Marti Kane, Michael Karmen, Jeffrey Keidel, Janice Kesler, Jeff Kiefer, Julie King, Judy Klippel,

Sherry Klosiewski, Dr. Cliff Knapp, Pat Knighten, Bill Koehler, Jackie Lane, Pat Lang, Mickey Larkins, Tim Lemon, Gretchen Leuenberger, Don MacCarter, Haile Macurdy, Barbara Marshall, Chris Martin, Roy Martin, Dale Mason, Colleen Matt, Beth McCanley, Shalon McCart, Jim McCollough, Jim McCullough, Terry McLaughlin, Jack McNeel, Mary Melican, Justine Menci, Patricia Mercker, Cathy Meyer, Brenda Miller, Debra Miller, Suzanne Miller, Susan Miller, Matt Miller, Sterling Miller, Gerald Mohr, Cheryl Mollohan, Marie Monfredo, Carrie Morgan, Tim Morgan, Fran Morris, Jane Moynihan, Margha Mulling, Kim Mumper, Stu Murrell, Jim Nelson, Tom Nelson, Deb Neuenschwander, Dorcas Newkirk, Rod Nichols, Connie O'Brien, Mike Overton, Helen Panagiotopoulos, Rod Parker, Lynette Parkhurst, Deborah Patton, Barbara Pietrucha, Mark Pochon, Deborah Poti, Polly Powell, Teresa Prather, Christine Raabe, Anna Radue, Janet Rasmussen, Barbara Reed, Marian Rendall, Earl Richardson, Ken Riddleberger, Dolores Ringdahl, Wanda Rowland, John Russell, Bob Samples, Linda Sand, Dave Sanger, Larry Sarner, Nancy Schneider, Rachel Schneider, Ann Seppenfield, Daphne Sewing, Mary Shapiro, M. Sharp, Dan Shaw, Art Shomo, Lisa Silverman-Gent, Rick Sinnott, James Slater, Lucy Slinger, Cecil Buckey Smith, Dean Smith, Marlies Smith, Dr. Cindi Smith-Walters, Heidi Solper, Jacquelyn Sparrow, Theresa Stabo, David St. Clair, Paula St. Clair, Catherine Stefanides, Michael Stephan, Regina Stovall, Mary Stuever, Caroline Sweigart, Jo Temte, Jean Terry, Tracey Thompson, Mary Todd, Jack Turner, Barbara Tucker, Kenneth Uhlhorn, Dennis Unkenholz, Larry Vanderlinden, Al Van Hoey, Karen Van Norman, Jane Vollmer, Mary Frances Wagner, Linda Walbruch, Bob Waller, Dave Walters, Dave Wanisko, Jennifer Warwick, Arthur Washburn, Luann Waters, Kenneth Watkins, Linda Watters, Brenda Weiser, Donna White, Elizabeth White, Ellen Wilken, Debbi Wilkinson, Frank Williams, Tim Williams, Don Winslow, Carl Wolfe, Laurie Woodall, Shirley Wright, Julie Yamamoto, Jill Yeager, Dr. Dennis Yockers, Eileen Yost, Janice Young, Kathie Zager, Cathy Zazanis, Judy Zeider, Dean Zimmerman, Sue Zimmerman, Darci Zolman, Nancy Zuschlag; Glossary: The glossary was compiled from four principal sources. The majority of the terms and definitions are reprinted with few changes from *Multidisciplinary Wildlife Teaching Activities*, developed and edited by William R. Hernbrode. (Columbus, OH: ERIC Clearinghouse for Science, Mathematics, and Environmental Education, 1978). Regarding the Project WILD Aquatic glossary, the next largest group of entries is derived from the glossary that appears in the *Project Learning Tree Environmental Education PreK–8 Activity Guide*. (Washington DC: American Forest Foundation, 1993). A number of entries are adapted or reprinted from Wildlife Aid No. 2. (Portland, OR: U.S. Forest Service, R-6, June 1965). Additional entries are based on the contributions of our Committee, members, staff, and reviewers. All glossary materials derived from previously published sources are adapted or reprinted with the permission of the copyright holder.

First Edition Contributors (1987–1992):

Bess Marie Adams, John Alderman, John Alesandrini, Judith Allard, Eileen Allen, Gene Allen, Jim Allen, Wendy Allen, Connie Alley, Debbie Alvey, Robin Anderson, Steve Andrews, Tony Angell, Neil Armantrout, Barbara Armentrout, Jim Armstrong, Pam Armstrong, Joseph W. Artmann, Daniel R. Baker, Wilma Baker-Nelson, Kerry Baldwin, Tana Baldwin, Howard Barbour, Jean Bateman, Ingeborg Baxter, Beverly Beard, Sue Beck, Carl Becker, Irene Begay, Nancy Belmont, Louise Belnay, Jim Bennett, Carol Bergevin, Barbara Berka, Jack Berryman, Connie Bersok, Joanna Bertolucci, Paul Bixler, Jim Black, Jerry Blackard, Sara Blanchard, Gary Bloemker, Rosalie Bock, Merilyn Bohm, Pat Bower, Steve Brandt, Bob Brantly, Judi Breuggeman, Kathleen Brian, Roxanne Brickell, Larry Broder, Sharon Broguard, Anna Brown, Daniel Brown, Hal Brown, Ann Bryan, Doug Buettner, Beverly Calloway, Marlena Campbell, Carolyn Cannava, Daniel Capuano, Beth Ann Carnes, Cleti Cervoni, Judi Chandler, Cheryl Charles, Tom Charles, Ed Chiosso, Chuck Clark, Corinne Clay, Dot Coates, James Cole, Betty Jo Collins, Sue Confer, Mike Conlin, Kim Contini, Susan Cook, Russ Cookingham, Dianne Corneau, Jean-Michel Cousteau, Connie Coutellier, Peggy Cowan, Dale Crider, Linda Crider, Gwen Criswell, Peter Croskery, Paul Cuplin, Patricia Currence, Atwood Curtis, Alice Cyr, Paula Davenport, Jay H. Davies, Meg Davis, Judy Dawson, Wayne DeFeo, Marilyn Delaney, Michael Demchik, Sandra Diamon, Kathleen Dilger, Christine Dixon, Kathleen Drake, Annette Dray, Tracy Drury, Frank Dunkle, Lynn Dunn, Miriam Dunne, Doug Ehorn, Bill Einsig, George Ek, Tamsey W. Ellis, Doug Emery, Environmental Education Association of Oregon, Denice Erb, Rick Estes, William Evans, Willis Evans, Debra Faast, Linda Falk, Patty Farthing, Kate Ferschweiler, Sheri Fetherman, Bill Finch, Steven Fish, Bambi Fisher, Sharon Fitzgerald, Tom Flatt, Lyn Fleming, Jim Flynn, CeCe Forget, Pete Fortune, Lucille Fortune, Don Friberg, Debbie Fritz-Quincy, Ronald Fritzsche, Brad Frohloff, Pat Fry, Jim Fugate, Barbara Fujimoto, Liz Fulton, Gene Gabriel, Connie Gahl, John Gahl, Frank Gallagher, Amelia Garcia, John Garner, Carol Gatzke, Lucille Gertz, Jeanette Gifford, Mary Gilbert, Judy Gillan, Suzie Gilley, John Goettl, Bev Graham, Celia Graham, David Grant, Paul Gregory, Stanley Griffin, Joy Grijalva, Loraine Gustafson, Della Haig, Penney M. Hall, Raydel Hall, Rita Hall, Anne Hallowell, Cliff Hamilton, Liz Hammerman, Bill Hammond, Duke Hammond, Debbie Dorsett Hanson, Keith Hanson, James E. Hardwick, Roberta Harlow, Pearlie Harris, Nancy Harte, Linda Haschke, Ken Hashagen, Bill Hastie, Bob Hayes, Jan Hayes, Bill Haynes, Jodi Heath, Lin Heinrich, Carroll Henderson, Sara Hepner, Bob Hernbrode, George Herrera, Carolyn Hill, Ilo Hiller, Jeffrey Hodges, Eric Hoeppner, Keith Holtzman, Ellie Horwitz, Carol Houck, Gary Hudson, Charlotte Hughes, Beth Huning, Ann Hymel, Catherine Isham, Carol Jackson, Laura Jackson, Gerald Jacobi, Diane Jacobson, Trish Jahnke, Dean Jamason, David E. James, Bob Jantzen, Dave Jensen, Sheri Jeter, Daniel Jeung, Andrew Joachim, Kathy Johnson, Mark Johnson, Ruby Johnson, Karen Olin Johnston, Carol Jones, Cydney Jones, Yolanda Orozco Juarez, Marti Kane, Pat Kane, Carol Kaney, Jeff Keidel, Carol Kelley, Mike Kendall, David Kennedy, Lois Kenney, Mike Kersten, Jo Ellen Kessler, Laura Key, Peggy Kinder, Roy King, Bill Kinman, Carolyn Kirk, Sandy Klein, Richard Klingbeil, Mary Ann Kobayashi, Rene Kochenberger, Kevin Kopp, Clifford Knapp, Robin Knox, Jan Kurke, Sara LaBorde, Joanna Lackey, David LaHart, Larry Lane, Kay Langstaff, Larry Langstaff, Fred C. Lapse, Sr., Howard N. Larsen, Floyd Larson, Richard Larson, Dennis L. Lee, Janet Lee, L. Janet Lee, Rick Lemon, John D. Leppink, Norma Livo, Marylyn Locandro, Nigel Lock, JoAnn Loersch, Mrs. Lovett, Kathy Luczynski, Renee Mabry, Don MacCarter, Jane S. MacCarter, Dotty MacVeigh, Neal Maine, Tim Manolis, Ken Manuel, Bruce Marganoff, Bill Martin, Donald Martin, Gary Mason, Jack Massie, Robert Matheson III, D. Maxwell, Gladys May, Milton McClaren, Kim McColman, Ernie McDonald, Roberta McFarland, Mary McIlwain, Susan McLane, Kathy McLean, John McMahon, Pat McQuown, June McSwain, Mike Mercer, Midge Michelason, John Miller, Marnie Miller, Alberto Mimo, Paul Mitschler, Richard Moats, Jan Moberly, Conley Moffett, Cheryl Mollohan, Jeanne Monteau, Karen Monteil, Linn Montgomery, Miriam Moore, Bill Morris, Doris Morris, Edward Morrows, Dalton Moultrie, Steven N. Moyer, Debbie

Mues, Bruce Munson, Luba Mycio-Mommers, Dick Myshak, Pat Naccarato, Robert Nappi, Dennis Nelson, Henry Neufeld, Don Newberry, Jake Nice, Rod Nichols, John Nickum, Brenda Niese, Donna Nye, Barbara Oestreich, Jane Okada, Harold Olson, Sarah Orleans, Vicki Osis, Mark Osokow, Russell Otto, Peter Paladino, Phyllis Parker, Susan K. Parker, Dave Patterson, Dennis Pelletier, Nan Peters, Nancy Peterson, Tom Peterson, Ellen Petrick-Underwood, Michelle Phillips, Linda Pils, Edward Pimentel, Loretta Pisani, Daniel A. Poole, Janet Posch, Tom Powell, Margie Prickett, Jim Pulliam, Catherine Quinn, Christine Raab, Gill Radonski, Robert Rawstron, Rhonda Reed, Marian Rendall, Jan Rensel, Sharon Richards, Steve Richardson, Patricia Riggins, Mark Robson, Marie Rocheleau, Don Roderick, LaVonne Roll, Sande Ross, Jane Rossman, Chuck Roth, Kathleen Rude, Toni Rumsey, Pat Ryan, Margery Salmon, Bob Samples, Stician Samples, Anita Sanchez, Suzanne Sanchez, Kay Sanders, Dave Sanger, Steve Sawyer, Mike Schaadt, Rudy Schafer, Jerry Schierloh, Nancy Schlietz, Brenda Schussman, Elena Scofield, Dolores Scott, Ned Serleth, Mary Shanks, Carole Sharo, Dan Shaw, Kathy Shaw, Barry Sheehan, Janet Sheldon, Peggy Shelton, Linda Sherman, Peter Sherrill, Art Shomo, Andrea Shotkin, Valerie Silva, Richard Simpson, Dan Sivek, Daniel Skanson, Jim Slaughter, Gloria Small, Dan Smith, Leroy Smith, Jr., Linda Smith, Karen Snavely, Caroline Snow, Charles Soria, Robert Sousa, Carol Spangler, Mary E. Sparrow, Mike Spears, Lundie Spence, Pam Stacey, Bob Stack, Peter Stekel, Gene Stephenson, Bob Stewart, Michael Stewart, P. Stewart, Roberta Stewart, Wanda Stinson, Sara Stokes, Larry Stonecipher, Brenda Stonecipher, Darleen Stoner, Carl Strang, Susan Streb, John S. Street, Carl Sullivan, Pat Sullivan, Pat Sumner, Meryl Sundove, Mary Sutherland, Pamela Swearingen, Flint Swerdfeger, Ray Tamppari, Jill Thayer, Craig Thompson, John T. Thompson, Karl Toft, Mary Sue Topper, Eileen Tramontana, Elma Tuomisalo, Marta Turksel, Linda Turnborn, Laurie Usher, Dolores Varela-Phillips, Rick Veatch, Joe Vogler, Rolf Wallenstrom, Bill Watt, Marianne Webster, Marilyn Wein, Cathy Ann Welch, Amy Welden, Susan Wells, Betty Ann Welsh, Art Whitney, Joyce Whittet, Andy White, Joel Wiens, Dean Williams, Stan Williamson, Maureen Wilson, Ruth Windmuller, Twyla Wofford, Scott Wolf, Susan Wolf, Jeannie Wood, Jan Woodhouse, John Woodling, Suzette Woods, Helen Woody, Lynn Worch, Barry Worczak, Sherrie Wren, Shirley Wright, Jeff Wymer, Patrice Wyzga, Bonnie Yeager, Dennis Yockers, Dell Young, Lee Young, Kathie Zagner, Patricia Zalo, Carolyn W. Zaugg, Bill Zeller, Kathy Zentmyer

These materials were originally developed in 1987 with the U.S. Fish and Wildlife Service. In 2000, the Council for Environmental Education revised these materials in response to a comprehensive Project WILD program evaluation and national education reform efforts. Funding for the development of the original materials was provided from monies made possible through the Wallop-Breaux Amendment to the Sport Fish Restoration Act. This federal legislation provides support for aquatic resources education to increase public understanding of, and responsibility toward, the nation's water resources and aquatic life forms.

Photo Credits

v Cahoon Elementary, FL ▪ viii Texas Parks & Wildlife Department ▪ xii (top) Evie Bradley, USFWS; (bottom) Laynna Burke ▪ xiii (top) Ken Hammond, USDA; (bottom) Dusty Jansky ▪ xvi Lori Haynes ▪ xviii USFWS ▪ xix (top) Galveston Bay Foundation; (bottom) USFWS ▪ xxi Lisa Koch ▪ xxii (top) Laynna Burke ▪ xxiii Galveston Bay Foundation ▪ xxiv (bottom) Smithsonian ▪ xxv Steve Hillebrand, USFWS ▪ xxvi Vilmarie Roman, Puerto Rico DRNA ▪ 4 Jennifer Paschke ▪ 11 USFWS ▪ 14 William C. Gladish ▪ 15 NOAA ▪ 21 Jim Williams ▪ 26 USFWS ▪ 27 Raymond Schobe ▪ 30 (top) Alex Panoiu; (bottom) Jim Williams ▪ 36 Barney Burke ▪ 38 Joe McDonald, Bruce Coleman, Inc. ▪ 41 (top) Maddie List, USFWS; (bottom) Everglades National Park ▪ 42 Steve Hillebrand, USFWS ▪ 46 - 52 USDA NRCS ▪ 55, 58 EPA ▪ 59 Eric Engbretson, USFWS ▪ 61 William C. Gladish ▪ 66 Jennifer Paschke ▪ 71 Steve Hillebrand, USFWS ▪ 83 USDA ▪ 88 - 90 USFWS ▪ 106 Thomas Quinn, U of Washington ▪ 110 Jennifer Paschke ▪ 111 Becky Skiba, USFWS ▪ 115 xavipat, flickr ▪ 121 Garry Tucker, USFWS ▪ 126 Jim Reid, USFWS ▪ 127 Mohammed Al Momany ▪ 129 FDA ▪ 132 NOAA ▪ 133 Jennifer Paschke ▪ 136 NOAA ▪ 140 (top) Puget Sound Watershed; (bottom) Jennifer Paschke ▪ 142 NOAA ▪ 144 NOAA NMFS ▪ 145 - 146 NOAA ▪ 148 Becky Skiba, USFWS ▪ 149 Steve Hillebrand, USFWS ▪ 161 Texas Parks & Wildlife Department ▪ 163 Mike Weimer, USFWS ▪ 164 USDA NRCS ▪ 165 (top) Chelsi Hornbaker, USFWS; (bottom) Michael Quinn, NPS ▪ 167 John Cleckler, USFWS ▪ 169 Tom Tetzner, USFWS ▪ 172 Geoff Gallice ▪ 173 Steve Hillebrand, USFWS ▪ 177 USFWS ▪ 178 (top) Denise Krebs; (bottom) Steve Hillebrand, USFWS ▪ 179 (top) Jim Williams; (bottom) USFWS ▪ 183 Erik Zobrist, NOAA Restoration Center ▪ 185 Garrett Peterson, USFWS ▪ 186 Tina Shaw, USFWS ▪ 188 USFWS ▪ 190 Bill Perry, USFWS ▪ 191 Chris Swenson, USFWS ▪ 192 Pete Leary, USFWS ▪ 193 Susan White, USFWS ▪ 194 London Permaculture ▪ 195 David Patte, USFWS ▪ 197 Jaclyn Kircher, USFWS ▪ 198 George Gentry, USFWS ▪ 205 Energy.gov ▪ 207 National Geographic ▪ 208 (top) Steve Martarano, USFWS; (bottom) Cary Bass ▪ 210 CEE ▪ 214 Toni Castro, EPA ▪ 218 Debbie Porter ▪ 225 Jennifer Paschke ▪ 227 Lynn Betts, USDA NRCS ▪ 229 Chris Yunker ▪ 230 David Goehring ▪ 234 RBFF ▪ 237 USFWS ▪ 250 USFWS ▪ 252 Kerry Wixted ▪ 255 Gary Kramer, USDA NRCS ▪ 256 USFWS ▪ 257 Brian Washburn ▪ 261 Jeff Vanuga, USDA NRCS ▪ 271 Portland Corp ▪ 273 Koy Coffer, Texas Wildlife Association ▪ 274 USFWS ▪ 278 RBFF ▪ 281 NOAA ▪ 286 (top) dannyman, flickr; (bottom) USDA ▪ 297 Catherine J. Hibbard, USFWS ▪ 298 Eric Vance, EPA ▪ 300 USFWS ▪ 315 Christopher Paschke ▪ 318 Steve Hillebrand, USFWS ▪ 319 Texas Parks and Wildlife Department ▪ 333 Laynna Burke ▪ 334 Steve Hillebrand, USFWS ▪ 341 likeaduck, flickr ▪ 342 Meghan Kearney, USFWS ▪ 343 Gary M. Stolz ▪ 344 (top left) Laurel Wilkerson, USFWS; (top right) Mary Hollinger, NOAA; (bottom left) Cyndi Souza; (bottom right) Chelsi Hornbaker ▪ 345 Sherry James, USFWS ▪ 346 Tom Koerner ▪ 348 USFWS ▪ 349 Chris Poulin ▪ 351 Lamar Gore, USFWS ▪ 353 USFWS ▪ 356 Jessica D. Alexander ▪ 357 (top) born1945; (bottom) Phalinn Ooi ▪ 358 Social Geek, flickr ▪ 363 Vincent De Groot, USAF ▪ 364 (top) Rick L. Hansen; (bottom) Tom Koerner, USFWS ▪ 365 (top) Josetta Hawthorne ▪ 368 Garry Tucker, USFWS ▪ 369 USFWS ▪ 370 Steve Hillebrand, USFWS ▪ 380 Dan Magneson ▪ 382 NASA ▪ 385 Luther Goldman, USFWS ▪ 386 Ryan Hagerty, USFWS ▪

Project WILD
Supplementary Resources

Resources Available for Download

The following resources may be downloaded from or viewed on the Project WILD website at *www.projectwild.org*. Each may be accessed by clicking "Just For Educators" and "Additional Classroom Resources," then clicking on the link to the desired resource.

Aquatic Extensions to Project WILD K–12 Activities, PDF format.

This compilation is to encourage use of both *Project WILD* and *Aquatic WILD K–12 Curriculum and Activity Guides* in a complementary manner to expand on concepts or to develop thematic units of study.

Project WILD and Aquatic WILD Student Pages, PDF format.

The accompanying student worksheets and activity cards found within these guides are also available for download from the Project WILD website.

Lesson Planning Worksheet 1 page, PDF format.

This planning aide provides space for notes under the following headings: Standards; Themes or units; Project WILD Activities; Grade(s); Materials; and Adaptations, enrichments, field trips, local resources.

Resources Available for Purchase

The following resources may be purchased from the Project WILD National Office. An order form may be obtained by accessing the Project WILD website at *www.projectwild.org* or by contacting the National Office by phone at (713) 520-1936 or by fax at (713) 520-8008.

Growing Up WILD: Exploring Nature with Young Children (128 pages)

This full-color early childhood guide is designed to help educators and caregivers engage children ages 3–7 in activities that encourage active exploration of nature. Each of the 27 developmentally appropriate activities includes reading suggestions, music and movement, math connections, art projects, centers and extensions, snack ideas, a "Helping Hands" conservation activity, and a "Take Me Outside" component. "Home Connections" cards in English and Spanish extend the learning at home for the entire family. The guide is correlated to Head Start domains and NAEYC standards. Educator training in the guide is available through many state wildlife agencies and regional training partners. For more information visit *www.pwgrowingupwild.org*.

Taking Action: An Educator's Guide to Involving Students in Environmental Action Projects (74 pages)

Developed in cooperation with the World Wildlife Fund, Taking Action inspires ideas and provides models for conducting effective environmental projects. From adopting species to protecting habitats to saving energy, this guide will help educators plan, implement, and evaluate environmental action projects. Samples of more than 30 projects from around the country provide a glimpse of how groups of students have recognized a need in their community and successfully worked together to implement change.

WILD About Elk: An Educator's Guide (80 pages)

This guide is a product of the Rocky Mountain Elk Foundation and the Council for Environmental Education. WILD About Elk provides a summary of the biology and ecology of elk. Topics addressed include elk's physical characteristics and adaptations, habitat and historical range, behavior, life cycles, social structure, migratory patterns, and the present and historical relationships between elk and humans. A primary message woven throughout the guide is the importance of habitat to the elk's survival. Activities in the guide assist educators in helping their students learn about elk and their habitat.

Proyecto WILD: Traducción en Español de Las Guías del Plan de Estudios y Actividades del Jardín de Niños Hasta La Preparatoria (240 pages)

This guide contains 34 translated activities taken from *Project WILD K–12 Curriculum and Activity Guide* and *Project WILD Aquatic K–12 Curriculum and Activity Guide*. The Spanish supplement introduces Project WILD to new audiences—teachers; scout leaders; school volunteers; parks and recreation staff members; and nature center, zoo, and museum staff members—who live and work in primarily Spanish-speaking communities. Project WILD hopes that these materials will open the outdoors to a new generation of students and volunteers.

Water Watchers: Conserving Water at Your School and Home (104 pages)

Water Watchers is an additional resource offered for purchase by the Council for Environmental Education. It is designed to provide educators with a framework for mentoring a student-driven audit of water use—and waste—at school and in their homes. Lessons in the guide are arranged to lead students from awareness of basic conservation concepts and issues to responsible action and stewardship of their water environment.

Educators will first introduce students to the water cycle, issues of water use, pollution, and potential water conservation measures. Students then have the opportunity to conduct a hands-on investigation of their school water system, monitor water use over time, and brainstorm ideas for ways water can be conserved. Using the results of a cost-benefit analysis, students take action by preparing and presenting a water conservation proposal for their school and tracking the results. Encouraging service learning, *Water Watchers* aims to inspire student leaders in water conservation. Visit **www.wetcity.org** for more information.

Fishable Waters: An Urban Fishing Activity for Middle and High School Students (16 pages)

This booklet features "Fishable Waters," an activity from the *Aquatic WILD K–12 Curriculum and Activity Guide*. Packaging this activity as a separate booklet allows its easy incorporation into fishing and angler education programs.

Let's Go Fishing!

Watching students experience the muscular strength of a fish in their hands or the thrill of the tug on their fishing line is not only highly rewarding, but can be educational as well. Noting the value of these experiences to students, a host of organizations and agencies have emerged with programs and resources to overcome the traditional barriers to getting students fishing. These new opportunities make it not only logistically possible to incorporate fishing into the curriculum, but cost-effective and in many cases, aligned with state and national education goals.

State/Provincial Fishing Programs

In an effort to provide direct instruction and equipment outreach for schools, many state/provincial fish and wildlife agencies have developed fishing outreach programs. These programs offer a variety of outreach options to schools and youth groups to encourage fishing education and provide direct outdoor fishing experiences. In many agencies, organized Angler Education programs exist with dedicated staff who provide in-school fishing clinics, equipment loan programs, and grant opportunities to pay for fishing field trip expenses. Some agencies have established fishing curriculum in alignment with state learning standards that blends both classroom and outdoor experiences into one cohesive unit. Angler education outreach staff, as well as Fisheries division staff, can offer valuable localized advice or presentation opportunities regarding the natural history of native fish species, conservation concerns, and restoration efforts specific to the students' home region. Beyond the classroom, these agencies also offer a variety of opportunities for the general public to become involved in fishing including youth fishing derbies, festivals, and family fishing days at state parks or other public natural areas. Contact your state/provincial natural resources or fish and wildlife agency for more information.

National Fishing in Schools Program

National Fishing in Schools Program (NFSP) is a nationwide, in-school program that teaches the positive lifetime activity of fishing to students in middle schools and high schools. NFSP educates students about fish, insects, aquatic habitats, resource stewardship, and conservation using fishing—and learning the skill of casting—as the instructional tool. The NFSP curriculum, *Cast A Fly, Catch A Student*, using fly rods, is specifically

created to address a broad and inclusive framework of National Academic Standards for language arts, physical education, science, and technology. *The Cast A Lure, Catch A Student* sequel, using traditional tackle, will do the same. Information regarding the cost and application procedure to participate in this program can be found at *www.fishinginschools.org*.

Online Resources

The Recreational Boating and Fishing Foundation (RBFF) has created *www.takemefishing.org*, a resourceful online destination for students to learn, plan, and equip for a lifetime of fishing. Students can explore "Fishlopedia" (includes the natural histories of different fish species), "How to Fish" tutorials, and more. The site offers educators a state-specific tour of the resources, contacts, and programs available locally to bring fishing into the classroom.

Yet another online resource, from the Environmental Protection Agency (EPA), *http://watersgeo.epa.gov/mywaterway/*, offers students the opportunity to investigate the health and potential fish contamination threat of local waterways by entering their zip codes.

Resources to help your students get hooked on fishing are available, so cast your line out today!

Grade Level Index

KEY

LE = Lower Elementary (K–2)   MS = Middle School (6–8)
UE = Upper Elementary (3–5)   HS = High School (9–12)

Activity	LE	UE	MS	HS
Riparian Retreat		●		
Sea Turtles International				●
Silt: A Dirty Word		●		
Sockeye Scents		●		
Something's Fishy Here!			●	
The Glass Menagerie				●
To Dam or Not to Dam			●	
Turtle Hurdles		●	●	
Urban Waterway Checkup			●	
Water Canaries			●	●
Water Plant Art	●	●		
Water Safari	●			
Water We Eating?		●		
Water Wings		●	●	
Water Works		●	●	
Watered-Down History			●	
Watershed			●	●
Wetland Metaphors		●		
Whale of a Tail			●	
What's in the Air?			●	
What's in the Water?			●	
Where Does Water Run?			●	●
Where Have All the Salmon Gone?			●	●
Working for Wildlife			●	●

KEY

LE = Lower Elementary (K–2)   MS = Middle School (6–8)
UE = Upper Elementary (3–5)   HS = High School (9–12)

Skills Index

Below is an alphabetical listing of all activities found in the *Aquatic WILD K–12 Curriculum and Activity Guide*. Also listed are the page numbers, suggested grade levels, and skills addressed for both cross discipline and subject-specific areas. Note that while all Aquatic WILD activities have outdoor components, the "Indoors or Outdoors" column indicates each activity's primary setting. Under Grade Level, **LE** indicates that the activity correlates to national learning standards for grades K–2, **UE** for grades 3–5, **MS** for grades 6–8, and **HS** for grades 9–12.

SYMBOL NOTE: The dot and triangle symbols are of equal value. They were used to help distinguish between the Cross-Discipline Skills and the Subject Area Skills.

Activity Name	Page Number	Grade Level/National Learning Standards Correlation	Indoors (I) or Outdoors (O)	Field Investigation	Analysis	Application	Classification	Comparison	Construction	Description	Evaluation	Generalization	Observation	Problem-solving	Research	Synthesis	Science	Math	Social Studies	Language Arts	Environmental Education	Expressive Arts
A Whale of an Issue	141	MS, HS	I		●	●			●	●	●					●			▲		▲	
Alice in Waterland	223	UE, MS	I,O						●	●	●	●	●	●			▲	▲	▲		▲	▲
Aqua Words	69	LE, UE	I						●	●	●	●	●	●			▲	▲	▲	▲	▲	▲
Aquatic Roots	251	MS, HS	I,O		●	●	●		●	●	●	●			●	●	▲		▲		▲	
Aquatic Times	264	UE, MS, HS	I,O		●	●			●	●				●	●	●				▲	▲	
Are You Me?	2	LE	I		●	●	●										▲				▲	
Blue Ribbon Niche	94	UE, MS	I,O		●	●		●	●	●	●		●	●		●	▲				▲	▲
Conservation Messaging	289	MS,HS	I,O		●	●				●	●			●	●	●	▲		▲	▲	▲	▲
Dam Design	269	MS, HS	I,O		●	●			●		●			●			▲		▲	▲	▲	▲
Designing a Habitat	34	UE, MS	I		●	●	●	●		●		●	●	●	●	●	▲			▲	▲	▲
Dragonfly Pond	282	UE, MS	I		●	●					●			●					▲		▲	
Eat and Glow	112	HS	I		●					●	●	●	●	●	●		▲	▲			▲	
Edge of Home	119	UE, MS	I,O	✔	●		●		●				●	●		●	▲			▲	▲	
Facts and Falsehoods	184	MS, HS	I		●	●		●			●			●	●	●				▲	▲	
Fashion a Fish	98	LE, UE	I,O		●	●			●	●		●					▲			▲	▲	▲
Fishable Waters	232	MS, HS	I		●	●		●	●	●	●		●	●		●	▲		▲		▲	
Fishy Who's Who	9	UE, MS	I		●	●	●	●			●		●		●		▲		▲	▲	▲	▲
Gone Fishing!	272	MS, HS	I,O	✔	●	●						●					▲				▲	▲
Got Water?	24	UE	I,O	✔	●	●		●		●	●		●		●		▲	▲			▲	▲
Hooks and Ladders	84	MS	I,O		●					●	●	●				●	▲		▲		▲	▲
How Wet Is Our Planet?	180	MS	I		●								●	●		●	▲	▲			▲	
Kelp Help	279	UE, MS	I		●	●			●						●	●	▲				▲	

Activity Name	Page Number	Grade Level/National Learning Standards Correlation	Indoors (I) or Outdoors (O)	Field Investigation	Cross-Discipline Skills												Subject Area Skills					
					Analysis	Application	Classification	Comparison	Construction	Description	Evaluation	Generalization	Observation	Problem-solving	Research	Synthesis	Science	Math	Social Studies	Language Arts	Environmental Education	Expressive Arts
Living Research: Aquatic Heroes and Heroines	293	HS	I,O		●	●			●						●	●			▲	▲	▲	
Marsh Munchers	75	UE	I,O		●				●		●		●			●	▲				▲	▲
Mermaids and Manatees	124	UE, MS	I,O		●	●	●		●			●			●	●			▲	▲	▲	▲
Micro Odyssey	91	UE, MS	I,O		●		●	●	●				●		●	●	▲				▲	
Migration Headache	18	MS	I,O		●		●			●	●	●	●			●	▲				▲	▲
Net Gain, Net Effect	131	MS	I,O		●		●					●	●			●	▲	▲	▲		▲	
Plastic Voyages	189	UE	I,O		●							●	●		●	●	▲	▲	▲		▲	
Pond Succession	108	MS	I		●			●					●			●	▲		▲		▲	▲
Puddle Wonders!	166	MS	I,O	✔	●	●	●	●	●	●	●	●	●		●	●	▲	▲			▲	▲
Riparian Retreat	175	UE	I,O		●								●	●		●					▲	▲
Sea Turtles International	147	HS	I		●					●	●	●				●			▲		▲	
Silt: A Dirty Word	266	UE	I,O		●		●		●		●	●	●				▲				▲	
Sockeye Scents	103	UE	I,O		●				●			●		●	●	●	▲		▲	▲	▲	▲
Something's Fishy Here!	212	MS	I,O		●				●	●	●	●	●	●		●				▲	▲	
The Glass Menagerie	228	HS	I,O		●		●		●			●	●			●	▲				▲	
To Dam or Not to Dam	260	MS	I		●	●		●	●	●						●			▲		▲	
Turtle Hurdles	246	UE, MS	I,O		●				●	●	●	●	●			●	▲		▲		▲	
Urban Waterway Checkup	54	MS	I		●	●		●		●	●			●		●	▲				▲	▲
Water Canaries	63	MS, HS	O	✔	●		●		●	●	●	●	●	●	●	●	▲				▲	▲
Water Plant Art	72	LE, UE	I,O		●		●	●	●								▲				▲	▲
Water Safari	37	LE	I,O	✔	●	●		●			●	●		●			▲				▲	▲
Water We Eating?	128	UE	I		●			●	●			●	●	●		●	▲		▲		▲	
Water Wings	160	UE, MS	I,O		●	●			●			●	●	●		●				▲	▲	▲
Water Works	216	UE, MS	I		●						●								▲		▲	
Watered-Down History	138	MS	I,O		●	●	●	●	●			●		●	●	●			▲		▲	
Watershed	196	MS, HS	I,O	✔	●			●	●	●	●		●			●		▲			▲	▲
Wetland Metaphors	80	UE	I,O		●		●		●		●	●				●					▲	▲
Whale of a Tail	12	MS	I,O		●		●		●		●	●				●					▲	▲
What's in the Air?	201	MS	I		●		●		●			●	●			●	▲	▲	▲		▲	
What's in the Water?	206	MS	I		●		●	●	●			●	●				▲	▲			▲	
Where Does Water Run?	44	MS, HS	I,O	✔	●	●		●	●	●	●		●	●	●	●	▲	▲			▲	▲
Where Have All the Salmon Gone?	254	MS, HS	I		●		●	●	●			●	●				▲	▲	▲		▲	
Working for Wildlife	296	MS, HS	I			●				●	●		●		●	●	▲		▲	▲	▲	

Topic Index

Below is an alphabetical listing of all of the activities found in the *Aquatic WILD K–12 Curriculum and Activity Guide*. Also listed are the approximate duration of the activity and the broad topic categories for each activity.

GRADE LEVEL NOTE: LE indicates that the activity correlates to national learning standards for grades K–2, **UE** for grades 3–5, **MS** for grades 6–8, and **HS** for grades 9–12.

DURATION NOTE: The length of the activity is listed by a letter code: **A** = up to 45 minutes, **B** = 45 to 60 minutes, **C** = 60 to 90 minutes, **D** = 90 minutes to 3 hours, **E** = over 3 hours, and **V** = variable length.

TOPIC NOTE: Many of the topics listed incorporate important subtopics. For instance, *Biodiversity* includes *Endangered, Invasive,* and *Exotic Species; Change* includes *Succession; Environmental Quality* includes *Pollution, Acid Rain, Erosion,* and *Eutrophication; Population Dynamics* includes *Predator* and *Prey Relationships* and *Limiting Factors; Sustainability* includes *Conservation;* and *Food Chains* includes *Food Webs, Energy Transfer,* and *Trophic Relationships.*

Additional topics are indexed in the **Expanded Topic Index** on pages 327–332.

SYMBOL NOTE: The dot and triangle symbols are of equal value. They are placed in alternating columns for ease of tracking down the column.

Activity Name	Page Number	Grade Level/National Learning Standards Correlation	Duration (A,B,C,D,E,V)	Adaptations	Biodiversity	Change	Consumptive Use	Culture	Economics/Commerce	Environmental Quality	Food Chains/Food Webs	Habitats	Interdependence	Issues	Land Use	Ocean/Marine	Political Processes	Population Dynamics	Resource Management	Responsible Action	Sustainability	Urban	Values
A Whale of an Issue	141	MS, HS	D						▲					●		●			▲	●	▲		
Alice in Waterland	223	UE, MS	D			●		●		●		●								●	▲	●	
Aqua Words	69	LE, UE	V									●	▲										▲
Aquatic Roots	251	MS, HS	D	▲	●					▲			▲				▲		▲				
Aquatic Times	264	UE, MS, HS	V									●										●	▲
Are You Me?	2	LE	A		●																		
Blue Ribbon Niche	94	UE, MS	D	▲	●				●	▲	●	▲			▲			●					
Conservation Messaging	289	MS,HS	V			●				●		●		●						▲	●		
Dam Design	269	MS, HS	E							▲		▲	●	▲			▲		▲	●	▲	●	
Designing a Habitat	34	UE, MS	D									●	▲										
Dragonfly Pond	282	UE, MS	D		▲	●			●	▲	●	▲	●		▲		▲		▲	●	▲		▲
Eat and Glow	112	HS	E	●		●						●						●					
Edge of Home	119	UE, MS	C		▲								▲										
Facts and Falsehoods	184	MS, HS	D				●							●						●			
Fashion a Fish	98	LE, UE	V	●								●											
Fishable Waters	232	MS, HS	C		▲	●	▲			▲	●	●		●	▲		▲		▲	●		●	
Fishy Who's Who	9	UE, MS	D		▲													●					▲
Gone Fishing!	272	MS, HS	E	●	▲							●								●			

Topic Index

Activity Name	Page Number	Grade Level/National Learning Standards Correlation	Duration (A,B,C,D,E,V)	Adaptations	Biodiversity	Change	Consumptive Use	Culture	Economics/Commerce	Environmental Quality	Food Chains/Food Webs	Habitats	Interdependence	Issues	Land Use	Ocean/Marine	Political Processes	Population Dynamics	Resource Management	Responsible Action	Sustainability	Urban	Values
Got Water?	24	UE	C		▲							●											
Hooks and Ladders	84	MS	B	●	▲	●	▲		▲		▲	●	▲	●		●		●	▲				
How Wet Is Our Planet?	180	MS	B				●						▲	●		●					▲	●	
Kelp Help	279	UE, MS	D				●					●	▲			●				●			▲
Living Research: Aquatic Heroes and Heroines	293	HS	V				●						●							●	▲	●	
Marsh Munchers	75	UE	B	●							▲	●	▲			●		●					▲
Mermaids and Manatees	124	UE, MS	C	●	▲			●				●											
Micro Odyssey	91	UE, MS	D	●							▲	●	▲					●					
Migration Headache	18	MS	A		▲					●		●	▲	●	▲			●	▲		▲		
Net Gain, Net Effect	131	MS	B		▲		▲						●			●	▲	●	▲		▲		
Plastic Voyages	189	UE	B			▲	●	▲	●				●			●	▲	●	▲	●			
Pond Succession	108	MS	B		▲	●						●	▲										
Puddle Wonders!	166	MS	E	●	▲	●						●	▲		▲							●	
Riparian Retreat	175	UE	A									●	▲										▲
Sea Turtles International	147	HS	C				▲	●	▲			▲	●	▲		●	▲		●	●	▲	●	▲
Silt: A Dirty Word	266	UE	B							●		●	▲	●	▲				●		▲		
Sockeye Scents	103	UE	D	●								●											
Something's Fishy Here!	212	MS	D			●		●	▲	●				●					●		●	▲	●
The Glass Menagerie	228	HS	E		▲	●					●	●	▲	●									
To Dam or Not to Dam	260	MS	V		▲	●	▲	●	▲			●		●	▲		▲		▲				
Turtle Hurdles	246	UE, MS	A		▲	●	▲		▲		▲	●		●		●	▲	●	▲	●	●	▲	▲
Urban Waterway Checkup	54	MS	V		▲					●									▲	●	▲	●	
Water Canaries	63	MS, HS	C		▲					●		●	▲										▲
Water Plant Art	72	LE, UE	A									●	▲										▲
Water Safari	37	LE	V		▲							●										●	
Water We Eating?	128	UE	V					●	▲		▲										●	●	
Water Wings	160	UE, MS	V			●						●	▲			●							▲
Water Works	216	UE, MS	B			▲							▲						▲			●	
Watered-Down History	138	MS	D			●		●				●	▲	●	▲					●			
Watershed	196	MS, HS	V							●		●	▲							●			
Wetland Metaphors	80	UE	V		▲	●						●	▲										▲
Whale of a Tail	12	MS	V		▲											●							
What's in the Air?	201	MS	V			●				●		●		●									
What's in the Water?	206	MS	A		▲	●		●	▲	●	●	●	●			●			●	▲	●	▲	
Where Does Water Run?	44	MS, HS	D			●				●		●	▲						▲	●		●	
Where Have All the Salmon Gone?	254	MS, HS	D			●		●	▲			●		●				●	▲	●			
Working for Wildlife	296	MS, HS	D																▲	●			▲

Unit Planning

Many of the activities in the *Aquatic WILD K–12 Curriculum and Activity Guide* can be easily integrated into units of study. The table below will help in choosing activities that work well together for four general units of study. See also the **Topic Index** and the **Expanded Topic Index** as you decide which activities to implement to address specific topics. You can also use the **Table of Contents** in the front of this guide to see which activities (and groups of activities) address specific concepts.

Units of Study	Aquatic WILD Activities by Grade Level			
	LE (K–2)	**UE (3–5)**	**MS (6–8)**	**HS (9–12)**
Waterbodies *(Types, Geography, Histories of, Characteristics)*		Alice in Waterland; Blue Ribbon Niche; Dragonfly Pond; Marsh Munchers; Riparian Retreat; Water Wings; Wetland Metaphors	Alice in Waterland; Blue Ribbon Niche; Dragonfly Pond; How Wet is Our Planet?; Puddle Wonders!; To Dam or Not To Dam; Water Wings; Watershed; Where Does Water Run?	The Glass Menagerie; Watershed; Where Does Water Run?
Aquatic Life *(Plant & Animal Life Found in Waters)*	Are You Me?; Fashion a Fish; Water Plant Art	Are You Me?; Blue Ribbon Niche; Designing a Habitat; The Edge of Home; Fashion a Fish; Fishy Who's Who; Got Water?; Marsh Munchers; Micro Odyssey; Riparian Retreat; Water Plant Art; Water We Eating?; Wetland Metaphors	Aquatic Roots; Blue Ribbon Niche; Designing a Habitat; Gone Fishing!; The Edge of Home; Fishy Who's Who; Micro Odyssey; Migration Headache; Puddle Wonders!; Water Canaries	Aquatic Roots; Gone Fishing!; Water Canaries
Ecosystems *See also "The Ecosystem Concept and Project WILD" in the appendix.*	Fashion a Fish; Water Safari;	Blue Ribbon Niche; Designing a Habitat; Dragonfly Pond; The Edge of Home; Fashion a Fish; Marsh Munchers; Micro Odyssey; Water We Eating?	Blue Ribbon Niche; Conservation Messaging; Designing a Habitat; Dragonfly Pond; The Edge of Home; Gone Fishing!; Micro Odyssey; Puddle Wonders!; Something's Fishy Here!; To Dam or Not To Dam; Water Canaries; Watershed; What's in the Air	Conservation Messaging; The Glass Menagerie; Gone Fishing!; Water Canaries; Watershed
People, Land, and Water *(Water Resources)*		Alice in Waterland; Aquatic Times; Blue Ribbon Niche; Designing a Habitat; Dragonfly Pond; Plastic Voyages; Riparian Retreat; Water We Eating?; Water Wings; Wetland Metaphors; Water Works	Alice in Waterland; Aquatic Roots; Aquatic Times; Blue Ribbon Niche; Conservation Messaging; Designing a Habitat; Dragonfly Pond; Migration Headache; Something's Fishy Here!; To Dam or Not To Dam; Water Canaries; Water Wings; What's in the Air?; What's in the Water?; Where Does Water Run?; Urban Waterway Checkup; Working for Wildlife; Water Works	Aquatic Roots; Aquatic Times; Conservation Messaging; The Glass Menagerie; Water Canaries; Where Does Water Run?; Working for Wildlife

Expanded Topic Index

The following is an alphabetical listing of topics included in Aquatic WILD activities. This is not a comprehensive listing; that is, it does not list every possible topic. It does, however, list topics that might be included in an elementary or secondary course of study in a variety of subject areas.

Activities are listed alphabetically, not according to the degree to which they emphasize the topic. We hope this serves to assist in your curriculum planning as you integrate Aquatic WILD activities into existing courses of study and other instructional programs.

Acid Precipitation or Rain
What's in the Air? (201)

Adaptation
Eat and Glow (112); Fashion a Fish (98); Hooks and Ladders (84); Marsh Munchers (75); Mermaids and Manatees (124); Micro Odyssey (91); Puddle Wonders! (166); Sockeye Scents (103)

Amphibians
Are You Me? (2); Blue Ribbon Niche (94); Puddle Wonders! (166)

Aquaculture
Designing a Habitat (34); Water We Eating (128)

Awareness
A Whale of an Issue (141); Aqua Words (69); Aquatic Times (264); Are You Me? (2); Conservation Messaging (289); Edge of Home (119); Fishy Who's Who (9); How Wet Is Our Planet? (180); Kelp Help (279); Marsh Munchers (75); Puddle Wonders! (166); Riparian Retreat (175); Something's Fishy Here! (212); Water Canaries (63); Water Plant Art (72) ;Water We Eating? (128); Water Wings (160); Wetland Metaphors (80); Whale of a Tail (12); Where Does Water Run? (44); Working for Wildlife (296)

Birds
Are You Me? (2); Blue Ribbon Niche (94); Migration Headache (18); Plastic Voyages (189); Riparian Retreat (175); To Dam or Not To Dam (260)

Carrying capacity
Fishable Waters (232); Got Water? (24); Hooks and Ladders (84); Migration Headache (18); Turtle Hurdles (246); Water Safari (37); Where Have All the Salmon gone (254)

Careers
Working for Wildlife (296)
For more on careers, see "WILD Work" in the sidebar of every Aquatic WILD activity.

Communications
Aquatic Times (264); Conservation Messaging (289); Facts and Falsehoods (184); Living Research: Aquatic Heroes and Heroines (293); Mermaids and Manatees (124); Working for Wildlife (296)

Community (cultural)
A Whale of an Issue (141); Alice in Waterland (223); Dragonfly Pond (282); Facts and Falsehoods (184); How Wet Is Our Planet? (180); Living Research: Aquatic Heroes and Heroines (293); Plastic Voyages (189); Something's Fishy Here! (212); To Dam or Not To Dam (260); Water We Eating? (128); Watered-Down History (138); What's in the Water? (206); Where Does Water Run? (44)

Community (ecological)
Blue Ribbon Niche (94); Dragonfly Pond (282); Fishable Waters (232); Fishy Who's Who (9); How Wet Is Our Planet? (180); Kelp Help (279); Marsh Munchers (75); Micro Odyssey (91); Migration Headache (18); Puddle Wonders! (166); Riparian Retreat (175); The Glass Menagerie (228); Water Canaries (63); Water Wings (160); Watered-Down History (138); Watershed (196); Wetland Metaphors (80); What's in the Water? (206); Where Does Water Run? (44)

Field Investigations

Edge of Home (119); Gone Fishing! (272); Got Water? (24); Puddle Wonders (166); Water Canaries (63); Water Safari (37); Watershed (196); Where Does Water Run? (44)

Fish

Aquatic Roots (251); Are You Me? (2); Blue Ribbon Niche (94); Fashion a Fish (98); Fishable Waters (232); Fishy Who's Who (9); Gone Fishing! (272); Hooks and Ladders (84); Marsh Munchers (75); Net Gain, Net Effect (131); Plastic Voyages (189); To Dam or Not To Dam (260); Urban Waterway Checkup (54); Where Have All the Salmon Gone? (254)

Fishing

A Whale of an Issue (141); Fishable Waters (232); Gone Fishing! (272); Hooks and Ladders (84); Net Gain, Net Effect (131); To Dam or Not To Dam (260); Turtle Hurdles (246); Where Have All the Salmon Gone? (254)

Food Chains, Food Webs

Blue Ribbon Niche (94); Fishable Waters (232); Hooks and Ladders (84); Marsh Munchers (75); Micro Odyssey (91); Plastic Voyages (189); Turtle Hurdles (246); Water We Eating? (128); What's in the Water? (206)

Government

A Whale of an Issue (141); Aquatic Roots (251); Dragonfly Pond (282); Fishable Waters (232); Net Gain, Net Effect (131); Plastic Voyages (189); To Dam or Not To Dam (260);

Groundwater

Alice in Waterland (223); Dragonfly Pond (282); How Wet Is Our Planet? (180); Water Wings (160); What's in the Water? (206); Where Does Water Run? (44)

Habitat

Alice in Waterland (223); Blue Ribbon Niche (94); Conservation Messaging (289); Designing a Habitat (34); Dragonfly Pond (282); Eat and Glow (112); Fashion a Fish (98); Fishable Waters (232); Fishy Who's Who (9); Got Water? (24); Hooks and Ladders (84); Kelp Help (279); Marsh Munchers (75); Mermaids and Manatees (124); Micro Odyssey (91); Migration Headache (18); Puddle Wonders! (166); Riparian Retreat (175); Silt:

A Dirty Word (266); Sockeye Scents (103); To Dam or Not To Dam (260); Turtle Hurdles (246); Urban Waterway Checkup (54); Water Canaries (63); Water Safari (37); Water Wings (160); Watered-Down History (138); Watershed (196); Wetland Metaphors (80); What's in the Air? (201); What's in the Water? (206); Where Does Water Run? (44); Where Have All the Salmon Gone? (254)

Insects

Are You Me? (2); Blue Ribbon Niche (94); Riparian Retreat (175); Water Canaries (63); Water Safari (37)

Interdependence

Aquatic Roots (251); Blue Ribbon Niche (94); Dam Design (269); Designing a Habitat (34); Dragonfly Pond (282); Edge of Home (119); Hooks and Ladders (84); How Wet Is Our Planet? (180); Kelp Help (279); Marsh Munchers (75); Micro Odyssey (91); Migration Headache (18); Puddle Wonders! (166); Riparian Retreat (175); Sea Turtles International (147); Silt: A Dirty Word (266); The Glass Menagerie (228); Water Canaries (63); Water Wings (160); Water Works (216); Watered-Down History (138); Watershed (196); Wetland Metaphors (80); What's in the Water? (206); Where Does Water Run? (44)

Invasive Species

Aquatic Roots (251); Conservation Messaging (289)

Issues

A Whale of an Issue (141); Aquatic Roots (251); Aquatic Times (264); Conservation Messaging (289); Dam Design (269); Dragonfly Pond (282); Facts and Falsehoods (184); Fishable Waters (232); Hooks and Ladders (84); How Wet Is Our Planet? (180); Living Research: Aquatic Heroes and Heroines (293); Migration Headache (18); Net Gain, Net Effect (131); Plastic Voyages (189); Sea Turtles International (147); Silt: A Dirty Word (266); Something's Fishy Here! (212); The Glass Menagerie (228); To Dam or Not To Dam (260); Turtle Hurdles (246); What's in the Air? (201); What's in the Water? (206); Working for Wildlife (296)

Lake Environment

Dragonfly Pond (282); Fishable Waters (232); Fishy Who's Who (9); How Wet Is Our Planet? (180); The Glass Menagerie (228); What's in the Water? (206)

Land Use Planning

Blue Ribbon Niche (94); Dragonfly Pond (282); Fishable Waters (232); Migration Headache (18); To Dam or Not To Dam (260); Turtle Hurdles (246); Watered-Down History (138); Working for Wildlife (296)

Laws

A Whale of an Issue (141); Aquatic Roots (251) ; Dragonfly Pond (282); Fishable Waters (232); Net Gain, Net Effect (131); Sea Turtles International (147); To Dam or Not To Dam (260); Turtle Hurdles (246); Where Have All the Salmon Gone? (254); Working for Wildlife (296)

Life Cycle

Are You Me? (2); Hooks and Ladders (84); Turtle Hurdles (246)

Limiting Factors

A Whale of an Issue (141); Got Water? (24); Hooks and Ladders (84); Migration Headache (18); Net Gain, Net Effect (131); Plastic Voyages (189); Turtle Hurdles (246); Where Have All the Salmon Gone? (254)

Mammals

A Whale of an Issue (141); Are You Me? (2); Blue Ribbon Niche (94); Hooks and Ladders (84); Mermaids and Manatees (124); To Dam or Not To Dam (260); Turtle Hurdles (246); Whale of a Tail (12)

Management

A Whale of an Issue (141); Aquatic Roots (251); Conservation Messaging (289); Dam Design (269); Dragonfly Pond (282); Fishable Waters (232); Hooks and Ladders (84); Migration Headache (18); Net Gain, Net Effect (131); Sea Turtles International (147); Silt: A Dirty Word (266); To Dam or Not To Dam (260); Urban Waterway Checkup (54); Water Works (216); What's in the Water? (206); Where Does Water Run? (44); Where Have All the Salmon Gone? (254); Working for Wildlife (296)

Mapping

Dragonfly Pond (282); Edge of Home (119); Fishy Who's Who (9); Gone Fishing! (272); Got Water? (24); Migration Headache (18); Plastic Voyage (189); Puddle Wonders (166); Sockeye Scents (103); Urban Waterway Checkup (54); Water Safari (37); Water We Eating? (128); Watered-Down History (138); Watershed (196); Whale of a Tail (12); Where Does Water Run? (44)

Marine Environment

A Whale of an Issue (141); Hooks and Ladders (84); Kelp Help (279); Marsh Munchers (75); Net Gain, Net Effect (131); Plastic Voyages (189); Sea Turtles International (147); Silt: A Dirty Word (266); Turtle Hurdles (246); Water Wings (160); Whale of a Tail (12)

Marine Mammals

A Whale of an Issue (141); Are You Me? (2); Plastic Voyages (189); Mermaids and Manatees (124); Whale of a Tail (12)

Marsh

Dragonfly Pond (282); Marsh Munchers (75); Migration Headache (18); Wetland Metaphors (80); What's in the Water? (206)

Migration

Dam Design (269); Fishable Waters (232); Hooks and Ladders (84); Migration Headache (18); Sockeye Scents (103); Turtle Hurdles (246); Whale of a Tail (12)

Native Species

Aquatic Roots (251); Conservation Messaging (289); Fishy Who's Who (9)

Neighborhood

Alice in Waterland (223); How Wet Is Our Planet? (180); Living Research: Aquatic Heroes and Heroines (293); Puddle Wonders! (166); Something's Fishy Here! (212); Water Safari (37); Water We Eating? (128); Water Wings (160); Watered-Down History (138); Watershed (196); Where Does Water Run? (44)

Nonpoint Source Pollution

Dragonfly Pond (282); Fishable Waters (232); Plastic Voyages (189); Silt: A Dirty Word (266); Something's Fishy Here (212); The Glass Menagerie (228); Water Canaries (63); Watershed (196); What's in the Air? (201); What's in the Water? (206); Where Does Water Run? (44)

Nutrient Loading

Fishable Waters (232); The Glass Menagerie (228); What's in the Water? (206)

Expanded Topic Index
© *Council for Environmental Education (CEE)*

Ocean

A Whale of an Issue (141); Dragonfly Pond (282); Fishy Who's Who (9); Hooks and Ladders (84); How Wet Is Our Planet? (180); Kelp Help (279); Marsh Munchers (75); Net Gain, Net Effect (131); Plastic Voyages (189); Sea Turtles International (147); Silt: A Dirty Word (266); Turtle Hurdles (246); Water Wings (160); Whale of a Tail (12); What's in the Water? (206); Where Have All the Salmon Gone? (254)

Plant Life

Aquatic Roots (251); Dragonfly Pond (282); Fishable Waters (232); Kelp Help (279); Marsh Munchers (75); Riparian Retreat (175); Urban Waterway Checkup (54); Water Plant Art (72); Water Wings (160); Watered-Down History (138); What's in the Air? (201)

Point Source Pollution

Fishable Waters (232); Something's Fishy Here (212); What's in the Water? (206)

Pollution

Alice in Waterland (223); Blue Ribbon Niche (94); Conservation Messaging (289); Dragonfly Pond (282); Fishable Waters (232); Migration Headache (18); Plastic Voyages (189); Something's Fishy Here! (212); The Glass Menagerie (228); Urban Waterway Checkup (54); What's in the Air? (201); What's in the Water? (206)

Pond Environment

Dragonfly Pond (282); Micro Odyssey (91); Migration Headache (18); Pond Succession (108); The Glass Menagerie (228); Water Canaries (63); What's in the Water? (206)

Precipitation

Puddle Wonders! (166); What's in the Air? (201); Where Does Water Run? (44)

Predator/Prey Relationships

Blue Ribbon Niche (94); Hooks and Ladders (84); Marsh Munchers (75); Micro Odyssey (91); Net Gain, Net Effect (131); Turtle Hurdles (246)

Producers, Consumers, Decomposers

Blue Ribbon Niche (94); Fishable Waters (232); Marsh Munchers (75); Micro Odyssey (91); What's in the Water? (206)

Recreation

Gone Fishing! (272); To Dam or Not To Dam (260)

Regulations

A Whale of an Issue (141); Aquatic Roots (251); Dragonfly Pond (282); Fishable Waters (232); Net Gain, Net Effect (131); Sea Turtles International (147); To Dam or Not To Dam (260); Turtle Hurdles (246); Where Have All the Salmon Gone? (254)

Responsible Human Actions

A Whale of an Issue (141); Alice in Waterland (223); Conservation Messaging (289); Dam Design (269); Dragonfly Pond (282); Facts and Falsehoods (184); Fishable Waters (232); Gone Fishing! (272); How Wet Is Our Planet? (180); Living Research: Aquatic Heroes and Heroines (293); Plastic Voyages (189); Sea Turtles International (147); Silt: A Dirty Word (266); Something's Fishy Here! (212); Turtle Hurdles (246); Urban Waterway Checkup (54); Watershed (196); What's in the Water? (206); Where Does Water Run? (44); Working for Wildlife (296)

Riparian Environment

Blue Ribbon Niche (94); Dragonfly Pond (282); Fishable Waters (232); Hooks and Ladders (84); Riparian Retreat (175); Watered-Down History (138); What's in the Water? (206)

River Environment

Blue Ribbon Niche (94); Dragonfly Pond (282); Fishable Waters (232); Fishy Who's Who (9); Hooks and Ladders (84); How Wet Is Our Planet? (180); Riparian Retreat (175); To Dam or Not To Dam (260); Watered-Down History (138); What's in the Water? (206); Where Have All the Salmon Gone? (254)

Salmon

Hooks and Ladders (84); To Dam or Not To Dam (260); Where Have All the Salmon Gone? (254)

Science and Society

A Whale of an Issue (141); Alice in Waterland (223); Aquatic Roots (251); Dragonfly Pond (282); Hooks and Ladders (84); How Wet Is Our Planet? (180); Kelp Help (279); Migration Headache (18); Net Gain, Net Effect (131); Plastic Voyages (189); Something's Fishy Here! (212); To Dam or Not To Dam (260);

Evaluating and Assessing Student Learning

As the nation moves toward educational reform and literacy in all subject areas, standards in assessment become vital. The National Research Council suggests that the following assessment standards be used with students:

- Assessment Standard A: Assessments must be consistent with the decisions they are designed to inform.

- Assessment Standard B: Achievement and opportunity to learn science (or other subject areas) must be assessed.

- Assessment Standard C: The technical quality of the data (or other information) collected is well matched to the decisions and actions taken on the basis of their interpretation.

- Assessment Standard D: Assessment practices must be fair.

- Assessment Standard E: The inferences made from assessments about student achievement and opportunity to learn must be sound.

Source: National Science Education Standards (Washington, DC: National Research Council, National Academy Press, 1996)

Project WILD and Aquatic WILD are designed to assist teachers as they assess student learning. Each activity has an evaluation section that suggests at least one way to evaluate students' work, accomplishments, or performance. This section correlates directly with the stated objectives. Some of the suggested evaluations assess student understanding of factual information. Many of them ask students to demonstrate a theoretical or applied conceptual understanding.

Exemplary practice outlines the following strategies when assessing students' learning. Aquatic WILD encourages educators to incorporate some of these methods when using this guide.

Educator-Generated Tests

Unlike commercially produced tests, educator-generated tests are created by the instructor. They can be multiple choice, fill-in-the-blank, true/false, or essay-type tests. Aquatic WILD recommends that this type of evaluation be used on a regular basis for ongoing evaluation rather than as a cumulative tool.

Portfolios

A portfolio is a collection of class or project work chosen to specifically address a student's progress. Portfolios usually include examples of student work, reflections, self-evaluations, and goal-setting items. The purpose of a portfolio is to document what has been taught and the national standards that have been met. It also allows subject area assessments to be integrated and student growth to be charted.

Performance Tasks

A performance task is an assessment tool (generally chosen by the student) that demonstrates an understanding of concepts and processes as they apply to everyday life. The task is usually meant for a larger audience rather than for the educator alone. It is carefully planned and evaluated with detailed scoring. Teachers can present students with a new scenario, for which they will need to

apply recently acquired ideas and information. For example, students may be asked to solve a problem (such as food shortages) faced by animals when they experience a loss of habitat. Performance tasks can range from solving a real-life problem to preparing a speech or project, demonstrating a specific skill, or writing a paper or report.

Student-Initiated Assessment

Ask students, either as individuals or in groups, to create a list of preconceptions before beginning a new topic or activity. This may be a straightforward list, a web or concept map, or a journal entry. After completing the activity, ask students to revisit what they recorded and consider how their thoughts may have changed and how their knowledge and skills may have increased. Journals and logs are tools for students to use to record their own learning in a less formal manner. Journals are usually a subjective account of a student's perspective on what has been learned. Logs are more detailed and give a direct account that follows a given format. To assess overall classroom interest and information retention, ask students to submit written questions derived from

newly learned information that will be discussed in an open-class forum. To read more on science notebooks and field journals, see page xxiii in "Aquatic WILD Field Investigations."

Visual Vocabulary

An alternative method of assessment for the expression of learned concepts is through pantomime and creative movement. Students review vocabulary they have researched and then select specific terms that demonstrate their understanding of the activity's concepts.

Observation Checklists

Educators can use observation checklists as a useful tool to monitor whether a student has mastered a specific skill.

Graphic Organizers

Web diagrams, charts, pictures, digital presentations, and other forms of graphics can be generated by students to demonstrate non-verbal assessments of what they have learned and how it has been organized into their thought processes.

Interviews and Conferences

Educators can assess learning by interviewing and conferencing with students using a systematic approach. When discussing a topic, students can clarify their thinking and educators can gather information on how students are processing what they have learned.

Rubrics

Rubrics are used for any of the assessment strategies outlined above. A rubric is a set of scoring criteria against which a product/activity is evaluated. Generally, rubrics identify levels of quality (such as "Excellent, Good, Needs Improvement" or numeric scores "4, 3, 2, 1," which can be added for a total score). A rubric allows students and educators to know specifically what is expected and how each student has measured up to those expectations; they can also be used in self-evaluation or evaluation by peers.

Inventory Methods
For Plants and Wildlife on School or Community Grounds

Part 1: Background

What is an Inventory?

While there are many ways to study species that inhabit a school yard or community, a great way to start is by conducting an inventory. When exploring local ecosystems, consider the diversity of plants and animals within the area, the habitats in which they live, and the current and past land use.

An inventory is a list of the plants, animals, soil types, etc., in a given area. It may list the species of birds in a school yard or the different types of trees within a watershed. Such lists provide good information but may not necessarily include the actual number or census of specific plants or animals. The type of information found depends on how the inventory is conducted and the environmental factor (plant or animal) being inventoried. It may be a fairly simple task to count and identify all the trees in a small school yard. In this case, a simple inventory based on observation, identification, and actual count results in an inventory that includes the census or number of trees.

However, it is more difficult to get the exact number of a particular species of bird or butterfly in a school yard. Typically, a bird and butterfly inventory will provide a list of the species found in a certain area. The numbers of each species observed during the inventory may also be recorded. These numbers can then be used as an index to provide an idea of which species may be more common in that area or during a certain time of year.

Inventories can be based on a standardized method and timing, or they may be based on informal sightings. Many parks keep a running inventory of their plants and animals. Visitors jot down their sightings that, if confirmed, are then added to the park's inventory list. Other methods may be more formal, with volunteers doing an inventory in a given area at a given time. Before starting an inventory,

educators and students should determine what it is they want to know. A variety of inventory methods exist to create lists of species, habitats, and land uses that exist in the area. To get an idea of numbers of each species, population density, or habitat use, consider using a more standardized method. (For many species, particular statistical methods and research techniques may need to be used to obtain accurate population estimates and population densities.)

Inventory data typically includes:

- Date
- Name of the observer
- Habitat
- Location
- Species identification
- Number of plants, animals, or signs of animals found

Examples of statewide or nationwide inventory projects are the Audubon Christmas Bird Counts, National Park Service Inventory and Monitoring Program, and Project Budburst, a citizen science program.

Designing a Monitoring Project

Monitoring takes it one step further by studying a population or habitat over a long period of time with multiple inventories. While conducting a one-time inventory of a habitat can be both educational and informative, students may be interested in comparing data from year to year. Studying a site over a long period of time can reveal changes in population, new species introduced to the habitat, or other trends that cannot be studied from a one-time visit. When developing an inventory method set to be used multiple times, it is important to establish a standard, repeatable procedure called a monitoring project.

Monitoring involves observing, surveying, or inventorying over a period of time. Monitoring projects have very specific procedures that are repeated. Two examples of inventory methods used in monitoring projects are:

- *Point Count Method.* Often used for birds but also can be used for butterflies and amphibians. In this method, participants are assigned a route. At established points along the route, all birds are identified and counted, both seen and heard, within a given radius. An example of a project using the point count method is the Breeding Bird Census, which used this method to determine the population density of breeding birds over time. It is performed each year along the same routes or in the same study areas.

- *Spot Mapping Method.* Used to determine estimates of population density over a period of time. The spot mapping method involves establishing a study area, visiting the area several times during the breeding season, identifying birds within the area, and plotting their locations on a grid map.

Whether students conduct a one-time inventory or complete a yearlong monitoring project, it is important to respect all wildlife and natural areas. Refer to "Field Ethics" (page 354) for best practices on navigating instruction in outdoor settings.

Species Identification

Before conducting the inventory, it is helpful for older students to be familiar with at least some common aquatic species they may encounter. Depending on the specific inventory planned, give them time to research typical birds, mammals, fish, and other species in aquatic habitats similar to the study site. Photos or illustrations, as well as information about possible signs (tracks, eggs, lodges, or nests), will help students determine whether a particular species is present at the site.

Have students make and laminate identification cards to take on the inventory. Plan to have appropriate field guides on hand. A great way to record details of an organism while building critical observational skills is to bring a drawing pad and create a sketch. Place this in science notebooks to identify and label back in the classroom.

Younger students need not be too concerned about identifying exact species. General terms like "tadpole," "frog," "fish," or "duck" are developmentally appropriate descriptions of the different types of wildlife found at a particular site. If students show an interest in learning more, use child-friendly field guides to teach them common local species for the next inventory.

Part 2: Preparation
Introducing the Inventory

An inventory study of an organism, population, or habitat can be conducted with many of the same procedures used during a field investigation. An initial inventory of a study site will help students develop greater knowledge of their local environment and is thus a technique fit for conducting descriptive field investigations. That is, data collected in an inventory will help students answer many questions that describe a study site. With this knowledge, students can then go on to develop more involved questions that compare and/or correlate attributes or phenomena on a site (comparative and correlative investigations).

For more information on field investigations, including a list of field investigation activities in this guide, see "Aquatic WILD Field Investigations" in the introductory pages. Refer to activities such as "Where Does Water Run?" (on page 44) and "Puddle Wonders!" (on page 166) for guidance on helping students develop researchable investigative questions.

When initiating an inventory, explain to students that they will be conducting an inventory to learn about what organisms live in or near a habitat. Point out that scientists conduct field investigations to learn about plants, animals, and other living and nonliving elements of a habitat. Like other scientific investigations, inventories usually start with a question. The question guides the investigation and helps them determine the what, where, when, and how of their study.

Write the following question on the board: What plants and animals use resources or live in the study site? Ask students how this question might guide their inventory of the study site. Does it give information about what we would be looking for and where?

If a more specific investigation question is needed to guide the inventory, have students propose possible questions to consider. What precisely do they want to find out about the site, or about the aquatic wildlife that lives there? Is there anything they are particularly curious about? Do they want to know if a particular animal lives there? Or do they want to get a basic idea of all the plants and wildlife that inhabit the site? Do they want a detailed inventory of a particular group like birds or amphibians to study the population over time?

Taking time to formulate good questions before planning the inventory will encourage student-driven research and provide a solid foundation from which to design the study.

Planning the Inventory

When conducting a survey of plants and wildlife, students should consider several factors:

Size. First, students must decide where to survey. Is the study area large or small? Then decide what to survey. Do they want to get a basic idea of all the plants and wildlife that inhabit the site? Do they want to make a list of all the plants that are in an area? Or, do they want to acquire general knowledge of common plants and wildlife with a more detailed inventory of a particular group like birds, trees, or amphibians?

Time. When should the survey occur? Approximately how long will it take? Will it occur once, or as an ongoing monitoring project? How much preparatory time is needed before students conduct the survey?

Level of Experience. How much survey experience do the students have? Which techniques might be easier and safer for them to use? Select an inventory method appropriate for the grade level.

Sampling Design. A sampling design is a step-by-step method of counting a species. Because an inventory is just a list, the design can be as formal or informal as desired. However, for accuracy and consistency, especially when conducting a long-term monitoring project, students must use a standardized method each time the inventory

> An inventory is a data collection technique students can use when conducting descriptive field investigations. That is, data collected in an inventory will help students answer many questions that describe a study site.

occurs. Standard methods or techniques exist for discovering various plants and wildlife that inhabit the site. Specific techniques tend to lend themselves more for inventorying the different groups of plants and animals (insects, mammals, birds, amphibians, or plants). **Plot studies** and **transect lines** are typical survey designs used in conducting inventorying and monitoring projects for a wide variety of plants and wildlife. The actual sampling design can be the same, but the techniques and timing to discover the organism differ.

For example, students may set up a transect line or simply walk a particular trail on site. At set distances, such as every 5 meters (or yards), check for mammals or signs of mammals in a 2-meter diameter from the observation point. Using the same design, they can also check for amphibians or birds. However, students will have to use different techniques to actually find the animal and may need to inventory at different times of the day. To find mammals, look on the ground, in trees and shrubs, etc. Students could also look for tracks, scat, eaten corn, etc. Amphibians can be found under logs or stones, and to find birds look for nests and listen for songs or calls. Refer to "Part 3: Inventory Methods" on the following page to learn more on inventorying different species.

Analysis and Reporting. Analyzing and sharing the information gathered through inventorying, monitoring, or research projects is very important.

Before sharing, prompt students to reflect thoroughly on the inventory and what was learned. Begin with questions like:

- What did you learn from the inventory or monitoring project?
- What surprised you?
- What questions did the study raise?
- Who else might be interested in what we learned?
- How could we share this information?
- What else could we study next?

All information contributes to the general knowledge base and may contribute to management and conservation programs. Contact your state wildlife and resources department (many have local offices) or a conservation organization to see if the inventory results could be valuable as a citizen science contribution. Adapt the results to a catchy report or "news" update on the school social media page or website. Students could also video the inventory and develop a short PSA for the morning announcements. Publishing in a pamphlet, newspaper, journal, or on a website is a great way to practice scientific writing skills.

Part 3: Inventory Methods

Inventorying and Monitoring: Wildlife Populations

A population is the number of a particular species of organisms that occupy a certain area at a certain time as defined by the people interested in the group. A population can be deer in Montgomery County in 1999 or the White Pines in the county park in 1884.

Conducting a census for wildlife has been done for centuries. There are many reasons to determine the population size of a given animal. However, the value of a one-time population estimate is limited. Noting trends in population size is much more valuable. This task is accomplished through repetitive estimates over time. For example, a one-time count gives the number at that time; it does not help assess the overall health or status of a population. However, population estimates over a period of years can indicate a decline or area of concern. Reasons for determining population size include the following:

- A species is endangered or threatened.
- The status of a species needs to be determined.
- A "nuisance" species needs to be monitored.
- Harvest size of a species needs to be determined or monitored.
- Habitat management practices require population information.
- Population information is needed to determine the environmental quality index.

Naturally, it would be ideal if all wildlife populations could be counted individual by individual. However, even if it appeared that all were counted, how would biologists be certain? The reality is that most counts are based on some type of sampling methods. Sampling methods inherently have problems; however, over the years, many methods have been shown to give fairly accurate population estimates. The following methods are examples of wildlife population assessment techniques:

Territorial Mapping Method of Bird Populations. This procedure involves participants observing individual birds during repeated visits and recording the location of the bird at each visit. These locations are mapped on a grid. Clusters on the grids are counted and used for determining breeding population densities in a given area.

Marked Sub-Sample Method. In this approach, a known number of animals are marked individually. A survey is conducted, often aerial, and the marked and unmarked animals are counted. Then, a ratio is used to determine the total population:

Total Population Estimate =

$$\frac{(\text{Number of marked animals}) \times (\text{Total animals observed})}{(\text{Number of marked animals seen in survey})}$$

Change-in-Ratio Methods. These methods remove the animal from the population by means of trapping or hunting. Change-in-ratio methods involve two types of animals (e.g., male and female, with antlers and without antlers, adults and juveniles). For instance, a pre-hunt road count is made of deer with and without antlers. A hunt takes place, and the road count is conducted again. Then, changes in proportions are determined, resulting in a total population estimate.

Inventory Methods
© *Council for Environmental Education (CEE)*

Capture-Recapture Methods. These methods entail capturing and marking a known number of animals and then recapturing or observing animals at a subsequent time. Capture-recapture can provide two types of information:

- Data from the recapture of marked animals can be used to help determine survival rates.
- Proportions of the marked and unmarked animals captured at each sampling can be used to estimate population abundance.

An example of this method is the **Lincoln Index**. To use the Lincoln Index, biologists capture a group of animals and mark them. The number of marked animals becomes the sample size. If the biologists captured and marked 100 bears, 100 would be the sample size. At a later date, perhaps a year later, the biologists then recapture 100 bears in the same area and determine how many bears were marked. Then they use the following equation.

Total Population Estimate =

$$\frac{\text{(Sample size)}}{\text{(Percentage of the sample that is marked)}}$$

There are many other techniques to measure populations. For more information, contact a local university or the state wildlife agency.

Inventorying and Monitoring: Plants

The composition of the plant communities in a particular site can be quantified in many different ways. The sampling method used depends on several factors, such as the sort of data the class is interested in obtaining, the type of vegetation, and the amount of time available. The methods described below consist of observing plants along one or more lines, which may be laid out systematically or randomly within a study area.

Point-Transect Line Method
This type of inventory is typically done in a field situation but could be used as part of a plot study in a forest or other location.

1. Decide on the area to be inventoried.

2. Set up transect lines through the area. Students can use posts and string to make the lines.

TRY IT OUT!

For experimenting with the capture-recapture method, have students use sunflower seeds, beans, or marbles as "organisms," or assign several students to be biologists and the other students to represent the organisms. Place the objects in a container or, if using student "organisms," have students spread out in a gym or outside. Collect a certain number of organisms for a sample and mark them. (Student biologists can use an armband to mark student organisms.) Then, "release" the organisms. Recapture the same number of organisms using the same method. Count the numbers that were marked within the recaptured group and use the equation to calculate the total population. (The calculation given in this text is the basic calculation with no corrections added for bias. To get an accurate count, the larger the sample size and the higher the percentage of marked organisms, the better the estimate will be.)

Developed by T. Alberici, PA Game Commission. Reference: *Research and Management Techniques for Wildlife and Habitat*, edited by Theodore A. Bookhout, The Wildlife Society, Bethesda, Maryland, 1994.

---

3. Have students walk the transect lines. At set intervals along the line, record the plant closest to that point. The interval depends on how long the transect line is. For example, if the transect line is 25 meters, students may want to record data every 5 meters. Students could be asked to record the height of the plant and whether it produces berries, seeds, or flowers that might be useful to wildlife.

4. Summarize the data. Students will be able to figure out the most common species by looking at the percentage of occurrence (i.e., at how many points did this plant occur).

Variation on the Point-Transect Line Method
This procedure can be used in large field areas or to gain a basic idea of the most common plants in the area.

l. Divide the area into grids by establishing and numbering points along the length and width of the area.

2. Students randomly choose points to start the study by writing the numbers assigned to the points along the length of the site on slips of paper and putting those numbers into a container. Do the same for the numbers assigned to the width, putting those slips into another container. Next, have someone select a number from the width container and a number from the length container. Choose several of these sets of numbers (depending on how many starting points the class would like). Locate where the points intercept on the site. Then, using a meter (or yard) stick, place the beginning of the stick directly where the numbers intercept. Make sure the meter (or yard) stick always goes the same direction from the starting point. Ask students to record and identify each plant found at a determined point along the stick (e.g., every 10 centimeters).

3. Summarize the data. Have students determine the most common plant on site by looking at the percentage of occurrence at each point. Report all results after the plant inventory is complete.

Inventorying and Monitoring: Birds

Many different methods can be used to inventory and monitor bird species within an area. Two methods based on the **point count method** are suggested in this activity. One method is for smaller areas, similar to a small backyard. The other is for larger areas or areas with several types of habitats. Birds are resident and migratory; therefore, the inventorying and monitoring observation days should occur at different times of the year. Most birds are active in the morning and evening, so these times are better to conduct observations. However any time during the school day will also do.

Point Count Method

l. Select the area to be monitored.

2. Establish observation points.

■ Option 1. If the area is small and this is a monitoring project, then establish one or two observation points, observation times, and procedures. For example, observe for 10 minutes between 8 a.m. and 10 a.m. Keep the length of each observation time consistent.

■ Option 2. If the area is large or contains many different habitat types, conduct the more typical point count method. Establish routes through the area. At established points along the route, stop, identify, and count all birds seen or heard within a predetermined radius for a specified amount of time (generally between 5 and 15 minutes).

3. Ask students to count and identify each species observed. At a minimum, data collection should include date, time, weather, observer, species, and number. If students decide to conduct the inventory several times a day (for example, one class does the observations in the morning and another in the afternoon), be careful how they report the numbers of birds in the area. To determine the number for the day, use the largest number of the one species of bird observed at one time. For example, the morning group observed five robins; later that afternoon, the tally for robins was three. The total number reported for the day would be five. (In addition, it might be interesting to compare morning to afternoon numbers over a period of time.)

4. Conduct the inventory at least several times during the year to get an overall picture of what birds inhabit the area. While selecting the observation dates, consider when each bird species migrates.

5. At the end of the each season, have students summarize the data.

6. Using data summaries, students can draw conclusions and report to their class or school.

Winter Feed Count Method

One way to inventory winter birds that come to a feeder is to do feeder counts. Keep in mind that not all birds come to feeders and even birds that will use feeders also use different habitats. A feeder count will not reveal all the birds on the site, but it is a good start. Before a bird feeder program is started, research the types of food preferred by different species. Have students clean the feeders and area under the feeder (remove old seeds and hulled seeds) to prevent the spread of disease. Some

people feed birds throughout the year, but keep in mind that other animals, such as squirrels, raccoons, and even bears will use the feeders, which can cause problems. People in areas with bears should not feed birds all year.

1. Research local birds that come to feeders.

2. Learn about the do's and don'ts of bird feeding by bringing in a guest speaker or conducting online research.

3. Select the area for a bird feeder or feeders. Feeders should be easy to refill and be within easy view of a window.

4. Establish observation times and points. Observations can be done once or multiple times a day. In this case (for example, one class does the observations in the morning and another in the afternoon), be careful how the numbers of birds are reported in the area. To determine the number for the day, use the largest number of the one species of bird observed at one time. For example, the morning group observed five chickadees; that afternoon the tally for chickadees was three. The total number reported for the day would be five. In addition, it might be interesting to compare morning to afternoon numbers over a period of time.

5. Count and identify each species observed. At a minimum, data collection should include date, time, weather, observer, species, and number.

6. Conduct the inventory at least once a week through the winter months.

7. At the end of the winter, have students summarize their data.

8. Using the data summary, have students draw conclusions and report them to their class or school.

If students would like to get involved with a national bird feeder inventory and monitoring project, contact Cornell University's Project FeederWatch program:

Project FeederWatch
Cornell Laboratory of Ornithology
159 Sapsucker Woods Road
Ithaca, NY 14850
Phone: (800) 843-BIRD (2473)
birds.cornell.edu/PFW

Inventorying and Monitoring: Mammals

Students often enjoy seeing mammals such as squirrels or deer near their school. Direct observation is the most obvious method to observe mammals, but unfortunately, mammals are not always cooperative. Before beginning any type of inventory, have students research the habitat at the study site and make a list of mammals that might be found. Next, consider the type of signs those mammals may leave behind. Most often, mammal inventories are based on signs, rather than sightings of the actual animal. Below are two methods for inventorying mammals, but if students are conducting a monitoring project, the **line transect method** is more appropriate.

Please do not allow students to touch, capture, corner, or chase any wild animal.

General Observation Method

1. Ask students to describe the habitats located at the study site. Examples are grassy, open areas, woods, creeks, gardens, or a deep pond.

2. Create a list of the mammals that may be found on site. Indicate those that definitely inhabit the study site. The latter can be done by confirmed sightings by students or nearby residents.

3. Have students research in teams the type of sign that the mammal or mammals they are counting may leave behind.

4. Divide area into sections. Make sure all habitat types are included.

5. In teams, have students walk the sections and search for signs of mammals and record information on a data sheet based on the sampling design. If possible, bring cameras or science notebooks to sketch the findings.

Mammal signs to search for include the following:

- Direct observation of the mammal
- Sounds and vocalization
- Scat (animal droppings)
- Tracks and trails
- Nests (for example, squirrels' nests among tree branches)
- Scratchings and rubbings (claw marks on trees from bears; rubbing marks from deer or elk)
- Gnawings
- Lodges and homes

6. Summarize the data collected.

7. Repeat this inventory several times during the year to include different seasons.

8. Publish an inventory of mammals on the site.

Developed by T. Alberici, Pennsylvania Game Commission. Based on "Wildlife Is Everywhere!" and "Environmental Barometer" from Project WILD, Council for Environmental Education © 2001.

Line Transect Method

1. With students, select an area to inventory and monitor.

2. Set up transect lines to cross the area. Make sure the lines are far enough apart that observers are not counting the same animal. If the site contains different habitats, have students place transect lines in the different habitats. If this is a monitoring project, then they must develop a standard procedure. Brightly colored yarn, string, rope, or flags can be used to mark the line.

3. Walk the transect lines and record the number and identification of all mammals observed. It is recommended to establish a maximum observation distance (e.g., 30 meters or 100 feet from the transect line). Suggested information to record includes observer, weather, length of transect line, habitat, animal, number, behavior of animal at time of

observation, and date and time observed. Different animals are active at different times of day and at different times of the year. Prior research and careful planning will increase the chances of observing an animal.

NOTE: To estimate deer populations in an area, see the activity "Dropping in on Deer" in the *Project WILD K–12 Curriculum and Activity Guide.*

4. Summarize the data collected. Keep in mind that if this is a monitoring project, the counts recorded are incomplete. Although they can be used as an "index" to the population, these counts do not provide a real census of the population.

5. Present the conclusions to schools, to the community, or to even broader audiences.

Adapted by T. Alberici from "Line Transects," *Research and Management Techniques for Wildlife and Habitats*, edited by Theodore A. Bookhout, published by The Wildlife Society, Bethesda, Maryland ©1994, 230–31.

Inventorying and Monitoring: Amphibians and Reptiles

Once a general inventory of the habitats and land use in the study site has been conducted and mapped, consider including reptiles and amphibians. Reptiles and amphibians are useful indicators when studying potential pollution, effects of drought, and insect populations. First, divide the site into quadrants. The boundaries of the blocks should be easily identifiable (street, streams, etc.) or based on a topographical map.

Before going out into the field to search for amphibians and reptiles, it is important to research which ones could be found in the area and which are venomous. Learn how to identify them. A resource person from a local university or state agency could be helpful during this process. Bring large color pictures of these species or a field guide to reference during the inventory.

Never allow students to approach or handle venomous animals.

The classes Amphibia and Reptilia possess groups with extreme variability, and no single technique will work to locate them. In general, amphibians and reptiles tend to be secretive in nature except during specific times of the year (e.g., mating season) and under specific environmental conditions such as high humidity or rainfall. Techniques for observing and collecting each group of amphibians and reptiles will be discussed separately.

Salamanders
Salamanders, especially terrestrial (land based) and semiterrestrial species, can usually be found by looking under cover objects, such as rocks, logs, bark, and vegetation. Aquatic forms, such as newts, can be observed swimming or floating in ponds or along the weedy, shallow margins of lakes. This is

also true of spotted salamanders during the breeding season; however, they are seldom found except in fishless ponds in and near woods. Other aquatic salamanders, such as hellbenders and mud puppies, occasionally can be located by lifting submerged objects in streams and other appropriate bodies of water. Remember to replace the cover items where they were found to minimize habitat disturbance.

Generally, salamanders are active on the surface and are nocturnal, so slowly walking about at night in the appropriate habitat with a flashlight or lantern may prove successful. Any area that is likely to yield salamanders during daytime collecting (e.g., spring seeps, stream margins, wooded ravines, etc.) will also be a good area to locate salamanders at night. Rainfall and high humidity tend to stimulate salamander activity, so nighttime collecting for terrestrial and semiaquatic species is most productive under these environmental conditions.

Frogs and Toads
The fact that frogs and toads are highly vocal during the spring and summer breeding seasons makes them most likely to be located at this time. Listening for choruses at night is the most effective method of locating frogs and toads. When they are not calling, frogs can most frequently be encountered by searching the margins of streams, rivers, lakes, and

TIGER SALAMANDER

ponds at night with a lantern or flashlight. Browse the internet to learn frog calls of local species. The cricket frog, for example, can be called by rubbing two stones together in a pattern of increasing frequency. Using tricks to call frogs may help locate them around a body of water.

EASTERN SPADEFOOT TOAD

NORTHERN WATER SNAKE

Lizards

Lizards are often found on exposed rocky areas in forested regions when it is sunny and the air is calm. Search tree trunks, fence posts, and areas with nooks that lizards might use for quick hiding. Most skinks are also located in open rocky spots in forested areas, usually in the vicinity of streams.

CHUCKWALLA LIZARD

Snakes

Small to medium-sized species of terrestrial snakes most likely will be found by looking under objects. Water snakes and queen snakes are best found by walking in and along streams and other bodies of water as well as by overturning objects, such as rocks and logs, along the margins of streams and ponds. Large species, such as black rat snakes and black racers, are usually found actively moving about in the open. In general, the best places to look for snakes are along the margins of streams and lakes, around human habitation, in open rocky areas and rocky slopes, and in areas where debris, such as boards and other building material, has been left outdoors. In early spring, open rocky areas with southern exposures may be especially likely to host snakes.

Turtles

Many species of turtles bask either at the surface of the water (e.g., a variety of snapping turtles) or on emergent objects such as rocks, logs, and sandbars (e.g., painted turtles, map turtles, red-bellied turtles, soft-shelled turtles, etc.). Careful and quiet observation of suitable bodies of water through binoculars or spotting scopes will often reveal the presence of turtles. Late spring and early summer is egg-laying season, when individual turtles can occasionally be found moving about on land in search of nesting sites. Sightings are particularly common along the edges of roads in the vicinity of streams and bridges. In addition, heavy summer rains will often initiate terrestrial activity in otherwise aquatic species.

SNAPPING TURTLE

Inventory Methods
© Council for Environmental Education (CEE)

Inventorying and Monitoring: Invertebrates

Conducting an inventory of invertebrates can often yield large and consistent data sets for a monitoring project. Insects respond quickly to environmental and human influences since they often reproduce in high numbers and live less than one year, which increases the ability to observe population fluctuations during a school year. Invertebrates are found in every habitat, and can be a good option if the class is unable to conduct an inventory offsite. A common way to inventory these organisms is the **capture-recapture method** (see "Inventorying and Monitoring: Wildlife Populations" on page 338 for procedure).

Sweep Net Method (Terrestrial Invertebrates)
1. Similar to reptiles and amphibians, many invertebrates can be discovered by overturning leaves, rocks, logs, and disturbing leaf litter. If the study site possesses a grassy area, a sweep net is a easy and fast way to sample hidden invertebrates.

2. Place students in teams and create transect lines for each team to walk. Another option is to divide the area into sections or quadrants that each team inventories.

3. Have students use the sweep net to gently but swiftly swipe the grasses back and forth as they walk the line or quadrant. Once they have completed the sweep, quickly flip the net over on itself to prevent invertebrates from escaping. Use jars to remove and observe any caught specimens.

Kick Seine and Dip Net Method (Aquatic Invertebrates)
Aquatic macroinverterbates are excellent bio indicators of freshwater health. Many terrestrial insects such as dragonflies, mayflies, deerflies, and mosquitoes begin and spend most of their lives under the water. Have students survey all bodies of water at the study site for signs of macroinvertebrates by observing mosquitoes, dragonflies, or other insects hovering above or around the water. There are many web resources that provide detailed lists of macroinvertebrates to use for their inventory sheet. To familiarize students with identifying aquatic insects, practice using an ID book or drawing sample insects in class to count appendages, study body shapes, and learn the sizes of common species. Complete the activity "Water

Canaries" on page 63 to provide a good foundation for the inventory as well. During the aquatic collection it may help to laminate the inventory sheets before arriving on site.

1. Select a collection site. Students could collect from a creek, pond, stream, or a river.

2. Gather the proper equipment. Any sturdy net will suffice, but a dip net provides a long handle to reach out into the water from the bank. Waders are knee or waist high boots that students can place over their clothes to carefully stand in the water and collect. Kick seines are made from two handles and a screen in the middle. Place one group member further up from the kick seine and have them churn up the water with their feet or a log. As the muddy water flows downstream, any invertebrates living in the bottom will be caught in the net.

3. Separate the class into teams and spread them evenly along the waterbody. Make sure to record locations on the inventory sheet. Macroinvertebrates can live in many different areas of a waterbody. Some move freely through the water such as caddisflies or mosquitoes. Many live along the bank to hide from predators. Have students assess the area to collect from all parts of the aquatic habitat.

4. Begin collection. Bring all nets and kick seines to the bank and place the macroinvetebrates in a shallow pan. White pans work best to help the organisms stand out against the sediment and debris.

5. Determine as a class if the invertebrates will be released back into the water or if several specimens will be taken back to the classroom for further observation or sketches. Refer to "Field Ethics" (page 354) and "The Benefits of a Classroom Aquarium" (page 356) to make an informed decision about removing organisms from their habitat.

6. Summarize the data and report results. Make inferences about the health of the waterbody based on the species collected.

Inventorying and Monitoring: For Younger Students

Do not be concerned about identifying exact species. For this age group, general terms like "tadpole," "frog," "fish," or "duck" are adequate. Encourage students to create their own names for organisms they observe and discuss how scientists might select common names based on color, habitat, or mannerisms.

Look On, Look Under, and Look Above
Take students to a spot where they can see into the water of an aquatic habitat. Students will focus on three parts of the habitat for about five minutes each, while the educator records their observations. First, have them focus on the water looking for insects, feathers, bubbles, or other wildlife signs on the surface. Then, have them focus under the water, looking for any fish, tadpoles, or other animals in the water. (Using polarized sunglasses will help reduce glare.) Finally, have them focus above the water, looking for birds, insects, or other wildlife just above the water, up in overhanging branches, or well into the sky. Back in the classroom, make a list of the types of wildlife that use this waterbody.

Hula Hoop Transect
Lay out hula hoops (or wire clothes hangers bent into circles) near the water's edge. Have pairs or small groups of students work together to investigate each circle transect. They can use their science notebooks to draw pictures of each different plant, insect, caterpillar, or other wildlife—or sign of wildlife—within the circle. Have them count (or estimate) the numbers of each and write the totals next to their drawings.

Promoting Stewardship through Inventorying and Monitoring

Using inventory and monitoring methods provides a framework for constructive observation and exploration of the natural environment. Conducting multiple inventories of a site close to the school connects students to wildlife that may not otherwise be noticed and can build a stewardship ethic among students. After teaching the ethics and procedures of an inventory with the class, encourage students to conduct an inventory in their backyards or at a nearby park with their family.

RUDDY DUCK DRAKES

Service Learning
Engaging Students In Environmental Action Projects

The following excerpt has been adapted from Project WILD's *Taking Action: An Educator's Guide to Involving Students in Environmental Action Projects*, published by the Council for Environmental Education in cooperation with World Wildlife Fund. For more information or to order this guide, please contact Project WILD, Council for Environmental Education, 5555 Morningside Drive, Suite 212, Houston, TX 77005, Phone: (713) 520-1936, E-mail *info@projectwild.org*, or visit the Project WILD website at *www.projectwild.org*.

What Is an Action Project?

Project WILD has defined environmental action projects as any activities that get students involved in tackling an environmental issue or problem or that aim at improving an environmental setting. Activities are often most successful when they are focused on the local community, such as the enhancement of outdoor habitats or the development of natural sites within a neighborhood or on the school grounds. Projects can also work on a much broader scope—raising money to adopt sea turtles, for example.

An action project can be simple or complex—as straightforward as putting up a community bulletin board of current environmental events, or as involved as developing and implementing a community plan for oil collection and recycling. However complex, most action projects will fit into a variety of educational settings. Many educators find that action education blends well with their regular teaching duties, while others choose to make it the basis for afterschool sessions. Action learning is effective in informal settings, too, involving young people through nature centers, zoos, aquaria, and scouting programs.

Who Can Do Action Projects?

Students of all ages can take part in service learning projects, matching the complexity of the tasks to the abilities of students. Older students can get involved in issues that require research, issue analysis, in-depth discussion, careful planning, and follow-up. Students might establish river monitoring activities or conduct community education initiatives. Younger students can begin with projects that don't involve heated controversy, long-term commitments, or complex solutions. Picking up litter, writing a letter about an environmental concern, or planting a butterfly garden are excellent starting points for younger students.

Some Tips to Keep in Mind

Encourage student ownership and initiative.

The more students are involved in the project, the more they will get out of it. To the extent possible, allow students to make their own decisions on which problem to focus, how to conduct the project, and how to share results. Help students chart their own course, evaluate the pros and cons of each choice, and then gauge how much direction is needed.

Encourage parents and other community members to support the project.

Conflict sometimes can surface when students interact with community members who don't agree with a specific activity or don't feel that action projects are an appropriate educational approach. In many cases, you can diffuse this response by discussing projects with parents and community members beforehand and by explaining how environmental action projects enhance educational goals.

Keep your opinions in perspective.

Allow students to research material, discuss the issues, and form their own perspectives on the issues. Allow everyone the chance to openly express his or her opinions, no matter how different they may be. It is also critical to keep students on track and focused on the facts. Emotionally charged debate and hotly contested points of view can obscure the real facts and divert students' attention from the issue under scrutiny.

Encourage student cooperation, compromise, and understanding.

Have students work in small groups as much as possible. Besides the well-documented educational benefits of cooperative learning, group work offers a taste of real-life problem solving. Teams of scientists, politicians, business people, and concerned citizens often arrive at a plan of action together. Ideally, each person brings his or her own perspectives and talents to the process, and the results reflect the strengths of those human resources. Multiple perspectives encourage thoughtful debate, boost critical thinking skills, and allow students to make informed choices—especially if opinions are accompanied by reliable information.

Help students evaluate their methods and change their plans if necessary.

From time to time over the course of a project, have students assess the overall scheme and evaluate their methods. Ask if they think things are running as smoothly as expected. If they think there's room for improvement, ask what might be done to adjust the situation. In some cases, problem-solving teams can brainstorm ways to deal with the snags and setbacks encountered along the way.

Help students appreciate the value of their work.

It's important for students to know that their project, no matter how small, is significant. Assure students that every action counts. Even if students' actions do not seem to have much effect right away, the long-term results can be very important.

Approaches to Environmental Action

Teach It!—The Educate-and-Inform Approach

Projects that focus on teaching others about environmental issues (These might include older students mentoring younger students, conducting community education programs, writing and performing songs and poems, or conducting workshops with school or community groups.)

Make the Case—The Persuasive Approach

Projects designed to convince people to support a certain course of action or point of view (Activities include creating posters or brochures, creating virtual discussion forums through social media, conducting debates, writing letters to the editor, giving speeches, and distributing public service announcements.)

Be on the Money—The Economic Approach

Strategies that encourage consumers to shop with the environment in mind, as well as projects that raise money to support specific organizations, programs, or individuals working on environmental issues (Activities might include promoting environmentally friendly products, asking for cash or in-kind donations of time and materials from businesses and community groups, or applying for grants.)

Get Physical—The "Ecomanagement" Approach

Projects that physically improve the environment, such as planting trees, landscaping school grounds, cleaning up neighborhood parks or streams, or building bird and bat houses

Make Decisions—The Political Action Approach

Projects focusing on political action that could include speaking at a public hearing, meeting with an elected representative to discuss specific legislation, testifying before lawmakers, circulating petitions and fliers, writing letters to the editor, or campaigning for candidates

Become Legal Eagles—The Courtroom Approach

Projects that attempt to create change through legislation, or that take legal action against an individual, corporation, community, or government agency (Although most projects that involve primary and secondary students will not involve actual legal action, many projects can educate youngsters about existing laws and the workings of the legal system.)

Source: "Approaches" adapted with permission from *Investigating and Evaluating Environmental Issues and Actions* by Harold R. Hungerford et al. (Champaign, IL: Stipes Publishing Co., 10–12 Chester St., 1992)

Seven Steps to Action

Here are some basic steps that will help students get action projects off the ground. While the steps are listed in order, it's important to note that planning and implementing a project is not always a clear-cut, linear process. In some cases, students will investigate an issue, discuss it, begin to work on it, and then change their strategy as they use new information. They might decide to narrow their focus or switch projects after realizing that the potential solutions are beyond their capabilities. Such adjustments are a normal part of the learning process.

1. Get Informed

Before students decide which environmental projects to pursue, they need to become informed about the possibilities. Students may collect a pool of information from web resources, newspapers, and magazines; interview community members and parents; or contact organizations and government agencies that focus on environmental issues.

Another important step in this initial process, if it can be arranged, is for students to get out and see local environmental problems firsthand. A field trip to a stream in need of cleanup is much more

powerful than reading about water pollution. Even if students eventually select a problem that's occurring thousands of miles from their community, the exposure to concerns in their own backyard will be an important learning experience.

2. Create a List of Possibilities

Once the students' search has highlighted a number of potential topics, have them work in groups to develop a list of the most interesting or worthwhile ones. Then have students draft a list of projects to address all or part of each topic.

Environmental topics can be very broad and there are almost always several project possibilities for each topic. For example, water quality in the community might encompass pollution in a local river, lead in the city water system, or leaks in a landfill. Projects might include monitoring the pollution levels in the river over time and presenting data to the city council, conducting an education campaign about lead in the city's drinking supply, or developing a recycling plan to reduce the pressure on a landfill. Have students list the topic they most want to tackle, then they can brainstorm specific projects that might help the situation, listing any additional information they'll need to evaluate each project.

3. Narrow the Choices

Once the groups have selected the issues and projects they are most interested in, they need to evaluate and narrow their choices. For each project listed, the groups need to realistically address what they might accomplish and what problems the project might solve.

Encourage students to discuss the feasibility of each possibility by asking specific questions that help them think about the details of accomplishing certain tasks. Students may want to develop criteria to help them first select a project and then decide how they will determine the most appropriate solution. How much time will the project take? How complex is it? What resources are needed? Whom will they need to talk to?

Sometimes it's difficult for students to decide among local, national, and global projects. Although each will provide learning opportunities, an advantage of a local project is that students will learn more about how their own community works. They'll also be more likely to see real results.

4. Select a Project

By this point, students should have narrowed the list to the top three to five projects. Give them adequate time to research. Then encourage the use of libraries, interviews with experts, surveys, newspaper articles, local TV news, and so on. Invite experts or resource people in to discuss problems, find potential solutions, and help evaluate students' ideas. The more your students know about specific possibilities, the better equipped they'll be to develop a realistic action plan.

As students approach their final decision, have each group present a case for one or more of the projects the group feels strongly about. Then hold a group vote or have a large group discussion to reach consensus. The important thing is to let students have as much say in the decision-making process as possible, choosing a project that they think is both interesting and achievable.

5. Create an Action Plan

Once students have done their research and selected a project, help them get started on their action plan by asking, "What do you hope you'll be able to accomplish by doing this project?" After students share their answers, guide them in developing a goal for the project and specific, concrete objectives that need to be accomplished along the way.

Remind students to keep the goal and objectives in mind as they work to complete a planning sheet that includes the following:

1. What environmental problem or issue will the project address?

2. How would you briefly describe the goal of the project and the strategy to accomplish this goal?

3. What are the specific objectives that will help the group reach its overall goal?

4. What are the approximate starting and ending dates of the project?

5. Did you list the tasks to accomplish to meet each objective? Include a tentative completion date for each task, the names of people responsible, the supplies and equipment needed, any funding needed, and ideas of where to get materials and funding.

6. Did you write down the names of people and organizations that may be able to provide useful information, specific skills, expertise, or other help?

7. Did you list ideas on how to publicize and generate support for the project?

8. Did you describe how your success will be measured?

A large-format task and timeline chart may help the groups keep track of responsibilities and deadlines. As students work on their action plan, guide them toward realistic objectives. One of the most common problems for students is thinking too big. Help them focus and simplify the project by discussing the responses to the questions on their planning sheet and by asking them to really consider hard questions. How will the funds be raised? Can the problem be tackled on a smaller scale?

6. Put the Plan into Action

Students' projects will work best if they keep careful records of what they've done, when they did it, whom they've contacted, etc. They will also need to keep track of who is doing what to make sure crucial tasks are being completed and to avoid duplicating efforts. It's important that students take stock of the project periodically to see if they are on target and to make modifications, if necessary. Remind them that it's acceptable to rethink their goals and objectives and to revise their plan of action in light of new information or unexpected obstacles.

To build support for action projects, publicize any successes and showcase the ways that action learning promotes educational goals and addresses community priorities. There are many ways to let others know what students have done—holding a community awards event, posting successes through social media, getting a reporter from the local newspaper or television station to cover a project, or sending out public service announcements (PSAs). Have students brainstorm ways to publicize their work.

7. Assess, Generalize, Apply, and Celebrate!

Taking time to reflect upon and evaluate an action project helps students understand what they've accomplished and allows them to recognize how their project has facilitated their personal growth. As a project nears completion, guide students in assessing the project itself, as well as their feelings about the experience. Remember to incorporate a celebration of the project's success! It's important for students to evaluate the success of each project and to think about improvements for the next time. It's also important that they look beyond the immediate impact to more long-term, broad-scale gains—skills, knowledge, and attitudes that they can apply to other aspects of their lives.

Ideas for Measuring Success

Assessing Student Knowledge

- Keep a video or photo log of project highlights. After the project is completed, use the video or photo scrapbook as a springboard for discussions in which students share what they learned and their feelings about the experience.

- Collect memorabilia (articles about the project, newspaper photos, students' own photos, planning schedules, and so on) to create an action project scrapbook that students can sign and write comments in.

- Ask students whether they've changed their thinking or behaviors as a result of the project. Have students write essays describing what those changes are and what students think prompted them.

- Have students keep a journal or blog to record feelings about the project, its progress, and its setbacks and to keep notes about working with others. After the project, students share parts of their journals with the group and discuss their perceptions.

- Have students evaluate other members of their group, as well as themselves. Before they do, give students pointers on positive, constructive feedback. Focus the session on specific points, such as contribution to the project, effort, conflict resolution approach, etc.

- Have community members who were involved in the project assess student performances. Educators can develop an assessment form or have students conduct short interviews.

Assessing Project Success

- Have students describe how well they think their project accomplished the objectives they outlined at the start.

- Have students conduct surveys, field studies, or interviews to assess the success of their completed project. What worked? What didn't? Why?

- Evaluate how students planned for ongoing maintenance and sustainability of the project.

- Have community members and others who were involved in the project assess project outcomes.

Using Local Resources

I n the course of conducting activities in Aquatic WILD, educators may find that local resource professionals would be of great assistance. Some topics covered in Aquatic WILD activities address areas in which many educators may not have extensive background experience. Experts from the community can be invited to share with students their special knowledge of wildlife, environmental, or natural resource topics. However, involving such resource people should be done in a manner that uses each expert's time effectively. Preparing in advance is important before inviting experts to speak to classes, sending students to interview them, or taking field trips to special facilities. Here are a few basic suggestions that may help you with this process.

Have students explore the question of who might have special knowledge to contribute to a particular activity or topic.

One of the important skills that students can learn is "How can we find out?" Part of this process may involve asking someone who knows more than we do. Students can conduct web searches for potential experts. Where could they find someone who knows about local water quality? At the local city health department? In the state water commission? In the Office of the Environment? Are any citizen groups interested in the topic? Do they publish any resource materials? Do local colleges and universities have people on their faculties with expertise in this area? Develop a list of "leads," possible avenues to explore in order to identify the experts on a topic in your area.

To some extent, everyone in a community is an expert on something. Perhaps students will want to know what something in the community looked like 20 or 40 years ago. If any public opinion surveys or other forms of interviews in public places are planned, students should be supervised by adults. People who might be concerned (businessowners, mall managers, etc.) need to be asked in advance and informed about the project and its purposes. If people do not want to be interviewed, thank them politely for their time. An in-class trial run or

practice session using role-playing techniques can be an effective preparation for actually conducting interviews. Students act the parts of interviewers and subjects while other students serve as constructive critics of their performances.

Develop a plan for approaching the agencies or organizations where "experts" may be found.

Once students have decided where experts might be found, they will need to decide how to approach those institutions in order to actually acquire the names of people who might be speakers, lead field trips, or be interviewed. Some governmental agencies, for example, have public affairs departments, and those departments might be the best place to start. Some public libraries have information librarians who specialize in this sort of task and know whom to approach. Some universities and colleges publish speaker lists that include topics faculty members are willing to speak about. Local businesses may also have people who are experts. Web searches of organizations and governmental agencies may result in staff biographies with e-mail addresses included. Sometimes you may be referred directly to the resource person. In this case, consider the next suggestion before proceeding with your project.

Once you have identified potential resource people, develop a strategy for determining whether they would be willing to act as experts for your class and, if so, how they would like to work.

As a teacher, it is recommended that you speak with resource people before inviting them to your class. Sometimes, an expert might recommend a colleague who would be better suited to speak on the topic of the project. Some experts are not comfortable speaking to large groups of people, especially young students. They may want to talk to a small group, or even one student, who can take the information back to the rest of the class. Some might not be able to get away from their work to visit your school during the day. In that case, consider whether a field visit would be possible for the class. The expert may suggest other sources of information, such as books, magazines, websites, or films.

If the resource person is willing to work directly with students, find out what advance preparation is needed and in what type of setting the expert would like to work. Would he or she like written questions from the class beforehand? Would he or she be willing to be recorded or videotaped or written up in the school or local newspaper? If the expert is coming to your school, what sort of special equipment will be needed (digital projector, etc.)? If the class will take a field trip to visit the resource person at his or her office, laboratory, business, or home, what should the class know in advance? Are any special clothes required? How long will the visit be? Where should the group report to start the visit? Attention to this kind of detail can make the trip more productive, effective, and appropriate.

Decide who will act as interviewers, recorders, moderators, and hosts. Brief the class about the roles each of these students will serve, and the responsibilities and expectations for behavior of all students.

A letter or e-mail to the resource person in advance will help to verify the details of their visit. When a guest arrives at the school, a student can meet and escort the visitor to the classroom. If student interviewers visit the resource person, they should be encouraged to send a letter of introduction prior to their visit, they should be briefed about how to interview the person, and they should operate in pairs or with adult supervision for personal safety. Students who leave the school grounds to interview people should see themselves as representing the school and your class in particular. They will want to leave a good impression. Whether guests come to school or students visit resource people in the community, the importance of courteous, considerate, and responsible behavior should be stressed.

Do advance work on the topic.

Resource people usually do not mind sharing their time with people they think can use it well. If you and the class have done some homework on the subject, you are more likely to ask intelligent

questions and be able to understand what the expert has to offer. This advanced preparation is strongly recommended in any circumstance.

Maintain respect and professionalism during an interview.

Students should be reminded to conduct themselves in a professional manner and to keep an interview focused on the purposes of the research. Rather than the students using the interview to expound their own views on the topic, their task is to learn the subject's views and respect those views even if they differ from their own. If any form of recording is desired, ask for permission in advance, and advise them how the information will be used. Before using a quote with the interviewee's name cited, give them the opportunity to see the written proceedings of the interview, review any excerpts to be used, or review the recording before any class or public use of the information takes place.

Remember that a little consideration and hospitality go a long way.

Resource professionals can become lifelong supporters of your school and its programs or lifelong critics. Which will happen depends not only on suggestions offered here, but also on courtesies such as thanking them at the time of their visit (or your visit) and following up with a letter. If the class uses the information from the resource person in some special way, send a picture or samples of the work to the resource person to show what was accomplished. If the local media produce an article, send along a copy to your expert. Do not expect or demand large amounts of additional time from the experts, but do let them know that their expertise was appreciated as well as how it was used.

Field Ethics

Exploring in nature exposes students to a variety of natural objects. Often students desire to take an object with them if it strikes them as beautiful, interesting, or unique. Yet removing objects from natural settings—either temporarily or permanently—may cause an unnatural impact on the environment, especially when multiplied by many others who wish to collect similar objects. Individual educators and their students must decide on the appropriateness of collecting objects from natural settings, based on thoughtful decision making, caution, and respect for the living environment. In most cases, Project WILD and Aquatic WILD urge no collecting at all and recommend instead simply leaving the natural environment as it is found, with as little impact as possible from students in the process of learning.

There are times, however, when it may seem appropriate and so instructionally powerful that some limited forms of collecting are desired. Collecting for instructional purposes can take a variety of forms. Sometimes it involves going outside and picking up fallen leaves on an autumn day or picking up shells at the seashore. Collection can also involve using a net and examining organisms found in pond water, perhaps keeping the organisms temporarily in a classroom.

If any collecting is to be done, it should begin with a respect for the environment. Educators should determine in advance what laws or restrictions may apply and closely adhere to these. Then, if collecting is permitted, involve students in deciding what, if anything, to collect and how much collecting is appropriate. By involving students in the process of deciding whether and what to collect, they are more likely to develop an ethic that considers the impact on ecosystems and individual species. This kind of thoughtful decision making about the consequences of our individual and collective actions is an important, lifelong skill.

The following list of field ethics was developed by a class of sixth graders in Illinois:

1. We should obey all laws protecting plants and animals.

2. We should ask the owner before we take anything.

3. We should collect an animal only if we know we can keep it alive long enough to learn from it.

4. We should not collect things that will hurt us.

5. We should collect something only if there are a lot of them in that place.

6. We should collect something only if we can learn something very important about it.

Obviously, any collecting for instructional purposes should alter the environment as little as possible and should not significantly damage wildlife or their habitat. Where possible, anything collected from the environment for instructional purposes should be returned to its original location at the conclusion of the activity.

Beyond the collecting issue, students must understand that humans can affect living things in other ways. For example, just by walking over fragile areas outdoors or observing animals under certain conditions, we can destroy or disturb organisms. Walking on rocks can remove new soil and crush mosses and lichens if they are present. Thoughtful decision-making and responsible behavior are not just an outcome or goal of Project WILD and Aquatic WILD, but a path to developing a lifelong conservation ethic.

Animals in the Classroom

The following is a portion of the NSTA Position Statement on "Responsible Use of Live Animals and Dissection in the Science Classroom." Please see the NSTA website www.nsta.org/about/positions.aspx to view the entire statement, which includes a section on dissection that is not represented below. Note that digital, interactive dissection software is now commercially available online.

NSTA supports the decision of science teachers and their school or school district to integrate live animals and dissection in the K–12 classroom. Student interaction with organisms is one of the most effective methods of achieving many of the goals outlined in the National Science Education Standards (NSES). To this end, NSTA encourages educators and school officials to make informed decisions about the integration of animals in the science curriculum. NSTA opposes regulations or legislation that would eliminate an educator's decision-making role regarding dissection or would deny students the opportunity to learn through actual animal dissection.

NSTA encourages districts to ensure that animals are properly cared for and treated humanely, responsibly, and ethically. Ultimately, decisions to incorporate organisms in the classroom should balance the ethical and responsible care of animals with their educational value.

While this position statement is primarily focused on vertebrate animals, NSTA recognizes the importance of following similar ethical practices for all living organisms.

Including Live Animals in the Classroom

NSTA supports including live animals as part of instruction in the K–12 science classroom because observing and working with animals firsthand can spark students' interest in science as well as a general respect for life while reinforcing key concepts as outlined in the NSES.

NSTA recommends that teachers

■ Educate themselves about the safe and responsible use of animals in the classroom. Teachers should seek information from reputable sources and familiarize themselves with laws and regulations in their state.

■ Become knowledgeable about the acquisition and care of animals appropriate to the species under study so that both students and the animals stay safe and healthy during all activities.

■ Follow local, state, and national laws, policies, and regulations when live organisms, particularly native species, are included in the classroom.

■ Integrate live animals into the science program based on sound curriculum and pedagogical decisions.

■ Develop activities that promote observation and comparison skills that instill in students an appreciation for the value of life and the importance of caring for animals responsibly.

■ Instruct students on safety precautions for handling live organisms and establish a plan for addressing such issues as allergies and fear of animals.

■ Develop and implement a plan for future care or disposition of animals at the conclusion of the study as well as during school breaks and summer vacations.

■ Espouse the importance of not conducting experimental procedures on animals if such procedures are likely to cause pain, induce nutritional deficiencies, or expose animals to parasites, hazardous/toxic chemicals, or radiation.

■ Shelter animals when the classroom is being cleaned with chemical cleaners, sprayed with pesticides, and during other times when potentially harmful chemicals are being used.*

■ Refrain from releasing animals into a nonindigenous environment.

Adopted by the NSTA Board of Directors June 2005

*Project WILD encourages the use of non-toxic, "green" cleansers.
Reference: National Research Council. (1996). National Science Education Standards. Washington, DC: National Academy Press.

The Benefits of a Classroom Aquarium

Filters, hoses, leaks, sand, pH, algae, air stones? It is easy to understand why maintaining a classroom aquarium can seem daunting. Buying supplies, selecting the appropriate ecosystem and organisms, and cultivating a mini habitat may easily turn an educator away. However, there are excellent reasons why integrating an aquarium into the classroom is worth the investment. While many options exist for aquariums, it is recommended to begin with a 10 to 30 gallon freshwater tank that balances the ability to accommodate a variety of species with a manageable level of maintenance. With the right planning, elevating a goldfish bowl into an operating aquatic ecosystem opens the door for many planned and unplanned teachable moments.

Ethics and Responsibility

Students are never too young to learn proper care and responsibility through pet ownership. While an aquarium may not compare to a family dog, integrating one into classroom responsibilities offers a chance to understand the commitment associated with caring for another organism. The feeding and cleaning may seem tedious to the educator, but many students take pride in the opportunity to care for and interact with the classroom pets. Aquarium tasks can be used as positive reinforcement for classroom management. Inviting students to fully participate in the set up and operations will promote lasting stewardship and responsibility in addition to learning.

Ecology

A surprising amount of ecology and life science concepts can be learned from an aquarium. At the simplest level, students can understand that an aquarium is a system with inputs and outputs. Most aquariums are not closed systems: owners add food, chemicals, and other organisms to properly balance the system so organisms can survive. Identify aquatic food chains in the tank and what it would take for the system/habitat to be completely self-sufficient. What do components such as the light, filter, and air pump simulate in a real aquatic habitat? If it is set up appropriately, an aquarium can house frogs, fish, or  invertebrates throughout its life cycle. Instead of buying dozens of butterflies or tadpoles for a one time study of life cycles, incorporating the aquarium into the lesson may be more sustainable.

Scientific Inquiry

Unexpected problems occur for even the most dedicated aquaria enthusiasts. However, in a classroom, the ups and downs of aquarium ownership provide a foundation for scientific inquiry. If a fish is found floating upside down one morning, while disheartening, the first thing students will ask is "Why?" Practice the scientific method to discover why new snails are popping up, algae are suddenly more prevalent than last week, or a favorite fish seems under the weather. When a problem occurs in the system, students will begin to understand how critical it is for an ecosystem to be in balance.

Scientists often keep journals to sketch and record observations that may later develop into a hypothesis. Utilize the aquarium during quiet time after a test or design a formal activity to record changes, observations, sketches, and questions.

Chemistry

An important and often challenging part of maintaining an aquarium is providing healthy water. Temperature, carbon dioxide, pH, and dissolved oxygen all need to be balanced to support life in the habitat. Too little oxygen can kill fish, while too many nutrients can cause thick algae growth and limit visibility. Assign small groups to research and control different chemical components of the aquarium. Practice titrations and other water quality methods with your students. A large part of successful learning is motivation, and a healthy classroom aquarium is an excellent motivator!

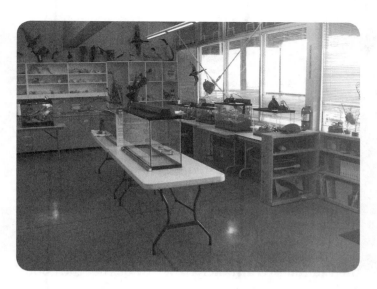

Special Needs

Many classroom pets can offer a feel of "hominess" or comfort to students. Aquariums are colorful and dynamic habitats with a variety of living organisms to observe. Special needs students, especially those with ADD, autism, or emotional disorders, may benefit from visiting the aquarium to take a break, relieve stress, or watch the animals to distract from a problem. Use the aquarium to divert a student away from a stressful situation to feed the fish or perform other tasks that may diffuse tension.

Whatever the reason (there are many more!), keeping an aquarium can be an enjoyable challenge for both you and your students. It may also inspire other educators to begin one too! Visit ***www.projectwild.org/aquatic*** to find resources on building and maintaining classroom aquaria.

Sustainable Seafood

Not all seafood dishes are created equal. Some turn into delicacies from flourishing species that are harvested sustainably, while others tax species already on the decline. Some seafood may be contaminated by pollutants such as mercury that are hazardous to human health.

Students can learn to effect social change through their families' consumer power by buying the good and boycotting the bad. Seafood Watch, a program of Monterey Bay Aquarium, makes the selection easy by providing lists of best choices (green), good alternatives (yellow), and items to avoid (red) for consumers living in different regions of the United States. Such recommendations come in a pocket-guide format, meant to be readily available when one contemplates a restaurant menu or supermarket display. Note that the answer to whether a type of seafood should be consumed is sometimes, "It depends." For instance, shrimp species caught or farmed in North America are mostly best choices or good alternatives, but those imported are to be avoided due to concerns related to water pollution and the destruction of mangrove forests by shrimp farms. So when in doubt, ask about the item's origin.

Distribute the pocket guides to students and encourage them to follow the recommendations before choosing their seafood. Collect menus to evaluate a local restaurant's ocean friendliness. Plan a field trip to a seafood market and conduct interviews on where each product comes from and whether it is farmed or wild caught. Have students

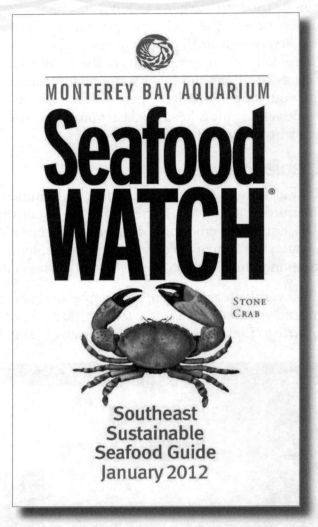

research the survival status of selected species and educate each other on why it is listed under a certain category. Students can also find sustainable seafood recipes to design a menu for a fictional restaurant.

In time, innovations may turn a poorly-managed fishing or aquaculture practice into a sustainable one that meets human demand and does not deplete resources. Make sure to check for updates from Seafood Watch and always follow the newest pocket guide.

Visit *www.montereyaquarium.org/seafoodwatch* for resources on sustainable seafood. To download the consumer pocket guide, click on "What Consumers Can Do."

© Council for Environmental Education (CEE)

Agencies and Organizations

The following federal agencies and organizations are involved in wildlife education. Please be advised that this is not a complete listing. State wildlife agencies may be contacted directly in each state. Project WILD and Aquatic WILD encourage educators and students to contact a range of organizations so they can make informed decisions. We recommend requests be as specific as possible and mailed or e-mailed on behalf of a class or group rather than each individual student.

Federal Agencies

Bureau of Land Management
Office of Public Affairs
1849 C Street, NW, Room 406-LS
Washington, DC 20240
(202) 452-5125
www.blm.gov

United States Department of Agriculture
Cooperative State Research, Education,
    and Extension Service
1400 Independence Avenue, SW, Stop 2201
Washington, DC 20250-2201
(202) 720-4423
www.nmfs.noaa.gov

National Marine Fisheries Service
NOAA Fisheries
1315 East-West Highway, 9th Floor
Silver Spring, MD 20910
(301) 713-2379
www.csrees.usda.gov

National Oceanic and Atmospheric
    Administration
1401 Constitution Avenue, NW, Room 5128
Washington, DC 20230
www.noaa.gov

National Park Service
1849 C Street, NW
Washington, DC 20240
(202) 208-6843
www.nps.gov

Natural Resources Conservation Service
U. S. Department of Agriculture
1400 Independence Avenue, SW, Room 5105-A
Washington, DC 20250
(202) 720-7246
www.nrcs.usda.gov

U.S. Army Corps of Engineers
Public Affairs
441 G Street, NW
Washington, DC 20314
(202) 761-0011
www.usace.army.mil

U.S. Department of Agriculture
1400 Independence Avenue, SW
Washington, DC 20250
(202) 720-4623
www.usda.gov

U.S. Environmental Protection Agency
Environmental Education Division
1200 Pennsylvania Avenue, NW
Washington, DC 20460
(202) 272-0167
www.epa.gov

U.S. Fish and Wildlife Service
Department of Interior
1849 C Street, NW
Washington, DC 20240
(800) 344-WILD
www.fws.gov

**U.S. Fish and Wildlife Service
Reference Center**
5430 Grosvenor Lane, Suite 110
Bethesda, MD 20814
(301) 492-6403
http://federalaid.fws.gov

USDA Forest Service
Natural Resource Conservation Education
1400 Independence Ave., SW
Washington, DC 20250-0003
(202) 205-8333
www.fs.fed.us

Regional Offices
U.S. Environmental Protection Agency

**U.S. EPA Region 1
Environmental Education Program**
1 Congress Street, Suite 1100
Boston, MA 02114-2023
(617) 918-1111
www.epa.gov/region1/

**U.S. EPA Region 2
Environmental Education Program**
290 Broadway
New York, NY 10007-1866
(212) 637-3660
www.epa.gov/region2/

**U.S. EPA Region 3
Environmental Education Program**
1650 Arch Street (3CG00)
Philadelphia, PA 19103-2029
(215) 814-5000
www.epa.gov/region3/

**U.S. EPA Region 4
Environmental Education Program**
Atlanta Federal Center
61 Forsyth Street, SW
Atlanta, GA 30303-8960
(404) 562-9900
www.epa.gov/region4/

**U.S. EPA Region 5
Environmental Education Program**
77 West Jackson Boulevard (PI-19J)
Chicago, IL 60604-3507
(312) 353-2000
www.epa.gov/region5/

**U.S. EPA Region 6
Environmental Education Program**
1445 Ross Avenue (6XA), Suite 1200
Dallas, TX 75202-2733
(214) 665-6444
www.epa.gov/region6/

**U.S. EPA Region 7
Environmental Education Program**
901 North Fifth Street
Kansas City, KS 66101
(913) 551-7003
www.epa.gov/region7/

**U.S. EPA Region 8
Environmental Education Program**
1595 Wynkoop Street
Denver, CO 80202-1129
(303) 312-6312
www.epa.gov/region8/

**U.S. EPA Region 9
Environmental Education Program**
75 Hawthorne Street
San Francisco, CA 94105
(415) 947-8000
www.epa.gov/region9/

**U.S. EPA Region 10
Environmental Education Program**
1200 Sixth Avenue, Suite 900
Seattle, WA 98101
(206) 553-1200
www.epa.gov/region10/

Organizations

**American Cetacean Society
National Headquarters**
P.O. Box 1391
San Pedro, CA 90733-1391
(310) 548-6279
www.acsonline.org

American Fisheries Society
5410 Grosvenor Lane
Bethesda, MD 20814-2199
(301) 897-8616
www.fisheries.org

American Rivers
1101 14th Street NW, Suite 1400
Washington, DC 20005
(202) 347-7550
www.americanrivers.org

American Sportfishing Association & Future Fisherman Foundation
225 Reinekers Lane, Suite 420
Alexandria, VA 22314
(703) 519-9691
www.asafishing.org

Animal Welfare Institute
P.O. Box 3650
Washington, DC 20027
(703) 836-4300
www.awionline.org

Aquatic Resources Education Association
www.areanet.org

Association of Fish and Wildlife Agencies
444 North Capitol Street, NW, Suite 725
Washington, DC 20001
(202) 624-7890
www.fishwildlife.org

California Coastal Commission
45 Fremont Street, Suite 200
San Francisco, CA 94105-2219
(415) 904-5200
http://www.coastal.ca.gov/

Center for Marine Conservation
1725 DeSales St., NW, Suite 600
Washington, DC 20036
(202) 429-5609
www.cmc-ocean.org

Cetacean Society International
P.O. Box 953
Georgetown, CT 06829
(203) 770-8615
csiwhalesalive.org

Chesapeake Bay Foundation
Philip Merrill Environmental Center
6 Herndon Avenue
Annapolis, MD 21403
(410) 268-8816
http://www.cbf.org/

Conservation and Environmental Education Resource Network
www.resourcecommons.org

Cousteau Society
710 Settlers Landing Road
Hampton, VA 23669
(757) 722-9300
www.cousteau.org

Defenders of Wildlife
1130 17th Street, NW
Washington, DC 20036
(800) 385-9712
www.defenders.org

Ducks Unlimited
1 Waterfowl Way
Memphis, TN 38120
(800) 45-DUCKS
www.ducks.org

Earth Island Institute
300 Broadway, Suite 28 3
San Francisco, CA 94133
(415) 788-3666
www.earthisland.org

Fund for Animals
200 W. 57th Street, Suite 705
New York, NY 10019
(888) 405-FUND
www.fundforanimals.org

Greenpeace
702 H Street, NW
Washington, DC 20001
(202) 462-1177
www.greenpeace.org/usa

The Groundwater Foundation
P.O. Box 22558
Lincoln, NE 68542-2558
(402) 434-2740
www.groundwater.org

International Whaling Commission
The Red House
135 Station Road
Impington, Cambridge,
Cambridgeshire CB4 9NP, UK
England +44(0)1223-233971
www.iwcoffice.org

Izaak Walton League of America
707 Conservation Lane
Gaithersburg, MD 20878-2983
(301) 548-0150
www.iwla.org

Marine Stewardship Council
2110 N. Pacific Street, Suite 102
Seattle, WA 98103
(206) 691-0188
www.msc.org

Monterey Bay Aquarium
886 Cannery Row
Monterey, CA 93940
(831) 648-4800
www.montereybayaquarium.org

**National Association for Humane and
   Environmental Education**
Humane Society of the United States
2100 L Street, NW
Washington, DC 20037
(202) 452-1100
www.hsus.org

National Association of Conservation Districts
509 Capitol Ct., NE
Washington, DC 20002
(202) 547-6223
www.nacdnet.org

National Audubon Society
225 Varick Street, 7th Floor
New York, NY 10014
(212) 979-3000
www.audubon.org

National Fish and Wildlife Foundation
1133 Fifteenth Street, N.W., Suite 1100
Washington, DC 20005
(202) 857-0166
www.nfwf.org

National Fishing in Schools Program
3601 Calvert, Suite 26
Lincoln, NE 68506
(970) 708-9373
www.schoolofflyfishing.com

National Geographic Society
1145 17th Street Northwest
Washington, DC 20036
(202) 857-7000
www.nationalgeographic.com

National Marine Educators Association
P.O. Box 1470
Ocean Springs, MS 39566-1470
(228) 896-9182
http://www.marine-ed.org

National Wildlife Federation
11100 Wildlife Center Drive
Reston, VA 20190-5362
(800) 822-9919
www.nwf.org

The Nature Conservancy
4245 North Fairfax Drive, Suite 100
Arlington, VA 22203
(703) 841-5300
www.nature.org

New England Aquarium
1 Central Wharf
Boston, MA 02110
(617) 973-5200
www.neaq.org

**North American Association for
   Environmental Education**
2000 P Street NW, Suite 540
Washington, DC 20036
(202) 419-0412
www.naaee.net

The Ocean Conservancy
1300 19th Street, NW 8th Floor
Washington, DC 20036
(800) 519-1541
www.oceanconservancy.org

Oceana
1350 Connecticut Ave., NW, 5th Floor
Washington, D.C. 20036
(202) 833-3900
www.oceana.org

Provincetown Center for Coastal Studies
115 Bradford Street
Provincetown, MA 02657
(508) 487-3622, ext. 101
www.coastalstudies.org

Recreational Boating and Fishing Foundation
500 Montgomery Street
Alexandria, VA 22314
(703) 519-0013
www.takemefishing.org

Save The Bay, Inc.
100 Save The Bay Dr.
Providence, RI 02905
(401) 324-6020
https://www.savebay.org/

Sierra Club
85 Second Street, 2nd Floor
San Francisco, CA 94105
(415) 977-5500
www.sierraclub.org

Trout in the Classroom
Trout Unlimited National Office
1300 North 17th St., Suite 500
Arlington, VA 22209
(703) 522-0200
www.troutintheclassroom.org

Whale Center of New England
P.O. Box 159
Gloucester, MA 01931-0159
(978) 281-6351
www.whalecenter.org

Wildlife Management Institute
1146 19th Street, NW, Suite 700
Washington, DC 20036
(202) 371-1808
www.wildlifemanagementinstitute.org

The Wildlife Society
5410 Grosvenor Lane, Suite 200
Bethesda, MD 20814-2144
(301) 897-9770
joomla.wildlife.org

World Wildlife Fund
1250 24th Street, NW
P.O. Box 97180
Washington, DC 20090-7180
(202) 293-4800
www.worldwildlife.org

Climate Change Education

Scientists, federal agencies, educators, and even wild plant and animal species, are all indicating Earth's climate is changing. Climate change indicates major changes in temperature, rainfall, snow, or wind lasting for decades or longer. Climate change is a result of both natural and human activities.

Global warming is an average increase in temperature near the Earth's surface and lowest layer of the atmosphere. Global warming is a result of the greenhouse effect, a natural occurrence in which heat from the sun is trapped in the atmosphere by clouds and greenhouse gases such as carbon dioxide. Without the greenhouse effect, Earth would be too cold to support the life we know today. However, scientists now believe that humans are accelerating the rate of global warming by releasing excess amounts of greenhouse gasses into the atmosphere. Global temperature data shows an average warming of 1.3°F over the past century. In this regard, global warming can be considered part of climate change along with precipitation, sea levels, and other indicators.

According to The National Oceanic and Atmospheric Administration (NOAA), within the past 30 years the rate of warming across the globe has been approximately three times greater than the rate over the last 100 years. Intergovernmental Panel on Climate Change (IPCC) scientists believe that there is a greater than "90% chance that most of the warming since the 1950s can be attributed to an increase in greenhouse gas emissions from human activities." The EPA estimates that if humans continue to emit greenhouse gases at or above the current pace the global temperatures will increase 3 to 7°F by the year 2100. While this may sound insignificant, this rate is larger and faster than any climate change over the last 10,000 years. This accelerated increase allows little time for plants and animals to adapt to the new conditions, especially for already threatened or endangered species.

Climate change impacts the amount and frequency of precipitation, causing an increase in drought conditions in some regions while inducing excessive storm activity in other locations, increasing the likelihood of floods. The prairie pothole region of the Northern Plains is a critical wetland breeding habitat for countless species of ducks, especially Canvasbacks. Droughts in the prairie potholes would force waterfowl to either move to a lower quality habitat or remain with fewer resources for successful offspring. Both of these scenarios would result in reduced nesting success.

Climate change can increase both the temperature and acidity of aquatic habitats. Rising acidity recently documented in the oceans is associated with increased levels of carbon dioxide dissolved in the water. Ocean acidity creates a problem for corals, the primary protection for Earth's coastlines. In Appalachian streams, recent studies have documented the correlation between increasing water temperatures and decreases in Brook Trout populations, a native fish which requires cold water to live and spawn.

Students can play a role in reducing greenhouse gases by practicing sustainable behaviors such as using alternative or mass transportation, lessening electricity needs, and reducing their waste. Service-learning experiences provide opportunities to empower students. Habitat improvement projects, public education campaigns, and waste reduction projects all help to further students' understanding. As citizen scientists, students can participate in meaningful research that documents the effects of climate change through the study of phenology (recurring plant and animal life cycle stages, especially their timing and relationships with weather and climate).

Across the world, classroom programs are available that invite individuals to participate in meaningful research by recording the everyday sightings of spawning fish, arriving migrants, or hatching turtles to create a baseline or add to existing databases that record the timing and occurrence of these trends. Through programs such as Journey North, students have confirmed scientists' hypotheses that birds are migrating north earlier in the spring; cherry blossoms in Washington, D.C. are blooming an average of six days earlier than 30 years ago, and species overall are shifting their geographic ranges at a rate of 11 miles north every decade. Researchers have been able to connect that across all genera of animal life, species are moving farther and faster in areas of the greatest temperature increases.

The Center for Essential Science has developed SPECIES (Students Predicting the Effects of Climate In Ecological Systems), a student resource which offers an 8- to 12-week online curriculum that focuses on climate change and climate change impacts. Likewise, the United States Global Change Research Program, a consortium of federal agencies, has created a comprehensive climate change website including "Climate Change, Wildlife, and Wildlands: A Toolkit for Formal and Informal Educators," complete with DVD accompaniment, activities/lesson plans, and an educator supportive background guide. The Environmental Protection Agency offers sound background information for the student and educator through its interactive climate change website. The National Wildlife Federation supports and rewards schools for reducing their carbon footprint through its Eco-Schools USA program. The NWF website also offers students over 15 cases detailing habitat areas and animal species already struggling with the effects of climate change. For links to these resources and more, visit *www.projectwild.org/aquatic*.

The *Aquatic WILD K–12 Curriculum and Activity Guide* provides a variety of experiences that lend themselves to discussions regarding critical trends and current topics in the environment. Natural resource agencies worldwide are currently investigating new ways in which they will need to adapt their management and conservation efforts in response to our changing climate. Aquatic WILD encourages students to become part of this discussion through classroom research and field experiences that allow students to formulate questions, test hypotheses, and evaluate conclusions.

Sources:

Cherry, Lynne. *How We Know What We Know About Our Changing Climate: Scientists and Kids Explore Global Warming.* Dawn Publications, 2008.

"Frequently Asked Questions About Global Warming and Climate Change: Back to Basics." Environmental Protection Agency, April 2009. *http://www.epa.gov/climatechange*

"Warming Planet Pushing Species Habitats Quicker Than Expected." LiveScience, August 2011. *http://www.livescience.com/15640-species-shifting-climate-change.html*

"Climate Change, Wildlife, and Wildlands: A Toolkit For Formal and Informal Educators." United States Global Change Research Program, June 2009. *http://globalchange.gov/resources/educators/toolkit*

"Summary of Key Findings." University of Michigan SPECIES Project. *http://sitemaker.umich.edu/essentialscience/files/ci_summary.pdf*

The Ecosystem Concept and Project WILD

*T*he *Project WILD K–12 Curriculum and Activity Guide* and *Aquatic WILD K–12 Curriculum and Activity Guide* are designed to invite students of all ages to ask questions about how ecosystems work. To address these questions, educators need not be professional ecologists nor have extensive backgrounds in biology or wildlife management. This appendix serves as a reference to help educators develop a few simple and powerful ecological concepts with students.

The Ecosystem

*E*cosystem combines two words: ecology and system. "Eco" comes from the Greek word "household" and can be thought of as the household of nature. A system is any group of parts that work together as a unit. Ecology regards a system as a set of living and nonliving parts that interact over time. Ecologists have offered a number of definitions of this concept. A question that often arises is the size and scope of an ecosystem. Some have seen pictures of Earth from space and heard the entire planet referred to as an ecosystem. This ecosystem is called the "global ecosystem" or "biosphere." Essentially, there is no closed natural ecosystem, even the biosphere, but scientists often create boundaries to study relationships between a set number of living and nonliving things.

The term ecosystem helps to categorize different sections of the natural world and identify differences in how each system operates. The redwood forests in California and the bottom of the Atlantic Ocean both have an energy source, but one uses the sun while the other uses hydrogen sulfide from thermal vents. We can draw an imaginary line around a section of the larger world, decide to treat its elements separately from the rest, and call it an ecosystem. When describing how organisms in the system behave, interact, grow, adapt; what they eat; how long they live; what happens to them when they die; and what they require to stay healthy or to reproduce, we are studying how the household system operates—and thinking SYSTEM-atically.

Connections between elements of a system are often subtle and hard to see or understand. Quite frequently, this is because they take a long time to happen. The life cycle of certain tree species in North American west coast forest ecosystems is 300 to 500 years. In an average human life span, we might see little change in those forests. But the life cycle of an ecosystem in a pond that dries up during the summer and is frozen in the winter might be 12 months. Life cycles in a jar of microbes might be measured in hours.

An ecosystem represents a concept rather than a place or set of things. When students set up a wide-mouth jar in the classroom with pond water, a few small animals, and some plants, then cap the bottle tightly, they have established an ecosystem. The jar contains biotic and abiotic elements. The biotic elements are all the living things in the jar: plants, snails, microbes, and so forth. The abiotic elements are the nonliving elements: air, water, rocks, and bottom debris. Both the biotic and abiotic elements will interact with each other in the ecosystem. The animals might use plants for food or shelter, while the plants recycle nutrients from their waste to grow.

This little ecosystem in a jar will quickly turn into a gooey mess unless placed under indirect sunlight. The system in the bottle is not going to operate without a source of energy, namely light energy. If there are not too many animals, or consumers, in the jar, the bottle can be sealed, even "air tight", and may operate as a self-contained environment for many years. It will slowly change over time as some organisms will die and decompose. Slow hatching eggs or spores may develop and germinate. The acidity of the water may change. The color of the water may change and absorb more heat and light. The system will undergo a life cycle of its own, slowly aging and changing. Throughout all these fluctuations the key to any self-sustaining, successful ecosystem is a balance of inputs and outputs. When the term ecosystem is used in Project WILD and Aquatic WILD, it describes a system in which there are living and nonliving components, and a primary source of energy interacting over time within a defined area. In most systems, the primary source of energy is the sun. We could establish organisms in various environments, but unless there was an appropriate balance or set of relations among them, the system would quickly or slowly go into crisis and die. Many people have seen examples of changed systems when they have cleaned out refrigerators or discovered last month's uneaten lunch in the bottom of their lockers.

One ecosystem often studied in school is a pond. "Pond" is not a word typically used with a precise definition and is similar to the word ecosystem in many ways. In some parts of the world, a pond is a small body of freshwater. In other places, a pond can be a lake quite reasonable in size and depth or a small bay with narrow entrances to the ocean. Here we use the term to refer to small, shallow, freshwater waterbody.

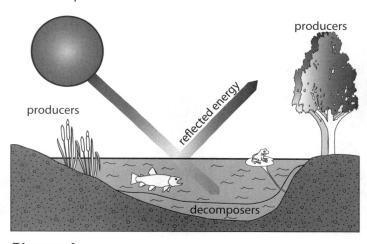

Diagram A

Diagram A shows a simple illustration of a pond and includes the basic elements of most ecosystems. The sun is the energy source and acts as the "engine" which drives the rest of the system. The biotic components are the green plants and animals. The green plants are direct "sun catchers." The wonderful process of capturing the sun's energy is known as photosynthesis—photo (light) and synthesis (assembly, connection, manufacture). The energy of the sun is stored in the form of chemical bonds in molecules. During photosynthesis, plant cells store solar energy by assembling complex molecules with six carbon atoms from building blocks of CO_2 and water. Animals are not capable of photosynthesis but rely on green plants to catch solar energy and to use it to assemble food materials. Known as producers,

green plants are the food factories in natural systems. Equally important, plants also provide oxygen as a byproduct of this process.

Not all animals eat plants directly. Those that eat plants and only plants are known as primary consumers, or herbivores. They are one step away from producers. Animals that eat other animals are two steps away from the sun, so they are often called secondary consumers, or carnivores (meat eaters). The sequence becomes more complex if we add animals that prey on other meat eaters: tertiary consumers (three steps away from the sun). **Diagram B** illustrates some of those relationships.

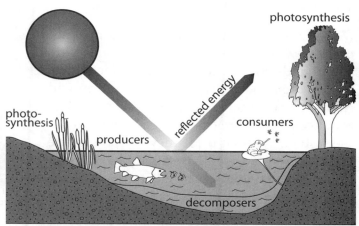

Diagram B

A diagram linking some of these organisms as producers and consumers is illustrated as a food chain. **Diagram C** shows a simple food chain that might be associated with a pond. In this diagram, the eagle eats the fish that eats the frog. In turn, the frog eats spiders and the spiders eat insects.

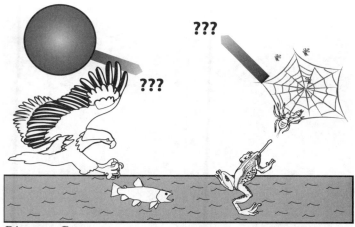

Diagram C

This food chain is not an ecosystem as important elements are missing. There are no direct producers capable of photosynthesis. The eagle cannot capture energy from the sun directly. It is at least three steps away from the sun's input of energy. In its tadpole stage, the frog eats plant material. The insect might feed on plant nectar, or its larval stage might eat leaves. The food chain describes only a portion of the connections in a pond ecosystem. If the diagram were more complex, then a food web would be produced. Food webs balance inputs and outputs in the ecosystem, allowing it to exist for long periods of time. It would include all the producers and consumers in the pond and introduce a new set of special consumers, called decomposers.

Decomposers are the garbage collectors of nature, breaking down a variety of materials into simpler compounds. Similar to consumers, decomposers receive their energy from other organisms and cannot perform photosynthesis. Decomposers produce CO_2 and release needed elements into the system. Without these recyclers, the entire ecosystem would gradually run down. Imagine a forest in which none of the fallen trees, branches, dead animals, and leaves ever rotted. Soon it would be impossible to move through the debris and nothing new could grow. Without decomposition in ponds, the accumulation of materials falling to the bottom would result in the pond's rapidly becoming so shallow that it would no longer hold water.

As a general principle, students should understand that both energy and materials constantly circulate in all ecosystems. Plants, through the process of photosynthesis, are the major point of entry of

the sun's energy into the natural system. However, that energy works in other ways throughout the ecosystem. Solar heating of the atmosphere and oceans produces winds and great patterns of air circulation in the atmosphere. The absorption of solar energy in the oceans is expressed in the flow of ocean currents. In a way, the entire planet is a great solar-powered engine. All materials cycle—some slowly, some quickly.

Carbon dioxide, for example, is a byproduct of respiration in plant and animal cells. The carbon of CO_2 is used by green plants in photosynthesis and becomes the building block of many biological molecules, including sugars, proteins, and fats. Once assembled into these materials, the carbon can be taken in by animals when they eat food materials—whether from plant or animal sources. Food is both a source of energy and a source of raw materials for biological construction.

Diagram D

The carbon cycle is one of the great cycles in natural systems. Nitrogen, water, and elements such as phosphorus are also involved in cycles. The passage of materials along food chains and through cycles is responsible for the concentration of chemicals such as pesticides. Small amounts of pesticide molecules passed along a food chain may accumulate when they reach the top consumer, whether that be an eagle or a human. Sometimes animals like the Humpback Whale "shorten" the steps between the input of solar energy and themselves by feeding directly on millions of small animals and plants that are closer to the source of solar energy. (See **Diagram D**.)

An ecosystem, therefore, may be viewed as a set of living and nonliving elements interacting over time within a defined locale. Ecologists attempt

The Ecosystem Concept and Project WILD
© *Council for Environmental Education (CEE)*

to define ecosystems in terms of sets of elements that directly or indirectly interact with each other. At a global level, all elements on the planet interact. The rain that falls today on the plains may have evaporated yesterday from the leaf of a tree in a coastal forest. But in practical terms, for studying and understanding the interactions among organisms in the environment it is useful to draw boundaries around certain groups of organisms that are normally interacting in a relatively direct way, as a community or neighborhood grouping. This grouping may be considered an ecosystem.

Within these biological neighborhoods, it is possible to assign organisms both an "address," describing their typical location in space, and an "occupation," or role that they play in the system. An organism's address is its habitat. The occupation of an organism in an ecosystem is called its niche. For many people, the term niche describes a location or group. Ecologists use the term to describe an organism's role or activities in the system. This definition can often be a source of confusion.

use surface tension to inhabit the narrow surface film zone at the top of the waterbody. Sometimes organisms inhabit different zones during different stages in their lives.

It is important to explore a variety of zones in multiple habitats because students might encounter quite different sets of organisms. Often, people tend to overlook certain zones—possibly because at first glance they seem devoid of life. It may seem tedious to sift through the muck on a pond bottom when dip nets are filled with interesting things found in the water or on rushes at the shore line. However, to develop an understanding of the diversity of life forms that inhabit an ecosystem we need to explore the whole range of addresses where they might be found.

Tips for Studying Ecosystems

A major purpose in having students study ecology is to develop an awareness and understanding of relationships. This process entails developing the ability to see systems, or sets of interactions, and think about how they have changed and will change with time. With enough exposure, students will begin to understand living systems as complex mosaics in which all the parts fit together to make a whole. The removal of one seemingly unimportant component can often have major consequences on the health and function of the ecosystem.

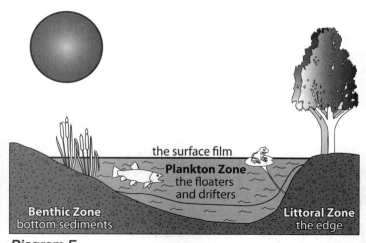

the surface film

Plankton Zone
the floaters and drifters

Benthic Zone
bottom sediments

Littoral Zone
the edge

Diagram E

Although there are many different aquatic ecosystems, all can be divided into a set of zones which are usually categorized by depth. **Diagram E** illustrates some of the zones that can be found in a typical pond ecosystem. Organisms occupying the edge or margins of the pond live in the littoral zone. The planktonic zone is named for microscopic organisms, plants or animals, that float and drift through the water without means of locomotion. Other organisms like catfish or aquatic insects live around or in the bottom sediments of the pond. Though few, organisms like water-striders

Building miniature ecosystems in jars or small glass aquariums can help students to begin thinking about what elements are needed to keep an ecosystem healthy. Foster an understanding of interactions by asking students to sketch a web connecting a natural object to as many other things, including themselves, they can think of. A dead leaf floating on the surface of a pond might be seen as unimportant to the ecosystems until—by drawing connections in as many directions and dimensions as possible—the student starts to see it as food, habitat, and former harvester of the sun's energy. These exercises help students appreciate all abiotic and biotic components in a habitat, even a dead leaf.

Individual organisms can be strange, beautiful, or even humorous. The next step in developing an ecosystem mindset is to try to appreciate the role played by an organism in the community of which it is a part. Is this a predator, or prey? Ultimately all organisms are "food" even if for microbes. Does one organism provide a home for other organisms? Do two different species work together to obtain resources they need but the other provides? Is it a producer that captures and stores solar energy? An important part of the activities in Project WILD and Aquatic WILD is asking students to think about these connections, and ultimately to connect themselves to the system as well.

Naming is often both an asset and an obstacle to the study of natural systems. When students visit a community, they want to know the names of the organisms they encounter. This is a good time to learn and recognize some plants and animals.

But often it is enough to appreciate differences and similarities, and encourage students to assign names of their own making to the things they see. Do not let a lack of detailed knowledge of names discourage study. Instead, use this opportunity to pose the "How can we find out?" questions. Emphasize characteristics of plants and animals and their interactions, rather than losing sight of those attributes in a quest to label the parts.

Finally, it can be a powerful experience for students to visit and revisit a natural setting at various seasons of the year. Spring is an ideal season to study ponds and streams. But it is a mistake for students to think of nature as dead, or even as largely dormant, in the winter. Seasonal changes are important to the economy of nature. Ecosystems change over time. The changes of the seasons are an important expression of continuing natural change in natural systems.

Have students follow an ecosystem—perhaps a pond, stream, lake, or river—through the seasons from late summer to fall, through winter and into spring and summer. School grounds can also provide useful opportunities of this kind. Some schools have adopted a local pond or stream and use it as the focus of studies by classes over many years. If the past data is saved, students can appreciate what is happening to their local ecosystems.

The Ecosystem Concept and Project WILD
© *Council for Environmental Education (CEE)*

Project WILD Conceptual Framework

This framework serves as the conceptual basis for activities in the *Project WILD* and *Aquatic WILD K–12 Curriculum and Activity Guides*. Every concept statement in a topic area is directly addressed by the activities listed for that topic. Activities under other topics may also support the concepts directly or indirectly.

Ecological Knowledge

Wildlife Populations (WP)

I. Characteristics
    A. Wildlife comprises all nonhuman and nondomesticated animals. Wildlife includes but is not limited to insects, spiders, birds, reptiles, fish, amphibians, and mammals.
        1. Wildlife is all around, although it may not be seen or heard or its presence otherwise sensed.
        2. Wildlife varies from forms that are microscopic to those more than 100 feet in length, and it occurs in a variety of forms, colors, and shapes.
    B. All living things go through a series of orderly changes in life cycles. Some species have distinct changes; the young of other species resemble their parents.
    C. Living things all need food, water, shelter, and a suitable place to live.
    D. Animals can be classified according to life needs, behavior, and physical characteristics, including body appearance, movement, habitat type, and relationship to humans (wild/domesticated).
II. Population Dynamics
    A. Wildlife numbers and species compositions are not static but are constantly changing.
        1. Systematic inventory of wildlife populations did not become a common practice until the 1930s, although journals of early explorers reflect considerable variation in historic population levels.
        2. Some wildlife populations exhibit cyclic patterns over time.
            a. Living things tend to reproduce in numbers greater than their habitat can support.
                (1) Carrying capacity is the dynamic equilibrium expressed by the availability of habitat components and the number of animals the habitat can support.
                (2) Each area of land or water, and ultimately the planet, has a carrying capacity of plants and animals.
                    (a) Carrying capacity is determined by climatic, geological, biological, or behavioral factors, along with human activities.
                    (b) Carrying capacity may fluctuate from season to season and year to year.
                    (c) Carrying capacity affects and is affected by wildlife behavior.
                        i.   The numbers, health, and distribution of wildlife are related to carrying capacity.
                        ii. Carrying capacity limitations can result in competition between and among domestic animals, wildlife, and humans.
            b. A population tends to increase in size until limited by one or more factors.
                (1) When one or more limiting factors exceed the tolerance range for an animal, population, or species, it directly affects the well-being of the animal(s) and may result in death or extinction.
                (2) Limiting factors include life history parameters such as food, water, shelter, space, disease, predation, and climatic conditions, as well as human activities such as development, pollution, and hunting.
    B. Natural laws are ultimately as binding on human populations as on wildlife.

Habitats, Ecosystems, and Niches (HN)

I. Distribution
   A. Wildlife is present in nearly all areas of the Earth.
   B. Each environment has characteristic life forms.
      1. The environment—created and shaped by natural forces or modified by humans—shapes life forms that occupy it.
      2. Each species occupies a niche within the range of environments in which it is found.
II. Importance
   A. Good habitat is the key to the survival of humans and wildlife.
      1. Habitat is composed of many integrated components including food, water, shelter or cover, space, and the suitable arrangement of these in relation to each other.
      2. In addition to supporting wildlife, ecosystems must furnish the products humans need to survive.
   B. Wildlife may be used as an indicator of the environmental health of an ecosystem.

Interdependence (ID)

I. Commonalities
   A. All living elements of an ecological system are interdependent.
      1. All forms of life depend on food, water, shelter, and space in a suitable arrangement.
      2. Humans and wildlife have similar basic needs.
         a. Humans and wildlife share environments and are subject to essentially the same environmental conditions.
         b. The health and well-being of humans and wildlife depend on the quality of the natural environment.
   B. Plants and animals in ecological systems live in a web of interdependence, in which each species contributes to the functioning of the overall system.
II. Interactions
   A. All living things are affected by and interact with their environments.
   B. In a naturally functioning ecosystem, life forms and environmental factors interact to keep wildlife populations in long-term dynamic equilibrium with each other and with their habitats.
      1. Many interactions result in a flow of energy and matter throughout the system.
         a. Energy takes a one-way course through an ecosystem and dissipates at every trophic level.
         b. Material substances, such as water, nitrogen, carbon, and phosphorus, cycle through ecosystems.
      2. Food webs illustrate the interrelationships of all living things.
         a. Either directly or indirectly, plants support nearly all forms of animal life, including humans.
            (1) Energy from the sun and organic matter enters the animal world through herbivores, those animals that eat plants.
            (2) A relatively large quantity of plant material is required to support herbivores (primary consumers), and herbivores can support only a smaller number of carnivores (secondary consumers).
            (3) Decomposers complete the cycle by breaking down organic matter formed by photosynthesis.
         b. Trophic relationships in an ecosystem may be complex and may vary depending on environmental conditions.
   C. Wildlife interacts with other wildlife and thereby affects the functioning of the ecological system.
      1. Interactions exist between different populations.
         a. Competition is a major determinant of community structure.
         b. Predation can be beneficial or harmful to a population as a whole.
         c. Symbiotic relationships may benefit or harm one or both of the partners.
      2. Interactions exist among members within a population, including competition and cooperation.

Changes and Adaptations (CA)

I. Environmental Changes
    A. Variation and change occur in all ecological systems.
    B. Succession is an orderly, gradual, and continuous replacement of one natural community of life by another.
        1. Succession influences what kinds of plants and animals live in an area.
            a. New communities arise when ecosystems change through succession.
            b. Newer communities may have less diversity.
            c. Species present in new communities will have traits that allow them to survive in the new environment.
            d. Over time, species diversity may increase in a new community.
        2. Natural events and human activities affect the rate and direction of succession.
    C. All forms of life are affected by changes in the quality, quantity, and distribution of their habitats.
II. Organism Adaptations
    A. All life forms exhibit adaptations to the environments in which they live.
        1. Fish and wildlife are adapted to their environment in ways that enable them to survive and maintain their populations.
            a. Many physical and behavioral adaptations, such as body coverings, hibernation, and migration, are associated with climatic conditions.
            b. Adaptations to predator and prey relationships may include behavioral (e.g., signaling, flight, freezing) as well as physical (e.g., camouflage, mimicry) variations.
            c. Reproductive strategies are adaptations that maximize species survival.
        2. Fish and wildlife species differ in their ability to adapt to changes in their habitats.
    B. Each habitat is suitable only to those life forms that are adapted to its ecological conditions.
    C. Isolated ecosystems are more vulnerable to environmental change.

Biodiversity (BD)

I. Types
    Biodiversity can refer to a variety of natural systems, a variety of species in an area, or a genetic diversity within a species.
    A. Ecosystem Diversity
        1. Ecosystem diversity is affected by many influences, such as climate and level of disturbance.
        2. Ecosystems undergo successional changes that are usually gradual.
        3. Species that are not able to adapt to ecosystem change may become extinct.
        4. A biologically healthy ecosystem is diverse over the range of the ecosystem, not necessarily within each community.
    B. Species Diversity
        1. Climate and habitats influence species diversity.
        2. Organisms that are not able to adjust to ecosystem changes will die.
        3. New ecosystems and ecosystems that are harsh tend to have relatively few species.
        4. Species diversity tends to be higher in the transition zone between ecosystems.
    C. Genetic Diversity
        1. Genetic variability is important to health within a species.
        2. Diversity facilitates adaptation to change and provides sources of new genetic material.
II. Human Influence
    A. Some wildlife species are not native but have been introduced to the area they presently occupy. Such introductions can be beneficial, harmful, or both to other species in the ecosystem.
    B. Adding or subtracting members from a community affects other members of the community.
    C. Human activities can affect the rate at which wildlife becomes threatened, endangered, or extinct.

III. The Importance of Habitat
   A. Habitat is the key to wildlife survival.
   B. Improving habitat improves wildlife populations.
   C. Reintroduction of wildlife into its former range may be possible if suitable habitat and suitable wild stock are available, and if such other conditions as weather and predator levels do not substantially interfere.
   D. Management of one species will affect other species in a community.
   E. For a wildlife population to sustain itself, there must be suitable habitat to support a viable breeding population, not just a few individuals.

Social and Political Knowledge

Cultural Perspectives (CP)

I. Cultural Development
   A. Human cultures and societies, past and present, affect and are affected by wildlife and its habitat.
   B. Values, ethics, and historical traditions of cultures and societies are reflected in their treatment of wildlife and other resources.
      1. Human and wildlife relationships are expressed through legends, myths, religious teachings and writings, symbols, protocols, ceremonies, and other cultural and societal activities.
      2. Appreciation of wildlife is often portrayed through creative expression of human relationships with wildlife in historic and contemporary times.

II. Appreciation
   Societies and cultures within societies may have different attitudes toward wildlife and its uses, formed and transmitted by family, community, and other social groups in a variety of ways.
   A. The aesthetic and spiritual values that humans place on wildlife vary from person to person and culture to culture.
   B. Different cultures may disagree over certain uses of and rights to wildlife and its habitat.
   C. Wildlife and its habitat are interpreted and treated differently by people viewing them from various cultural perspectives and frames of reference.
      1. Increasing separation of people from direct contact with the natural world has influenced human actions and attitudes toward wildlife. Therefore, actions and attitudes toward wildlife may be positive, negative, naïve, or misguided.
      2. Formal and nonformal education and the media shape the attitude of people toward wildlife and its habitat.

Economic, Commercial, and Recreational Considerations (EC)

I. Economic Considerations
   A. Natural resources include water, air, minerals, soil, fossil fuels, and plant life, as well as aquatic and terrestrial wildlife.
      1. Nonrenewable natural resources are those available on a finite basis.
      2. Renewable natural resources, including wildlife, can replenish themselves independently or with human assistance.
   B. The distribution and abundance of wildlife can affect the economy of an area.
      1. Some wildlife provides products of commercial value or subsistence needs to humans.
      2. Members of some cultures still depend on wildlife to supply a portion of their requirements for food, shelter, and clothing.
      3. Human use of wildlife directly and indirectly creates job opportunities for people.
   C. Economic trends, in addition to increased human population and mobility, have important influences on wildlife and its habitat.
   D. The human culture and economic condition of an area affect and are affected by the available resources, including wildlife and its habitat.

II. Commercial, Recreational, and Other Economic Considerations
  A. Historically, when conflict between recreational and commercial harvest of a wildlife species became severe, the commercial use had been eliminated.
  B. Recreational trends affect wildlife and its habitat.
    1. Wildlife-based recreation is of major importance to many millions of North Americans.
      a. Consumptive wildlife-based activities, such as hunting and fishing, provide U.S. and Canadian citizens with millions of days of outdoor recreation each year.
      b. Nonconsumptive activities, such as wildlife photography, painting, feeding, and observation, also provide millions of days of recreation annually.
    2. More leisure time and the growing popularity of outdoor activities are increasing the pressures on wildlife and habitat.
  C. Funds provided by consumptive users, not general tax dollars, historically have been the primary source of income for most state wildlife management programs and some federal programs.
    1. Charging an access fee to hunt, fish, camp, play, or trap on private land is common.
    2. Reductions in income from direct consumptive uses of wildlife (hunting, fishing, etc.) and nonconsumptive uses (camping, bird watching, etc.) have resulted in a loss of revenue for natural resource agencies.

Historical and Geographic Development (HG)

I. Development of Society
  Historically, wildlife affected the development, movement, and size of human societies.
  A. Human societies and cultures developed in various ways, partly because environmental factors produced different types of plants and animals in different places.
  B. Wildlife has played a significant role in the development of human culture through its influence on art, religion, and commerce.
  C. Wildlife questions and issues have influenced alliances and conflicts between and within communities, societies, states, and nations.
II. Development of Commerce
  Throughout history humans have used wildlife for food, shelter, clothing, and other products.
  A. All livestock and pet animals were domesticated and developed from wildlife species as humans sought to provide themselves with food, shelter, medicines, and companionship, and to satisfy other needs or wants.
  B. The ways in which humans value wildlife and natural resources have changed over time.
  C. As human populations have grown and pressures on wildlife populations have increased, people have developed systems to study wildlife and to regulate human impact on wildlife and habitats.

Political and Legislative Frameworks (PL)

I. United States
  A. Political trends affect wildlife and other natural resources.
  B. In the United States, wildlife is considered to be a public resource. Ownership of land or water alone does not secure ownership of wildlife on that land or in that water as it does in some other countries.
    1. Public decisions that affect wildlife and the environment are made through social and political processes designed to represent the wishes of the society.
    2. Primary responsibility for most wildlife conservation programs in the United States is delegated to governmental agencies.
      a. States are considered to have a greater responsibility for wildlife conservation programs than does the federal government. State wildlife agencies are legally responsible for managing most wildlife on public and private lands within their geographic jurisdictions.
      b. Federal agencies, in cooperation with state agencies, are legally responsible for managing wildlife affecting national interest, such as most threatened and endangered species and migratory wildlife.

3. Nongovernmental institutions play significant roles in influencing environmental policy and direction.
   a. Wildlife interest groups use judicial, legislative, and regulatory systems in reaching their objectives.
   b. Private organizations, industrial interests, and individual citizens also conduct wildlife conservation activities.
   C. Societies develop programs and policies relating to wildlife and its habitat through a variety of social mechanisms.
II. International
   A. Other nations and governments have different policies and philosophies relating to wildlife ownership and protection and to habitat management.
   B. Many wildlife species regularly move across national boundaries, necessitating the adoption of international agreements and the formation of international agencies and organizations to ensure protection and management of these species.

Sustaining Fish and Wildlife Resources

Attitudes and Awareness (AA)

I. Awareness
   A. Humans may find peace and inspiration through study and observation of wildlife, or simply through knowledge of its existence.
   B. Citizens benefit from experiencing and enjoying their natural resources.
II. Values
   A. Wildlife has intrinsic value, although humans often recognize only values based upon human wants and needs.
      1. The value placed on wildlife is commonly an issue in resource management decisions because value is often intangible and varies from person to person.
      2. Various groups interested in wildlife represent a wide range of philosophies and ethics concerning wildlife and how best to ensure its long range health and viability.
   B. Ecosystems have a finite capacity to provide for wildlife and human needs and wants. Sustainable living requires humans to live within the limits of the ecosystem capacity.

Human Impacts (HI)

I. The Importance of Impacts
   A. Human effects on fish and wildlife and their habitats are a driving force affecting environmental quality worldwide.
   B. The presence of people affects wildlife in positive and negative ways.
II. Impacts
   A. Humans have the capacity to sustain themselves and wildlife.
      1. Although all organisms affect their environment, only humans have the capacity to consider the effects of their actions and to develop a community that is sustainable into the future.
      2. A sustainable community is one that is in balance with a healthy environment and perpetuates a healthy environment for future generations.
      3. The development and adoption of sustainable human lifestyles and social decisions can change the negative effects of human activity on wildlife.
         a. Individual lifestyle decisions including recreational choices, transportation options, housing selections, vocation, food, clothing, and energy use affect wildlife directly and indirectly.
         b. Community conservation practices, plus social, cultural, and economic values affect environmental programs and activities.

Project WILD Conceptual Framework
© Council for Environmental Education (CEE)

B. Human populations and technologies often require space and activities that are detrimental to wildlife and its habitat.
   1. Human development encroaches on wildlife habitat, decreasing the amount of available habitat.
   2. Wildlife habitats are being fragmented by urban sprawl, resulting in restricted wildlife movement.
   3. Some habitats are being altered by human development activities such as water storage and landscaping.
   4. Contaminants and their bio-accumulative risks to both wildlife and humans threaten sustainable environments.
   5. Pollutants fall into a number of categories including acid rain, terrestrial runoff, biological (exotics, disease, waste), industrial waste and spills, post-consumer petroleum products, sewage, silt or sediment, thermal pollution, and radioactive and solid waste. Each of these pollutants creates particular effects on habitats and, if severe enough, may cause habitat loss.
C. Loss and degradation of habitat are considered the greatest problems facing wildlife today.
   1. Wildlife habitat loss because of natural trends or human activities is a condition common in nearly all nations.
   2. One specific cause of habitat degradation is pollutants, which can negatively affect environmental quality.
   3. Many critical habitats have been, and are, under pressure from historic and current development. Many have been damaged or lost.
   4. Remaining critical habitats can be, and in some cases are being, protected and maintained; damaged habitats can be, and in some cases are being, rehabilitated.

Issues and Trends (IT)

I. Global Perspectives
   A. Current wildlife issues and trends are complex, involve alternatives, and affect the environment.
   B. Many problems, issues, and trends involving wildlife in other parts of the world are similar to those in this country.
      1. Wildlife issues can affect global and international as well as national, regional, and local political activities—particularly regarding human harvesting practices, transmission of pollutants and their secondary impacts, migratory species, and aquatic habitats.
      2. Consumptive uses of wildlife have been excessive in some settings and continue as a persistent problems in other parts of the world.
      3. Commercial sale of wildlife and wildlife products is controversial and has worldwide implications.
II. Wildlife Populations
   A. Human activities increasingly determine which species of plants and animals will flourish and which will decline or disappear.
      1. Most species that are endangered or threatened became so from natural or human-caused changes in their habitat and their inability to adapt or adjust to such changes.
      2. Exotic species introduced into a community can change the functioning of that system.
         a. Evaluation of the impact of non-native plants and animals on ecosystems is important to the management and conservation of those ecosystems.
         b. Citizens must be aware of their potential role in the dispersal of non-native species and the transmission of disease, and must take steps to avoid contributing to these problems.
   B. Private landowners play an important role in sustaining and improving wildlife habitat.
III. Land Use
   A. As human populations increase and become significantly urban, land usage is altered dramatically.
      1. Individual transportation systems that allow increased accessibility spearhead development and drive land-use changes.
      2. Natural areas are being converted to agricultural, recreational, residential, and commercial purposes.

3. Fragmentation of biological communities, caused by human activities, affects wildlife diversity and populations.
   B. Consumer changes lead to agricultural production changes.
IV. Human Perspectives
   A. Wildlife issues involve conflicts between different interest groups.
   B. Issues involving wildlife and its habitat are often products of cultural differences and priorities.
   C. Well-informed individuals can assist resource management through increased involvement.
V. Consumptive and Nonconsumptive Uses
   A. Conflicts exist within and between consumptive and nonconsumptive resource users. Any resolution must consider the needs of all groups and the sustainability of the resource.
      1. Whether uses of wildlife should be consumptive or nonconsumptive is of concern to many people.
      2. Among consumptive groups, conflicts often involve how, when, and how much wildlife populations are used.
   B. Nongame species have begun to receive greater and more specific management attention.

Wildlife Management (WM)

I. Basic Concepts
   A. For management purposes, wildlife often has been divided into categories, including game, nongame, endangered, and threatened.
      1. Game species are those that are hunted, fished, or trapped for recreational or economic purposes by humans.
      2. Nongame species are those that are not hunted, fished, or trapped for either recreational or economic purposes by humans.
      3. Endangered species are those in danger of extinction throughout all or a significant portion of their ranges.
      4. Threatened species are those likely to become endangered.
   B. Wildlife management is the application of scientific knowledge and technical skills to the protection, preservation, conservation, limitation, or enhancement of wildlife and its habitat.
   C. Conservation is the use of natural resources in a way that assumes their continuing availability to future generations through the wise use or protection of natural resources.
II. Management Considerations
   A. Wildlife resources can be managed and conserved.
   B. Wildlife species are important components of a larger ecosystem and should be managed within the context of that ecosystem.
      1. Management of one species of wildlife may have positive or negative consequences for other species within the same ecosystem.
      2. Management of aquatic wildlife and its habitat is directly influenced by land-based activities in the surrounding watershed.
   C. Wildlife management considers the needs and desires of people as well as wildlife.
      1. Humans differ in how they value wildlife and its habitat, and the total demand on each may exceed the supply.
      2. Wildlife management decisions must consider political, social, economic, and biological concerns; such decisions should involve all interested or potentially affected constituencies.
      3. These same factors may limit the scope and effectiveness of wildlife management activities.
   D. Philosophies and practices in wildlife management have been both supported and criticized by individuals, as well as by public and private organizations.
   E. Most wildlife exists on land or in waters that are not directly controlled by state or federal wildlife management agencies.

III. Management Practices

Wildlife managers combine an understanding of species biology and of ecosystem structure and function with population- and land-manipulation techniques to accomplish management goals.

A. Wildlife management is based on natural sciences such as biology, ecology, geography, and soil science, as well as on many other disciplines.

1. Wildlife management practices have been developed through extensive research on ecosystems, through both observation and experimentation.

2. Habitat management practices are often intended to mimic the effects of natural ecosystem processes, especially disturbance.

B. Wildlife management practices involve population and habitat inventory and monitoring, direct management of wildlife species through manipulation of populations, indirect management of wildlife species through protection and manipulation of habitat, and public regulation and education.

1. Surveys of wildlife populations and their habitat provide important baseline information to guide management decisions.

2. Wildlife populations are manipulated through practices such as artificial propagation, stocking, transplanting, predator and damage control, and regulated harvest.

3. Acquisition, protection, improvement, and restoration of habitat are considered to be the most successful and cost-effective long-range techniques for managing wildlife species.

4. Regulations are necessary for wildlife conservation, but they cannot substitute for the availability of suitable habitat, nor can they maintain the population of a species whose habitat has been depleted or destroyed.

5. A public that is well educated about wildlife management issues is critical to the long-term success of wildlife management programs.

C. Scientific knowledge of all aspects of wildlife, including biological and social, is growing.

1. Technology changes affect environmental management decisions by allowing more sophisticated science-based analysis.

2. Wildlife agencies employ persons with a variety of scientific training and vocational skills.

Responsible Action (RA)

I. All plants and animals (human and wildlife) must live within the limits of their natural resources.

A. Both consumptive and nonconsumptive resource uses by people can strengthen their sense of responsibility toward the environment and encourage ethical actions.

B. It is the responsibility of citizens, government, and industry to avoid waste and destructive exploitation of natural resources, including wildlife.

C. Communities can learn to live in a sustainable manner by understanding the effects of their actions on the long-term health of the environment.

1. Citizens must understand their rights, privileges, and responsibilities, plus the consequences of their actions. That is, they should be aware of methods to help protect and improve the resource and should have the opportunity to practice and apply them.

2. Private decisions that affect wildlife and the environment are made through personal judgments. Each person makes such decisions each day, including use of time and energy, consumer choices, and vocational and leisure time activities.

3. Citizens can become involved in the management of wildlife, habitat, and the environment by direct participation in the political process or through local, state, national, or international organizations.

4. Individuals can influence public processes by voting, demonstrating, lobbying, seeking office, and supporting compatible interest groups.

5. All users of wildlife must respect the rights and property of others, consider effects on the habitat, and observe rules and regulations relating to wildlife.

6. Communities can learn to live in a sustainable manner by understanding the effects of their actions on the long-term health of the environment.

7. Education can help landowners so that they can prosper while maintaining environmental quality and integrity into the future.

D. Each individual has a responsibility to act in ways that can directly or indirectly reduce the impact of pollutants on the environment.

II. Conservation, restoration, and enhancement of natural resource habitats benefit humans.

Project WILD Conceptual Framework
© *Council for Environmental Education (CEE)*

Glossary

This is a limited glossary. However, it does include many terms that are specifically helpful when studying water resources and aquatic environments.

acid precipitation: all forms of precipitation that have an acidity lower than normal rainfall (pH 5.6)

acre-foot: the amount of water needed to cover 1 acre of surface area to the depth of 1 foot (12 inches)

adaptation: an alteration or adjustment in structure or habits by which a species or individual improves its condition in relationship to its environment

advocacy: public support for wildlife and its protection in the environment

aerate: to supply with air or oxygen; to supply the blood with oxygen as in the function of lungs; to supply running water with additional oxygen as when a stream runs over falls or rapids or when wind creates waves on a lake

alevin: a young salmon during the first 2 weeks after hatching until the yolk sac has been absorbed

algae: simple one-celled or many-celled plants capable of photosynthesis; usually aquatic

algin: any hydrophilic, colloidal substance found in or obtained from various kelps

alluvial: coming from loose, unconsolidated soil which has not formed into a rock and has been transported to a non-marine setting

amphibian: an animal that typically lives in an aquatic habitat breathing by gills as young, and primarily in a terrestrial habitat breathing by lungs and through moist glandular skin as an adult (e.g., frog)

anadromous: species of fish that live their lives in the ocean and migrate to fresh water to spawn

angling: fishing with a rod, reel, fishing line, and bait

aquaculture: deliberate growing of plants and animals in freshwater environments

aquatic: growing, living in, or frequenting water

area: the size of a surface

arrangement: the location, in relation to one another, of sources of food, water, and shelter in an animal's habitat

bag limit: the maximum number of animals allowed to be taken by an individual in regulated fishing or hunting

baleen: a system, composed of bristles or hairs, located inside the mouths of baleen whales which is used to filter animals from water that the whales then consume

biodegradable: capable of being decomposed by biological agents, especially bacteria

biodiversity: a term used to represent the variety of life forms in a given area

biomagnification: an increase in concentration of some substance at higher levels within a food chain

biomass: the mass of living organisms in a given area

biotic index: the number of living organisms found in an ecosystem

bog: a wetland formed where low oxygen levels and soil temperature cause incomplete decomposition and limited drainage, and an accumulation of fibrous peat

buoyancy: the tendency of an object to float when immersed in a fluid

career: an occupation undertaken for a significant period of a person's life and with opportunities for progress

catadromous: a species of fish that begins its life in the ocean, lives most of its life in fresh water, and returns to the ocean to spawn

catch-and-release: a practice used in fishing in which fish are released after being caught, in order to conserve fish populations

cetacea: an order of marine mammals; whales, dolphins, and porpoises belong to this order

climax community: the steady state reached by an area of vegetation after going through ecological succession and eventually becoming adapted to local conditions

clinch knot: a knot used to secure the bait used in fishing to the fishing line

coloration: a genetically controlled pattern or markings that protects an individual organism

comparative questions: questions that will provide answers which make comparisons between two or more topics

condensation: the process of a substance changing from a gas to a liquid, usually as a result of cooling

conservation: the use of natural resources in a way that ensures their continuing availability to future generations; the wise and intelligent use or protection of natural resources

consumer: the first part of an ecosystem is the nonliving substance; the second part consists of those organisms that are called "producers," or food makers; the third part of this system is called the "consumer" because it uses the producer for its food; it may in turn be used as food by a secondary consumer

control: to verify a scientific experiment by conducting a parallel experiment or by comparing with another standard

controlled variable: a way in a scientific experiment to control how measurements are taken, samples are collected, and observations are made in order to ensure these are being done the same way every time

correlative questions: questions that will provide answers which show how two topics are related or connected

debris: the remains of something broken or destroyed

decomposer: those organisms (e.g. bacteria, fungi) that convert dead organic materials into inorganic materials

dehydrate: to remove water from

depth: the distance from the top or surface of something to its bottom

descriptive questions: questions that will provide answers which describe or explain

detritus: dead plant, animal, and other organic matter

direct water use: water that is visibly used or consumed (e.g., bathing, drinking, and cooking)

dissolved oxygen: molecules of oxygen gas dissolved in water

diurnal: active by daylight; the opposite of nocturnal

ecology: the study of the relation of organisms or groups of organisms to their environment; the science of the interrelations between living organisms and their environment

ecosystem: a natural unit that includes living and nonliving parts interacting to produce a stable system in which the exchange of materials between the living and nonliving parts follows closed paths

edge effect: the tendency of wildlife to use the areas where two vegetative types come together forming an edge

effluent: any matter that enters the environment from a specific source; the term generally refers to waste water from a sewage treatment or industrial plant

endangered: a species that is in danger of extinction throughout all or a significant portion of its range

entangled: the state of being twisted or caught up in something else

environment: the circumstances and conditions surrounding an organism that influences its existence, including physical, biological, and all other factors

environmental issue: a situation in which there is disagreement about solutions to an environmental problem, often because of differing values and beliefs

environmental problem: a difficult situation involving the interaction between people and the environment

erosion: the removal or wearing away of soil or rock by water, wind, or other forces or processes

estuary: a site where the sea and river meet and mix fresh water and salt water

eutrophication: enrichment of soils and water resulting from fertilization, sewage, effluent, or other waters that carry a high plant-nutrient component

evaporation: the process of a substance changing from a liquid to a gas by exposure to air, heat or both

evapo-transpiration: the process of transferring moisture from the ground to the atmosphere by evaporation of water and transpiration from plants

exotic: a plant or animal that is not native to a habitat

extinction: the condition of having been removed from existence

extirpated: the extinction of a species within a contained geographic area, but not everywhere

field investigation: a set of procedures used to systematically collect data in an outdoor setting in order to answer a question through description, comparison, or correlation of environmental conditions or phenomena. Field investigations contribute to scientific knowledge of natural systems.

fish ladder: a series of ascending pools of water constructed by humans as mechanisms to enable salmon or other fish to swim upstream around or over a dam

fishery: a system that includes: fish or shellfish populations; the habitats and communities of species in which those populations live; and the people who affect and use those populations

fishing ethics: a set of practices used in recreational fishing that are meant to conserve fish populations and provide a safe environment for all fishers

food chain: the transfer of food energy from one organism to another as each consumes a lower member and in turn is preyed upon by a higher member

food web: an interlocking pattern of food chains

freshwater: water that is not salty, especially when considered as a natural resource

freshwater marsh: a wetland where standing fresh water exists year-round in most conditions

fry: small young fish that have recently hatched

gill net: a curtain-like fishing net, suspended vertically in the water, with meshes of such a size as to catch a fish by the gills when it has thrust its head through the mesh netting

green-collar job: a job with the purpose of improving the quality of the environment (e.g., waste management workers, recycling managers, and environmental consultants)

ground water: water found under the Earth's surface between saturated soil and rock supplying wells and springs

habitat: the arrangement of food, water, shelter, or cover and space suitable to animals' needs

harvest: the intentional gathering of plants, animals, and other natural resources for use

hatchery: a place where fish eggs are hatched and raised

home range: the area where an animal travels in the scope of normal activities

hydrology: the study of the properties, distribution, and effects of water of the Earth and in the atmosphere

impervious: a surface or material that does not absorb water well, such as paved areas, buildings, and compacted soil

indicator: an instrument that is used to monitor or predict a certain condition, such as pH

indirect water use: total amount of water used to produce goods and services that are consumed by people (e.g., water needed to grow grains for bread or water needed to produce steel used in automobiles)

infiltration: a process by which water or some other substance enters the soil

ingest: to take food, water, or another substance into the body by swallowing or absorption

international agency: an agency that has representation from more than one nation

introduced species: a non-native species that is intentionally or accidentally brought into an ecosystem

inventory: a detailed, itemized list used in the process of identifying and counting animals

invertebrate: animals that do not have a backbone

isolated ecosystems: an ecosystem that is separated from another ecosystems

job fair: a fair or exposition for employers, recruiters, and job seekers; job seekers can learn more about organizations and the positions they offer, and employers can recruit potential applicants

job interview: an interview between an employer and a job seeker to determine whether the job seeker is suitable for employment

land use: usually refers to how the land is used by people

leach: to remove a mineral or chemical from some material by passing a liquid through the material

life cycle: the continuous sequence of changes undergone by an organism from one primary form to the development of the same form again

limiting factors: influences in the life history of any animal, population of animals, or species (e.g., food, water, shelter, space, disease, predation, climatic conditions, pollution, hunting, poaching, and accidents)

limnology: the area of science dealing with the study of fresh water aquatic ecology

litter: (1) carelessly discarded garbage; (2) the number of young born per birthing to a mammal

macroinvertebrates: invertebrate animals (animals without backbones) large enough to be observed without the aid of a microscope or other magnification

management: in general terms related to wildlife, the intentional manipulation or nonmanipulation of habitat or the organisms within the habitat

manipulated variable (independent variable): a condition in a scientific experiment which will be changed

mariculture: deliberate cultivation of plants and animals, including fish and kelp, in estuarine, coastal, and other marine areas

meter: a unit of measurement of length in the metric system

Glossary
© Council for Environmental Education (CEE)

microorganism: an organism microscopic in size, observable only through a microscope

migration: the periodic movement of animals from one area to another and back again as a natural part of their lives

mitigate: to make up for; to substitute some benefit for losses incurred

native: a plant or animal species that was produced, grew, or originated in a certain region

needs: in biological terms, the things that a plant or animal needs to survive

niche: the function or position of an organism or a population within an ecological community

nocturnal: active by night; the opposite of diurnal

non-native: in conservation terms, an organism that has been introduced into a new area

nonpoint source pollution: widespread overland runoff containing pollutants; the contamination does not originate from one specific location, and pollution discharges over a wide land area

nutrients: compounds found in the environment that plants and animals require for growth and survival

occupation: a person's usual work or business, as a means of earning a living

organic matter: chemical compounds of carbon combined with other chemical elements and generally manufactured in the life processes of plants and animals

permeability: a measure of the ability of a material (e.g., porous rock, sediment, or soil) to transmit water

permeable: capable of transmitting water (e.g., porous rock, sediment, or soil)

pervious: a surface or material that allows water to infiltrate, such as natural areas with well-rooted vegetation

pH: a measure that indicates the relative acidity or alkalinity of a substance (The pH scale ranges from 0 [most acid] to 14 [most basic], with a pH of 7 being neutral.)

plankton: those organisms suspended in an aquatic habitat that controls their movements; usually microscopic, including bacteria, algae, protozoan, rotifers, larvae, and small crustaceans (Phytoplankton are the plant plankton; zooplankton are the animal species.)

plastic: (1) a petroleum-based product; (2) capable of being formed or shaped

political process: the process relating to the study, structure, or affairs of government or politics

pollution: contamination of soil, water, or atmosphere by the discharge of harmful substances

population: the number of a particular species in a defined area

precipitation: water falling, in a liquid or solid state, from the atmosphere to Earth (e.g., rain, snow)

predator: an animal that kills and eats other animals

prey: animals that are killed and eaten by other animals

producer: a green plant or bacterium that uses photosynthesis or chemosynthesis; constitutes first trophic level in food chain

protection: the prevention of harm to wildlife

puddle: a collection of water, typically rainwater, that has flown and formed in a low spot or depression on the land's surface

responding variable (dependent variable): a condition in a scientific experiment which will be observed/measured

restoration: the act or process or bringing something back to a previous condition or position

ridgeline: an area, typically long and narrow, that separates two adjacent streams or watersheds

riffle: a short, shallow section of a stream or river in which ripples form due to the increased velocity of the water

riparian: located or relating to the banks of a stream, river, or other body of water

runoff: water that drains or flows off the surface of the land

salt marsh: a marshy land area that is wet with salt water or flooded by the sea

scavenger: an organism that habitually feeds on refuse or carrion

scent: a smell and odor

sediment: fragmented organic or inorganic material derived from the weathering of soil, alluvial, and rock materials; removed by erosion and transported by water, wind, ice, and gravity

seine net: a fishing net that hangs vertically in the water, with floats at the upper edge and sinkers at the lower

seral: part of a transitional stage during the ecological succession of an area of vegetation before reaching a steady state in which the species are adapted to local conditions

shelter: cover for natal activity or bedding and for protection from weather

silt: the fine-grained sediment carried by water

siltation: the pollution of water by fine mineral particles

slough: a hollow filled with mud and water (e.g., an inlet from a river, backwater, or tidal flat)

smolt: a young, silvery salmon migrating to the sea

solubility: the capacity to be dissolved or liquefied

spawning: to produce and deposit eggs

species: a population of individuals that are more or less alike and that are able to breed and produce fertile offspring under natural conditions; a category of biological classification immediately below the genus or subgenus

spin casting: a technique in angling, or fishing with a rod, that uses a spinning lure in order to entice fish to bite

sport fishing: fishing with a rod, reel, fishing line, and bait, or angling, done for sport or recreation

state wildlife agency: the government agency that has the legal responsibility for management of some or all wildlife in a state, including habitat protection, restoration, and alteration; planning; land acquisition; research; education; information; endangered species; consumptive uses; nonconsumptive programs; and regulations and usually law enforcement

subsistence: the act or means to exist; to find ones supply of food from hunting and fishing

succession: the orderly, gradual, and continuous replacement of one plant or animal by another

sustainability: maintaining resources in such a way to be able to renew themselves over time or to keep in existence and supply with necessities

swamp: a type of wetland where the soil is saturated and often inundated with water and trees as the dominant cover vegetation

terminal blade: the last blade to grow on a kelp frond nearest to the surface

threatened: in wildlife terms, a species present in its range but in danger because of a decline in numbers

tolerance: the ability to deal with an adverse environmental condition; the amount of variance from a standard that is allowed

treatment: the act, manner, or method of handling a situation

trophic level: a group of living things that share the same level in the food chain

variable: the part of an experiment that can be changed or manipulated

vegetation: the mass of plants that covers a given area

vernal: of or occurring in the spring

vernal pool: isolated and temporary puddles or ponds

volume: the amount of space occupied by a three-dimensional object

wants: those things that are not considered a need to survive but are desirable

water conservation: the use of water-saving methods to reduce the amount of water needed for homes, lawns, farming, and industry, and thus increasing water supplies for optimum long-term economic and social benefits

water cycle: the continuous circulation of water in systems throughout the planet, involving condensation, precipitation, runoff, evaporation, and transpiration

water source: a place where a living organism gets the water it needs to survive; the place where the water used by a municipal water system originates

waterfowl: water birds, usually ducks, but including shore and wading birds, geese, and so forth

watershed: the land area from which surface runoff drains into stream channel, lake, reservoir, or other body of water; also called a drainage basin

waterway: a river, canal or other body of water used as a route or way of travel or transportation

wetlands: any land area that tends to be regularly wet or a lowland area that is saturated with moisture, such as a marsh or swamp

wild: not tamed or domesticated, living in a basically free condition (A wild animal provides for its own food, shelter, and other needs in an environment that serves as a suitable habitat.)

wildlife: animals that are not tamed or domesticated and includes, but is not limited to, insects, spiders, birds, reptiles, fish, amphibians, and mammals, if nondomesticated

wildlife manager: a person who manages wildlife habitat, other related human activities, or both

zooplankton: plankton that is composed of tiny animals and animal matter

What's My Question?

Preparing for a successful field investigation begins with developing a question that is researchable. While there are numerous important "big picture" questions about the environment and how people interact with the environment, many questions are too broad to be answered with a single investigation. Asking a question that can be tested or researched is a key part of scientific inquiry.

As you consider questions about your local environment to investigate, it is important to consider what observations you will be able to make, and whether those observations will help answer your investigative question. One way to help with this process is to categorize your investigative questions into one of three categories. Use the boxes below to record researchable questions you would like to investigate.

1. Questions about the big picture. List questions here that are too big to answer with a single field investigation:

2. Questions that help us describe. List questions here that focus on a single aspect of your local environment—questions that you can find answers to by measuring, observing, describing or mapping. These questions help us describe parts of a natural system such as how many, how frequently, how much, what happened, when, and where?

3. Questions that help us compare. List questions here that compare changes within a population or differences between groups. Observations may be made either on a single population under various conditions (time of year, location) or on different populations. Comparative questions ask, what will happen to the measured variable when one of the changes occurs?

4. Questions that help us correlate. List questions here that involve measuring or observing two variables and searching for a pattern. Correlative questions ask, what is the relationship between two variables?

Adapted from *Field Investigations: Using Outdoor Environments to Foster Student Learning of Scientific Processes.* 2007. Pacific Education Institute and Association of Fish & Wildlife Agencies.

Conclusions and Next Steps

1. Restate your investigative question:

2. Were you able to answer your research question with the data and observations you collected? If yes, go to Step 3. If no, explain why not. For example, were you able to make the kinds of observations you were planning to make?

How can you modify or rewrite your question so you are able to answer it using observations you can make at your study site?

3. Write a concise answer to your research question:

4. Now elaborate. What natural occurrences were happening at your study site that explain the data you collected? Be sure to include evidence or observations to support your answer.

5. How could knowing this answer help you or others take actions to benefit people and wildlife?

6. What other questions about your study site could you or others investigate?

7. Choose one question you listed in Step 6 above. Describe the kind of information you would need to collect in order to answer this question. How would you go about collecting that information?

Data Collection Form

Observer's Name: _____

City/County/State: _____

Describe your surroundings (forest, seashore, prairie, urban, suburb, rural, park, etc.):

_____

_____

_____

Date	Time	Weather	Species Name/ Description	How Observed? (Viewed, heard, tracks, etc.)	Latitude	Longitude	How many did you see? #	Is this an estimate? ?

Data Collection Form
© Council for Environmental Education (CEE)

Metric Conversion Chart
Approximations

Symbol	When You Know	Multipy By	To Find	Symbol
		Length		
in	inches	2.5	centimeters	cm
ft	feet	30.0	centimeters	cm
yd	yards	0.9	meters	m
mi	miles	1.6	kilometers	km
cm	centimeters	0.4	inches	in
m	meters	3.3	feet	ft
m	meters	1.09	yards	yd
km	kilometers	0.6	miles	mi
		Area		
in2	square inches	6.5	square centimeters	cm2
ft2	square feet	0.09	square meters	m2
yd2	square yards	0.84	square meters	m2
mi2	square miles (640 acres)	2.6	square kilometers	km2
acre	acre (43,560 ft2)	0.4	hectares	ha
cm2	square centimeter	0.16	square inches	in2
m2	square meter	10.8	square feet	ft2
m2	square meter	1.2	square yards	yd2
km2	square kilometer	0.4	square miles	mi2
ha	hectare	2.5	acres	acre
		Mass		
oz	ounces (avoirdupois)	28.0	grams	g
lb	pound	0.45	kilograms	kg
t	short tons (2,000 lb)	0.9	tonnes (metric ton)	t
g	grams	0.035	ounces (avoirdupois)	oz
kg	kilograms	2.2	pounds	lb
t	tonnes (metric tons)	1.1	short tons (2,000 lb)	t
		Volume		
tsp	teaspoons	5.0	grams	ml
Tbs	tablespoons	15.0	kilograms	ml
fl oz	fluid ounces	30.0	tonnes (metric ton)	ml
c	cups (liquid)	0.24	ounces (avoirdupois)	l
pt	pints (liquid)	0.47	pounds	l
qt	quarts (liquid)	0.95	short tons (2,000 lb)	l
gal	gallons	3.8	grams	l
ft3	cubic feet	0.03	kilograms	m3
yd3	cubic yards	0.76	cubic meters	m3
ml	milliliters	0.2	teaspoons	tsp
ml	milliliters	0.07	tablespoons	Tbs
ml	milliliters	0.03	fluid ounces	fl oz
l	liters	4.2	cups (liquid)	c
l	liters	2.1	pints (liquid)	pt
l	liters	1.06	quarts (liquid)	qt
l	liters	0.26	gallons	gal
m3	cubic meters	35.0	cubic feet	ft3
m3	cubic meters	1.3	cubic yards	yd3
		Temperature		
°C	degrees Celsius	(9/5 x °C) + 32	degrees Celsius	°F
°F	degrees Fahrenheit	5/9 x (°F-32)	degrees Fahrenheit	°C

Notes

Notes

Notes

Get More WILD!
Other Programs Administered by CEE

Project WILD

Project **WILD**®

This "terrestrial" companion to Aquatic WILD is an interdisciplinary conservation and environmental education program emphasizing wildlife. The goal of Project WILD is to assist K–12 students in developing awareness, knowledge, skills, and commitment to result in informed decisions, responsible behavior, and constructive actions concerning wildlife and the environment.
Web: *www.projectWILD.org*

Growing Up WILD

Growing Up **WILD**

This early childhood education program builds on children's sense of wonder about nature and invites them to explore wildlife and the world around them. Through a wide range of activities and experiences, Growing Up WILD provides an early foundation for developing positive impressions about the natural world and lifelong social and academic skills.
Web: *www.pwGrowingUpWILD.org*

Flying WILD

Flying **WILD**®

Introducing students to bird conservation, Flying WILD uses standards-based classroom activities and environmental stewardship projects. Flying WILD encourages schools to work closely with conservation organizations, community groups, and businesses involved with birds to implement school bird festivals and bird conservation projects.
Web: *www.flyingwild.org*

The Bird Education Network (BEN)

BEN is a CEE initiative that seeks to connect and support the community of bird education professionals. Currently, 3,900 individuals representing over 400 organizations receive communications and engage in professional dialogue through the BEN-supported Bird Education Listserv. Join us!
Web: *www.birdeducation.org*

BEN
Bird Education Network

WET in the City

WET
in the city®
Water Education for Teachers

WET in the City engages K–12 youth in hands-on activities that creatively explore the science of water, its cultural context, and complex issues surrounding its management and stewardship. The program is delivered at the local level, city by city, and targets urban educators with relevant, localized water education.

Science and Civics

Serving as a guide for involving high school students in conservation, Science and Civics is filled with environmental action projects aimed at benefitting local wildlife found in a community. It involves young people in decisions affecting people, wildlife, and their shared habitat in the community.
Web: *www.projectwild.org/ScienceandCivics.htm*

Science and Civics:
Sustaining Wildlife
Project WILD
Curriculum Guide for Grades 9–12

For more information

Please contact us for more information on any of these programs:

Council for Environmental Education
5555 Morningside Drive, Suite 212
Houston, Texas 77005
Phone: (713) 520-1936
Web: *www.councilforee.org*

CEE
COUNCIL FOR
ENVIRONMENTAL
EDUCATION

Alphabetical Listing